Advances in

PARASITOLOGY

VOLUME 1

Advances in
PARASITOLOGY

Edited by

BEN DAWES

Department of Zoology, King's College,
University of London, England

VOLUME 1

1963

ACADEMIC PRESS
London and New York

ACADEMIC PRESS INC. (LONDON) LTD.
Berkeley Square House
Berkeley Square
London, W.1

U.S. Edition published by
ACADEMIC PRESS INC.
111 Fifth Avenue
New York 3, New York

Library of Congress Catalog Card Number: 62–22124

Second Printing 1966

ARNO REPRINT INC. N.Y.
PRINTED IN U.S.A.

CONTRIBUTORS TO VOLUME 1

C. HORTON-SMITH, *Houghton Poultry Research Station, Houghton, Huntingdon, England* (p. 67)

CLAY G. HUFF, *Naval Medical Research Institute, Bethesda, Maryland, U.S.A.* (p. 1)

JOHN E. LARSH, JR., *Schools of Public Health and Medicine, University of North Carolina, Chapel Hill, and School of Medicine, Duke University, Durham, North Carolina, U.S.A.* (p. 213)

J. LLEWELLYN, *Department of Zoology and Comparative Physiology, The University, Birmingham, England* (p. 287)

P. L. LONG, *Houghton Poultry Research Station, Houghton, Huntingdon, England* (p. 67)

D. POYNTER, *Parasitology Department, Allen & Hanbury's Ltd., Ware, Hertfordshire, England* (p. 179)

W. P. ROGERS, *University of Adelaide, South Australia* (p. 109)

R. I. SOMMERVILLE, *McMaster Laboratory, Division of Animal Health, C.S.I.R.O., Glebe, N.S.W., Australia* (p. 109)

PREFACE

Recent intensification of research throughout the world has induced much specialization in biological fields, creating a situation in which researchers preoccupied with particular projects tend to become comparatively uninformed about progress in matters which are of subsidiary interest to them. Text books soon become out of date and teachers no longer have the power to abstract and collate ideas and information which are sufficient to their needs from the original literature of science. Those who seek research projects for postgraduate students are anxious to know what has been done or is being done in other colleges, universities and research institutions in this or some other country. Books of the *Advances* type are a boon to students, teachers and professional scientists, satisfying an urgent need in modern life.

Parasitology has its roots in morphology and taxonomy and its branches in ecology, embryology and physiology, with some recent spreading into biophysics and biochemistry. *Advances in Parasitology* will provide authentic, well documented reviews of progress in various fields of endeavour, extending its scope towards the limits of existing knowledge and indicating where research effort can best be expended in the future. Considering how difficult it is to persuade specialists in research to lay down their tools, or labour farther into the night, writing down the results of their enquiries on the wave-front of knowledge in special fields, it has been my good fortune to get a satisfying initial response. This probably indicates not only a willingness to impart highly technical information in interesting ways, but also firm convictions that such writing will have great appeal to an army of biologists marching towards a worthy goal—greater understanding of the unique, intimate relationship between parasites and their hosts.

The first contribution concerns avian malaria and in it Clay G. Huff deplores the undesirable and unwarranted decline in interest on research in this field. The eradication of human malaria is not complete, and by neglecting the subject of avian malaria we are allowing valuable tools for combating malaria to rust away, placing ourselves in a disadvantageous position should there be future epidemics of the disease. Research on obligate parasites, particularly intracellular forms, has found many ways of dealing with fundamental problems the solution of which could not have emerged from the exclusive study of free-living forms of life. Huff deals with progress in respect of a wide variety of topics, many of which have arisen since the publication of Hewitt's monograph in 1940. In the section on parasitology, he considers high altitude effects on infections, natural immunity and susceptibility of the host, effects of irradiation on exogenous stages of the parasite and the hosts, the cytology and genetics of the parasite, the growth of exogenous stages *in vivo* and *in vitro*, periodicity of asexual reproduction, the natural immunity and susceptibility of mosquitoes, the effects on the parasites of other microbial agents and the action of low temperatures on the parasite. Following sections are just as far-reaching, concerning such topics as methods of *in vitro* culture; the application of the methods of physiology and biochemistry to malariology; exoerythrocytic stages and host cell preferences; the fine structure of asexual stages, gametocytes, ookinetes, EE stages, oocysts and sporozoites; immunological considerations which include the role of the spleen and RES, humoral immunity and relapse; and some aspects of pathology. Significant researches on *Haemoproteus* and *Leucocytozoon* come into the picture and, when the present status of research on avian malaria has been evaluated, areas for future development are briefly delineated.

C. Horton-Smith and P. L. Long are concerned with coccidians of the genus *Eimeria* and with the disease coccidiosis, which has economic rather than medical significance. The determination of degrees of pathogenicity is a matter of some consequence in regard to the afflictions of poultry, and problems of control of the disease depend on immunological methods of research. Cytochemical methods of research also come into prominence, because of the relatively large size of *Eimeria* spp., as protozoan animals. This contribution is divided into sections dealing with the pathology and the life cycle of six species of Eimeria in fowls and of three species which occur in turkeys. In chickens of Britain, *E. acervulina* has acquired greater importance as a widespread pathogen, *E. brunetti* is extending its range and increasing its economic importance, *E. maxima* is pathogenic under field conditions and causes deaths in commercial flocks, and heavy infections of *E. mitis* retard the growth of chickens. In turkeys, *E. adenoeides* is very pathogenic to birds less than 5 weeks old but less pathogenic to older birds, but *E. meleagridis* is non-pathogenic. One of the most pathogenic species in turkeys is *E. meleagrimitis*. The factor which has a direct bearing on possible economic losses of poultry is oocyst-production, which in some instances is relatively greater in light infections than in heavy infections. Thus an inoculum of 200 sporulated oocysts of *E. necatrix* produced, in 2–3 week old chicks, a yield of 50,000 oocysts per cyst administered, while an inoculum of 2,000 oocysts yielded only 2,500 oocysts per cyst administered. Differences in oocyst potential explain variability in the epidemiology of various forms of coccidiosis. *E. tenella* is a highly pathogenic species and a heavy producer of oocysts, while *E. necatrix* is equally virulent but a poor producer of oocysts; the resultant effect is that the former species soon causes coccidiosis in chickens only a few weeks old, while the latter species produces the disease in older birds.

The cytological observations on stages in the life cycle of *Eimeria* spp. concern forms of nucleic acid (DNA and RNA), proteins, lipids, carbohydrates, protein-carbohydrates complexes, mucopolysaccharides and enzyme activity. The section on immunity concerns the phase of the life cycle which induces the immune response, the immunization of chickens and the immunizing power of different species of coccidians, the fate of second generation merozoites of *E. tenella* in fully immune chickens, the duration of immunity in the absence of reinfection, the transference of resistance to *E. tenella* from one caecum to the other in individual fowls, the detection of precipitating antibodies and tests for the specificity of the reactions, precipitating antibodies associated with immunity to four species of *Eimeria* in fowls, detection of lysins in the sera of fowls immune to *E. tenella*, attempts to induce a passive immunity to infection with *E. tenella*, and cellular responses.

W. P. Rogers and R. I. Sommerville concern themselves with the infective stages of nematode parasites which affect numerous vertebrate and invertebrate hosts and also many plants. The hatching of the eggs, the moulting of larvae and modifications of the life cycle to further dispersal and parasitism are important considerations. The treatment of appropriate problems combines the physiological and behavioural viewpoints and concerns the question of survival of infective stages. Infection by way of the alimentary tract of the host involves various factors which constitute a "stimulus", which is due to the effects of carbon dioxide, reducing agents, salts, hydrogen ion concentration, etc. The physiological action of this "stimulus" is concerned with the exsheathment of larvae and involves a "trigger" mechanism. The process of infection by way of the skin provides a new set of problems and involves arthropods as agents of infection. The infection of plants is related to secretions of the host, soil conditions, the location of the plant, and attachment to the plant. The nature of "infectiousness", which is the capacity of the parasite to infect and live in or on its host, merits and receives special treatment. The infective larval stage is regarded as a "bridge" by which the parasite moves from one environment to another, one environment at least being part of the body of another organism. This larva may have to withstand changes of temperature, osmotic pressure and diet. In its early environment harmful factors tend to be mainly climatic, but in the later environment the parasite has to cope with factors which include antibodies, antienzymes and unspecified tissue reactions of the host. Metazoan parasites have this capacity to live in a new environment by virtue of some form of metamorphosis, which may be associated with the change from a free-living mode of life to parasitism, or change from life in an invertebrate animal to life in some vertebrate animal. The mechanisms of moulting and metamorphosis, it is claimed, may be as closely analogous in parasitic nematodes and insects as they are in insects and amphibians. Possibly, some similar intrinsic mechanism is involved, a mechanism which is influenced by external conditions and may induce neurosecretion. This is a topic which Rogers and Sommerville discuss in some detail, leading up to the formulation of a general hypothesis of infectiousness as an adaptation to parasitism.

D. Poynter deals with the problem of *Dictyocaulus viviparus*, the causal agent of parasitic bronchitis in cattle, first considering the parasite in the bovine host and also larvae which live in pastures, giving us a picture of the pathological condition and some ideas concerning treatment of the disease. Other topics include naturally acquired immunity, passive and active forms of immunization and the measurement of helminth immunity. The control of this disease by vaccination is unique in the sense that husk is the only helminthic disease for which a vaccine is available, its basis lying in the biological effect of X-irradiation of the infective larvae of *Dictyocaulus viviparus*, classical work which is discussed. Remarkable progress is reported. The Weybridge group and others have contributed to our knowledge of the ecology of *Dictyocaulus* and the epidemiology of the disease. The Glasgow school extended epidemiological results, studied the pathological and clinical aspects of the disease and, most notably, investigated the immunology of husk and discovered a method of vaccination. Contributions to progress have been made also by commercial houses who developed chemical compounds which are active against lungworms and instituted large-scale production of X-irradiated vaccine. This is a stimulating example of successful biological co-operation between academicians, professional parasitologists and commercial undertakings in researches of historical importance.

The contribution of J. E. Larsh, Jr. is a survey of progress in experimental trichiniasis from about 1950 to the present time. He has eliminated advances concerned with the chemical composition and metabolic activities of larval *Trichinella spiralis*, detailed antigenic analyses and serological studies which have occupied other recent reviewers and are more appropriate to other *Advances* series. His account is restricted also to researches using mice, rats and hamsters, which have been most popular, although rabbits do come in for some consideration. His special concern has been with known anatomical and physiological alterations in the host's body at precise periods during infections which are very complex and even today little understood, and with various aspects of acquired immunity. Larsh draws our attention to new information on morphology which electron microscopy has provided, to details concerning the life cycle which influence designs of experimentation, and to the activities and chemical composition of the parasite. He is inclined to believe the greatest advance to have been that which indicates how long-encysted larvae actively exchange metabolites with the host. However, much new information has come to light concerning the responses of the host to the parasite at specified periods during infection. Certain anatomical and physiological alterations have been recognized in the excretory, endocrine, gastro-intestinal, cardiovascular and muscular systems, and much new information has been gained concerning acquired immunity. Despite recent advances, however, many gaps remain in our knowledge about host-parasite relationships in experimental trichiniasis, the research efforts so far having "only scratched the tough surface holding great stores of future knowledge". The reader then gets the benefit of a forecast of some of the problems which will concern parasitologists engaged on future research in this field.

The contribution of J. Llewellyn turns our attention to one of the groups of the Platyhelminthes, namely the monogenetic trematodes or Monogenea. These forms have been classified almost entirely on adult characters for almost one hundred years. This has been due to a shortage of information concerning the larval forms, of which only about thirty had been discovered by 1957, whereas more than 100 have now been described. These new studies have greatly extended the taxonomic range represented, which has made it possible for Llewellyn to attempt to trace out possible lines of evolution within the group. His contribution is by way of being a critique of the scheme of classification recently erected by Bychowsky, and while he disagrees with many of the taxonomic allocations which are made in this scheme, he agrees that monogeneans should be divorced from digeneans and associated with the gyrocotylidean cestodes, because of points of larval structure which are discussed. In this matter, as in others with which we have been concerned, there is much scope for future research.

In conclusion, it is necessary to make clear to the reader that the editor and the publishers appreciate the sensitivities of authors in respect to methods of spelling. In the biomedical literature of the U.S.A. nearly all words referring to "blood" are given the prefix "hemo-" instead of "haemo-", and in two contributions in this book many such words, and also other words, are given their American form; for instance, analyse, anemia, behavior, defense, diaphram, edema, esophagus, favor and favorable, fecal and feces, fiber, meager, molt, program, sulfadiazine and sulfate. The practice of this publishing house is to prepare manuscripts by American authors according to Webster and those by

English authors according to the Oxford rules, with slight variations. We owe a debt of gratitude to the staff of the Academic Press for efforts towards consistency in these respects, and in other matters concerning the preparation of this book. It is hoped that authors and readers will bear with minor irritations of spelling, word-building, hyphenation and literary style in the interests of international co-operation in book production.

BEN DAWES
Professor of Zoology

KING'S COLLEGE   (Parasitology)
UNIVERSITY OF LONDON
STRAND, LONDON, W.C.2   September 1962

CONTENTS

CONTRIBUTORS TO VOLUME 1 v
PREFACE vii

Experimental Research on Avian Malaria

CLAY G. HUFF

I. Introduction 1
II. Historical 2
III. Recent Advances in Research on Plasmodium 3
    A. Parasitology 3
    B. Cultivation 28
    C. Physiology and Cytochemistry 29
    D. Exoerythrocytic Stages 35
    E. Fine Structure 40
    F. Immunology 46
    G. Pathology 50
IV. Research on Haemoproteus 53
V. Research on Leucocytozoon 55
    A. Schizogony and Type of Host Cell 55
    B. Pathology 56
    C. Differences in Host Response 57
    D. Transmission 58
VI. Present Status of Research on Avian Malaria 60
VII. Areas for Future Development 60
    References 61

Coccidia and Coccidiosis
in the Domestic Fowl and Turkey

C. HORTON-SMITH AND P. L. LONG

I. Introduction 68
II. The Pathology and the Life Cycles of the Species of *Eimeria* in Fowls .. 68
    A. The Pathogenicity of *E. acervulina* 68
    B. The Pathogenicity and Life Cycle of *E. brunetti* ... 69
    C. The Life Cycle of *E. maxima* 70
    D. The Life Cycle and Pathology of *E. mitis* 73
    E. The Life Cycles of *E. necatrix* and *E. tenella* ... 74
III. The Pathology and the Life Cycle of the Species of *Eimeria* occurring in Turkeys 76
    A. The Life History of *E. adenoeides* 76
    B. The Life History and Pathogenicity of *E. meleagridis* .. 76
    C. The Life History and Pathogenicity of *E. meleagrimitis* .. 78
IV. Oocyst Production of Different Species 82
V. Cytochemical Observations on Stages of the Coccidial Life Cycle 83
    A. Desoxyribonucleic Acid (DNA) 83
    B. Ribonucleic Acid (RNA) 84

C. Proteins 85
D. Lipids 85
E. Carbohydrates 85
F. Protein-Carbohydrate Complex 88
G. Mucopolysaccharides 90
H. Enzyme Activity 91
VI. Immunity to Coccidiosis 91
A. The Phase of the Life Cycle Inducing the Immune Response...... 91
B. The Immunization of Chickens and the Immunizing Power of Different Species of Coccidia 92
    ent Species of Coccidia 92
C. The Fate of Sporozoites and Second Generation Merozoites of *E. tenella* in Fully Immune Chickens 93
D. The Duration of Immunity to Coccidiosis in the Absence of Reinfection 95
E. The Transference of Resistance to *E. tenella* from one Caecum to the to the Other in Individual Fowls........................... 96
F. Detection of Precipitating Antibodies and Tests for the Specificity of the Reactions 97
G. Precipitating Antibodies Associated with Immunity to Four Species of *Eimeria* in Fowls 98
H. Electrophoretic Studies 100
I. Detection of Lysins in the Sera of *E. tenella*- Immune Fowls 100
J. Attempts to Demonstrate Antibodies in Caecal Tissue of *E. tenella*-Immune Fowls 101
K. Attempts to Induce a Passive Immunity to *E. tenella* Infection.... 102
L. Cellular Responses....................................... 103
References 104

The Infective Stage of Nematode Parasites and its Significance in Parasitism

W. P. ROGERS AND R. I. SOMMERVILLE

I. Introduction 109
II. General Form of the Life Cycle 110
A. Introduction 110
B. Hatching of Eggs 111
C. The Moulting of Larvae 115
III. Modifications of the Life Cycle for Dispersal and Parasitism 118
IV. Infective Stages.. 122
A. Ensheathed Larvae as Agents of Infection................... 122
B. Eggs as Agents of Infection............................. 123
V. The Physiology of Infective Stages........................... 124
A. The Food Reserves 126
B. Oxygen Requirements 124
C. Metabolism... 120
D. End-Products of Metabolism 128
E. Permeability and Osmoregulation 139
VI. The Behaviour of Infective Stages........................... 131
A. The Behaviour of Trichostrongyles on Pasture................ 132
B. Behaviour and Infection via the Skin..................... 135
C. The Behaviour of Nematodes Infecting Plants................ 136
D. Periodicity of Microfilariae 137
VII. The Survival of Infective Stages............................. 138
A. Infective Larvae of Animal Parasites...................... 138
B. The Survival of Infective Eggs.......................... 140
C. The Survival of Plant-Parasitic Nematodes 141
D. General Comments on Survival Studies.................... 144

VIII. The Process of Infection 145
       A. The Infection of Animals *via* the Gut......................... 146
       B. Infection *via* the Surface of the Host......................... 154
       C. The Infection of Plants....................................... 156
  IX. The Nature of Infectiousness 163
       A. Metamorphosis and Infectiousness 164
       B. Mechanisms of Moulting and Metamorphosis.................... 165
       C. A General Hypothesis of Infectiousness as an Adaptation to
           Parasitism 166
       D. The Action of the Stimulus from the Host..................... 167
           Acknowledgement 171
           References 171

Parasitic Bronchitis

D. POYNTER

    I. Introduction 179
   II. The Parasite 179
  III. The Parasite in the Pasture.................................... 181
   IV. Pathology 187
    V. The Treatment of Husk.. 194
   VI. Naturally Acquired Immunity.................................... 195
  VII. Passive Immunization 196
 VIII. Active Immunization 197
   IX. The Measurement of Helminth Immunity.......................... 199
    X. Vaccination 201
   XI. The Mechanism of Immunity 206
  XII. Conclusion 208
        Acknowledgement 209
        References 209

Experimental Trichiniasis

JOHN E. LARSH, JR.

    I. Introduction 213
   II. Anatomical and Physiological Alterations in Hamsters, Rats and Mice 215
       A. Hamsters 215
       B. Rats... 221
       C. Mice... 237
  III. Summary and Forecast.. 280
        References 282

Larvae and Larval Development of Monogeneans

J. LLEWELLYN

    I. Introduction 287
   II. Morphology of Monogenean Larvae 288
       A. General Features 288
       B. External Ciliation 290
       C. The Haptor... 293
       D. The Alimentary Canal 303
       E. The Osmo-Regulatory System................................ 305
       F. Glands.. 307

G. Nervous System and Sense Organs.......................... 308
III. Post Onco miracidial Development............................... 309
IV. The Development of the Haptor of the Adult in Polyopisthocoty-
lineans.. 312
V. Discussion 315
VI. Summary 322
References 323

AUTHOR INDEX... 327
SUBJECT INDEX... 337

Experimental Research on Avian Malaria*

CLAY G. HUFF

*Naval Medical Research Institute, Bethesda,
Maryland, U.S.A.*

I. Introduction... 1
II. Historical.. 2
III. Recent Advances in Research on Plasmodium 3
    A. Parasitology 3
    B. Cultivation.. 28
    C. Physiology and Cytochemistry 29
    D. Exoerythrocytic Stages 35
    E. Fine Structure 40
    F. Immunology.. 46
    G. Pathology 50
IV. Research on Haemoproteus 53
V. Research on Leucocytozoon 55
    A. Schizogony and Type of Host Cell..................................... 55
    B. Pathology 56
    C. Differences in Host Response... 57
    D. Transmission.. 58
VI. Present Status of Research on Avian Malaria 60
VII. Areas for Future Development.. 60
    References... 61

I. INTRODUCTION

In attempting to review recent advances made in the study of bird malaria one immediately becomes aware of the large gap which exists between the last general review (Hewitt, 1940) of this field, and also of the question of the appropriateness of segregating this portion of malariology from the consideration of malariology as a whole. Since Hewitt's monograph was published tremendous advances have been made in many aspects of malariology through the study of avian malarial parasites. During World War II intensive efforts were made in this field. These were completed after the war ended. No review of this great mass of work has been published except what has been mentioned in reviews on chemotherapy, exoerythrocytic stages, physiology or other special divisions of malariology generally. Some bridge will need to be built over which we can pass to the advances of the past 5 to 7 years which

---

* The opinions or assertions contained herein are the private ones of the writer and are not to be construed as officia or reflecting the views of the Navy Department or the Naval Service at large.

1

is the period covered by this review. This bridge will be an unsatisfactory structure at best, but it will have to serve in lieu of a more complete pathway which is impossible to build within the confines of the allotted space. Nevertheless, an attempt will be made to sketch the broad scope of work accomplished during that period without reference to specific authors and publications.

There are many reasons against the artificial separation of work done upon the malaria of birds and that of other animals and of man. However, the reason for the separation is the need to keep this review within manageable proportions. Although malariology fortunately has developed as a whole without much emphasis having been placed upon the kind of host or of parasite, there are advantages in separating the work done on birds in that this points to certain differences that exist between the various aspects of the avian parasites and the mammalian ones as well as the differences in the physiology of birds and of mammals. Extrapolations from studies on one group of malarial infections to those on another have been very beneficial on the whole, but we must realize that extrapolations have their limitations.

As the title indicates we shall be concerned here with experimental research. Descriptions of new species, new host records, and other subjects not of an experimental nature are excluded. Moreover, the work on chemotherapy of avian malaria is omitted because of the belief that it has been adequately covered elsewhere. "Avian malaria" is here intended to include work upon *Haemoproteus* and *Leucocytozoon* as well as upon *Plasmodium*. "Recent" is a flexible term covering the period, 1955 to 1962 but somewhat earlier work is included in instances where discussion of the earlier work is necessary to an understanding of recent work. Otherwise references to earlier work are made for the convenience of the reader who wishes to supplement his knowledge of work discussed here by reading older papers having a direct bearing upon that work. Although there is some implication that inclusion of a review of a paper is considered to be an "advance" in knowledge, it is perhaps best for the sake of completeness to include most of the work which has been published in the period in question leaving to the reader the decision whether it is an "advance". However, omission of papers falling within this period should not necessarily be interpreted as belief that such papers are unworthy of inclusion by the reviewer because it is possible that some really significant papers have been inadvertently omitted.

II. HISTORICAL

The period between the appearance of Hewitt's (1940) monograph and the recent work covered by the present review saw a very great increase in the amount of experimental work on avian malaria. This increase was largely due to the increased importance of human malaria during World War II. Avian malarial parasites were already known to be excellent screening agents for antimalarial work and, in fact had contributed significantly to the chemotherapy of malaria before World War II. *P. gallinaceum* had been discovered in 1935 and *P. lophurae* in 1938. These organisms were capable of infecting domestic fowl. This proved to be a great boon to the screening program carried out during the war since the more readily available domestic chick could be used in great numbers whereas, previous to this time the canary was the chief laboratory animal. *P. lophurae* was soon adapted to domestic ducklings thus adding another species available in large numbers to the screening program. Both of these species of *Plasmodium* could also be studied in large chickens. This great collaborative effort toward the development of adequate therapeutic agents for malaria which still continues today is mentioned only to indicate its stimulus for malarial studies of various kinds. During the period of about 15 years with which we are concerned in this historical review the following research activities were either initiated or greatly accelerated: (1) the relationship between the sporozoite and the exoerythrocytic stage; (2) the use of the chick embryo as a host; (3) *in vitro* cultivation of both endogenous and exogenous stages; (4) the physiology of erythrocytic stages; (5) immunology; and (6) miscellaneous parasitological studies. Also significant research was carried out on *Leucocytozoon* and *Haemoproteus* infections. The history of malariology will record this period as one in which research on avian malaria will rank in importance along with the part it played in the discovery of the transmission of malaria. From this great burst of interest and effort many new problems were uncovered and new techniques developed. The remainder of this review will be concerned with progress within the past 5 to 7 years.

III. Recent Advances in Research on Plasmodium

A. PARASITOLOGY

Some attempt has been made to group together papers covering a wide range of subjects under this heading. The following subheadings will not in all cases include papers related only to the subheading because there is considerable overlap among the latter. However, this method of grouping appears preferable to a greater subdivision with the consequent cross references to individual papers which this would entail.

1. *Effects of High Altitude on Infections in the Vertebrate Host*

It has long been claimed that human malaria was mitigated by transfer of the patient to high altitudes. The two following reports touch upon this question. Geigy and Freyvogel (1954) compared the infections with *P. gallinaceum* in chickens under three different conditions: (1) at Basle; (2) at Jungfraujoch Station; and (3) in a low pressure chamber at Basle. They found scarcely any difference between the control infection in Basle and the corresponding series in the low pressure chamber and concluded that the decrease in oxygen tension is not the factor responsible for the influence of high altitudes on malarial infections. Likewise the parasitemia in the animals on Jungfraujoch Station was very similar to that in the animals in the other two circumstances. However, in the latter case the exoerythrocytic stages were strikingly higher in numbers, being nearly twice as many as in the controls. They point to the possibility that the non-specific host defenses may be improved at the higher altitude through activation of the reticulo-endothelial system. Since no indication is given in their paper of the numbers of animals employed in the experiments it is not possible to rule out the role of chance in explaining the higher degree of exoerythrocytic infection in the chickens held at the high altitude. Hughes and Tatum (1955) found that infections of canaries with *P. cathemerium* when kept in an atmosphere deficient in oxygen (75 mm Hg partial pressure) required a ten-fold increase of Primaquine for suppression as compared with similarly infected birds kept in the normal air pressure for 800 ft altitude. Comparison of the two sets of experiments is complicated by the fact that they involved different host animals, different parasites, and the possibility of the *cathemerium* infections being low in exoerythrocytic stages whereas in Geigy and Freyvogel's experiments these stages were numerous at the higher altitudes. It is apparent that the therapeutic effect of high altitude on human malarial infection is neither strengthened or disproved by these animal experiments.

2. *Natural Immunity and Susceptibility of the Vertebrate Host*

The following studies on isolation of new strains and testing of new hosts for known strains are valuable in increasing the number of possible host-parasite combinations available to the experimentalist for his specific need and also in adding to the fund of knowledge which ultimately may make possible an understanding of the factors which contribute to natural immunity and susceptibility of the host and to infectivity or non-infectivity of the parasite.

Manwell *et al.* (1957) isolated a strain of *P. circumflexum* from the White-Throated Sparrow (*Zonotrichia albicollis*) which produced "heavy and infrequently fatal infections in canaries", but produced only light or ephemeral infections in ducks (Peking ducklings). When inoculated into splenectomized ducklings there was no indication that innate immunity was weakened by splenectomy. A strain of *P. elongatum* isolated from the song sparrow (*Melospiza m. melodia*) was highly infectious to ducklings; mortality was as high as 25%. Parasites were found in the blood for 3–4 weeks. Splenectomy of ducklings younger than 3 weeks resulted in higher and more prolonged parasitemia. Normal ducklings developed an age resistance to *elongatum* at about 20 days of age. If splenectomy was performed on older ducklings the effect of age was almost completely nullified. A small minority (5%) exhibited age immunity in spite of splenectomy. They conclude that age immunity possibly differs in some way from innate as well as acquired immunity and that "possibly the importance of the spleen as a part of the immune mechanism may differ somewhat in different types of malaria and at different times in the course of infection". They found that the weight of the spleen relative to total body weight reaches a maximum at about 20 days of age. The correlation with the beginning of age resistance to *elongatum* should be noted. Polizzi Sciarrone (1957) found that chicks were non-susceptible to *P. praecox* (*relictum*) (Corradetti's strain) when erythrocytic stages were inoculated intramuscularly, intravenously, and intraperitoneally, Furthermore, blood from chicks taken 1 min after inoculation from canaries was not infectious when subinoculated to canaries. Since these results are contrary to earlier ones reported by Manwell (1933) the author interprets the difference in results to differences in strains. It is to be noted, however, that Manwell used larger dosages of parasites than were used by Polizzi Sciarrone.

The known capability of *P. lophurae* for infecting a wide spectrum of hosts was given more extended study by Jordan (1957) who reported on the behavior of this parasite in four species of birds: Chinese pheasants (*Phasianus colchicus*), coots (*Fulica americana*), domestic pigeons and (for comparison) domestic chickens. She found that in coots the length of the asexual cycle averaged less than 36 h; in pigeons about 56 h; and in pheasants about 36 h. The average number of merozoites per mature schizont was respectively 15.43 ± 0.11; 11.05 ± 0.05; 11.71 ± 0.22; and 13.77 ± 0.06 for these four hosts. The parasiticidal effects of innate immunity were fairly uniform in chickens and pheasants during the acute rise of parasitemia; about 65% of the merozoites being destroyed in the chicken and 75–80% in the pheasants. The added action of acquired immunity resulted in a rapid drop of parasitemia in both of these hosts. In chickens there was a decrease in production and an increase in the ability to destroy the parasite; hence a sharp drop in parasitemia following the crisis. In pheasants the rate of reproduction remained fairly constant throughout the infection but the height of parasitemia was lower than in chickens. This was interpreted as innate differences in the hosts in reference to their abilities to produce parasiticidal antibodies. Reproduction was lowest in pigeons and highest in coots. Parasite destruction in pigeons was 50% in the first segmentation, 75% in the second, 83% in the third and nearly complete in the three subsequent segmentations. In coots there was less than 25% destruction in the first, nearly 80% in the second and over 98% in the third segmentation. In spite of the difference in rate of destruction in the two hosts the parasitemia progressively increased. The result in the pigeon was recovery and latency whereas it was usually death in the coot. Analysis of the factors involved in the different behavior of the parasite in these four hosts and of their effects upon the host were proposed by the author. These explanations may possibly be on unsafe ground in certain particulars because of her acceptance of the point of view that a lowering of mean merozoite number is a result (and therefore a measure) of acquired immunity. Some doubt has been cast upon this assumption by work reported elsewhere in this review (Huff and Marchbank, 1955; Huff et al., 1958).

An enhanced virulence of a strain of P. lophurae normally maintained in turkey poults was observed when it was passed serially in hybrid New Hampshire x White Rock chicks for 4 years (Hull, 1958). It was possible by regulating inoculum size to attain peak parasitemias of 50–60% consistently on the 4th post inoculation day.

Since Pipkin and Jensen (1958) reviewed the published reports on attempts to establish various species of avian malaria in chick embryos additional attempts have been reported. Manwell and Robinson (1962) attempted to adapt Plasmodium elongatum and P. hexamerium to chick and duck embryos. The former had been isolated from a song sparrow (Melospiza melodia melodia) in 1953 and the latter from a Lincoln's sparrow (Melospiza lincolni) in 1947. P. elongatum is unique in its ability to invade all blood and blood-forming cells and P. hexamerium is representative of a fairly coherent group of species characterized by their small size and small number of merozoites produced by the schizonts; some related forms are P. vaughani and P. rouxi. They found that duck embryos are susceptible to both species. Ten embryos of Khaki Campbell ducks that lived for 72 h following inoculation of erythrocytic forms of P. hexamerium became infected and the parasitemias increased until the death of the embryos. None of the embryos hatched and none lived beyond 11 days after inoculation. In embryos of White Peking ducks infections were accomplished in twenty-two experiments involving 480 embryos. Three serial passages were made. Peak parasitemias were usually higher than in donor birds. Embryos of all ages were infected and two of them hatched with parasitemias which continued until they were sacrificed. No exoerythrocytic stages were seen in impression preparations of liver, spleen, brain, bone marrow, heart and skeletal muscles. (In the reviewer's experience exoerythrocytic stages may easily be missed in impression smears when they can be found in sections of the same organ.) Chick embryos were only slightly infected with *P. elongatum*. Only nine of 623 inoculated embryos showed any evidence of infection and the parasitemia did not exceed 50% per 10,000 blood cells. Two of the embryos inoculated on the 14th day of incubation hatched and maintained parasites in their blood for 2 days. Only about half of the chick embryos inoculated with *P. hexamerium* became infected and most of these died even though the parasitemia had passed its peak in some of them. It was not possible to transmit infections to other chicks from the chicks which hatched from infected embryos. No alteration in morphology or periodicity of schizogonic development was observed. No exoerythrocytic stages were found.

In view of the rather general acceptance of the existence of a fairly strict host specificity of species of *Plasmodium* the papers of McGhee describing successful adaptation of an avian species of this genus to mice and of a mammalian species to avian embryos have necessitated a change in our thinking about the absolute character of host specificity. In 1951 he was able by intravenous inoculation of chick embryo blood heavily parasitized with *P. lophurae* into infant mice to produce a low grade infection in the latter host. Then by alternating embryo and mouse passages he was able to produce progressively higher peaks of parasitemia in the mouse and after four such passages he was able to pass the infection from one infant mouse to another without diminution of viability in the parasite. Since the erythrocytes of mature mice were as susceptible as those of infant mice the difficulties in making the transfer from avian to mammalian host were not explicable on basis of the age of the erythrocyte *per se* but must have been due to the rapidly developing ability of the mouse to destroy avian cells. Therefore the defense mechanisms of the growing mouse were the most important factor. At first the morphology of *P. lophurae* underwent changes in the mouse but these tended to diminish with passage. It is interesting that the parasite was able to utilize the hemoglobin of the new host and to produce malarial pigment somewhat different in the mouse. The mouse adapted strain was maintained for 3 years without returning it to the chick embryo (McGhee, 1956). During the first 15 months the average height of the parasitemia increased steadily and a comparison of the course of infection in individual mice of the strain during its 1st and 3rd years of passage indicated a consistently higher degree and a longer duration of the parasitemia. Gametocytes appeared after 9 months residence in the mouse and the mean number of merozoites per mature schizont had been temporarily disturbed by residence in the mouse. In this connection it may be mentioned that Huff (1958) reviewed the host influences on Haemosporidian parasites and found, in general, that most of the effects, so far observed, were of such an evanescent nature as those described by McGhee.

McGhee (1957) tested the comparative susceptibility of the red cells of five species of birds and three species of mammals to four species of avian malaria. The washed red cells were injected intravenously into chicken and duck embryos 2 days following the inoculation of malarial parasites at the age of 10 and 13–14 days respectively. Counts of the numbers of parasites in the introduced cells were made at 4 and 24 h and compared with the calculated number of infective organisms in the blood of the bird immediately after the introduction of the foreign cells. The index of susceptibility of the erythrocytes was the percentage of merozoites which invaded the foreign erythrocytes. Some degree of susceptibility was found in all avian cells for all four of the avian parasites. In addition *Plasmodium lophurae* invaded erythrocytes of the rabbit, mouse, and baby rat. *P. circumflexum* was similar to *P. lophurae* in ability to invade avian red cells but was able, of the mammalian cells, to invade only the cells of the baby rat. Invasion of avian cells by *cathemerium* was less than in *lophurae* and *circumflexum* and of mammalian cells only an exceptional cell from adult rats was invaded. *P. gallinaceum* had the lowest degree of invasiveness of the four parasites tested. Aside from chick erythrocytes it invaded the avian cells only to a slight degree and was not found to invade any of the mammalian erythrocytes. His results led to the conclusion that invasion of the erythrocytes is determined by some substance originating in the parasite rather than by differences in the strength of the host membranes or the mechanical ability of parasites to penetrate these membranes.

A comprehensive study of the loss and replacement of red blood cells in infections of mammalian and avian hosts by various species of *Plasmodium* was made by Zuckerman. We shall deal here only with her paper on avian infections (1960b). References to her previous publications on mammalian malaria will be found in this paper. Using untreated and prebled mature chickens infected with *P. gallinaceum* and with *P. lophurae* as compared with infections with these two parasites in untreated chicks she found a close similarity in the extent, duration, blood loss sustained by the host, and reticulocyte response in the peripheral circulation in the infections. No significant differences were observed between infections in untreated and prebled adults when infected with either parasite. Initial infections with *P. gallinaceum* were severe and uniformly fatal; initial infections with *P. lophurae* were severe in chicks and severe to mild in adults (all but one, a prebled adult, survived the infection). There was a clear reticulocyte response to both infections; very marked in chicks which died after 2 weeks infection with *P. gallinaceum*; varied in extent with the degree of parasitemia with *P. lophurae* and was clearly evident in one animal with a maximum parasitemia of 1%. Blood loss was very extensive in adult birds infected with *gallinaceum* and could all be attributed to the rupture of cells by emerging parasites. In *lophurae* infections blood loss was extensive throughout and in infections which were moderate or mild it was in excess of that due to rupture of cells by emerging parasites. The invasion of various stages of the developing erythrocyte was random in both infections but with a slight bias in favor of reticulocytes of sparse reticulation in *gallinaceum* infections and in favor of normocytes in *lophurae* infections. Zuckerman could not determine from a study of the blood loss or parasitemia the reason for 100% mortality of hosts infected with *gallinaceum* and its absence in hosts infected with *lophurae*. The reviewer suggests the possibility that exoerythrocytic stages might account for the high mortality in chickens infected with *gallinaceum*, whereas the known scarcity of these forms in chickens infected with *lophurae* would spare the hosts from death. If the two infections had been studied in turkeys the opposite result in mortality would have been expected.

Since the analysis of the factors which determine compatibility between host and parasite are so complex *in vivo*, Huff *et al.* (1960b) attempted to utilize a technique, developed by Algire *et al.* (1954), for sequestering exoerythrocytic stages of *P. gallinaceum* and *P. fallax* in both susceptible and insusceptible hosts. The technique (described in detail in Algire's papers) consisted of constructing lucite rings to which were attached discs of millepore membranes of different porosities. Two sizes of rings were used such that one fitted snugly within the other and could be sealed, thus enclosing the infected material. The whole chamber was then inserted into various locations inside the hosts (including embryonated eggs) and later removed for observation or viability tests. Chick embryo tissues heavily infected with exoerythrocytic stages of *P. gallinaceum* placed in chambers of $0.45 \pm 0.02\mu$ pore size and inserted into chickens resulted in infections in eleven of sixty-six of the recipients. Nine turkeys serving as recipients of similar chambers became infected whereas no infections resulted in ducks in which such chambers remained for 2–14 days. It was thus shown that some stage of the parasite was capable of passing through membranes of the above pore size. Development of exoerythrocytic states within chambers placed inside embryonated eggs occurred in two of twenty attempts. In one of these the growth was heavier than observed in any tissue yet observed, either *in vivo* or in tissue cultures. Tissues heavily infected with exoerythrocytic stages of *P. fallax* were placed in chambers with millepore membranes of three different porosities; in addition to that mentioned above,

B*

ones of pore size $0.3 \pm 0.02\mu$ and 50 ± 3 mμ were used. Such chambers placed subcutaneously into mice were removed at 3-, 7-, 14-, and 21-day intervals and their contents inoculated into turkey poults. Parasites in six of twenty chambers were found to be viable after residence of 7, 14, and 21 days whereas no infections resulted in the mice. These latter experiments further confirm the findings of McGhee (1951) reported elsewhere in this review about the broader capabilities of an avian parasite to live in foreign hosts than formerly believed.

The duration of the viability of sporozoites of *P. gallinaceum* in the blood of canaries and rats was tested by Raffaele (1955). Subinoculation of blood from canaries into chicks at intervals of 10, 30 and 45 min following the inoculation of sporozoites into the donors resulted in infections in the chicks receiving blood at the 10-, and 30-min intervals but not in those at the 45-min interval. He carried out control experiments in which the sporozoites were inoculated initially into chicks. He reported viability of sporozoites in these experiments after 1 h of residence in the plasma of the chicks which received the initial inoculations of sporozoites. Similar experiments were carried out using rats as the initial recipients of the sporozoites. Viable sporozoites were recovered from the rats (as shown by subinoculation to chicks) after being in the plasma of the rats from 15 to 105 min. The hypothesis is advanced that natural immunity of the host resides in the cellular rather than the humoral elements of the blood

3. *Effects of Irradiation on Exogenous Stages and their Hosts*

Terzian (1953) found that although *Aedes aegypti* was extremely resistant to X-irradiation (30 000 to 40 000 r being required to produce 100% mortality on the 12th – 21st-post-irradiation day), doses of 5000–30 000 r produced a significant increase in innate resistance to *P. gallinaceum*. This effect was quantitatively correlated with increasing doses of irradiation. He found, however, that both penicillin and sulfadiazine which he had previously shown to be capable of increasing the mosquito susceptibility to infection is capable of reversing the effect of X-irradiation (5000–30 000 r) on susceptibility in this host-parasite combination when these compounds were administered between the irradiation and the time of infection.

Terzian (1961) extended his previous studies on irradiation by exposing various stages of the sporogonous cycle of *P. gallinaceum* to γ-radiation. No development was completed in parasites given dosages of 20 000 r or more. Dosages of 5000 to 30 000 r at the end of 24 h produced no visible evidence until the 4th day of development. Depending upon the dosage administered certain percentages of oocysts developed a small vacuole on the 4th day in the main aggregate of pigment granules. The vacuole in certain oocysts appeared to originate around the more active granule which he termed the "k-granule". This was the first observable effect of the radiation. Progressively the surviving oocysts contained more clearly defined vacuoles and were retarded in their development. At 5000 r only 50% of the parasites developed into mature oocysts; at 10 000 r 22% and at 15 000 r less than 1% developed into normal, mature oocysts. After the 6th day other degenerative changes consisting of a wide variety of morphological modifications began to occur. These included changes in the general appearance and breaking up and shrinking of the protoplasm. As in the case of his work on the effects of various drugs on the sporogonous cycle (1955), meaningful descriptions are difficult to make, so to better understand their appearance the reader is urged to study the thirty-three photomicrographs which are a part of his report. In his opinion the effects of radiation are manifested through interference with individual systems which make up the physiological complex of the parasite, the time of the effect upon each one being probably important in producing the wide variety of effects observed.

Irradiation studies on gametocytes and immature stages of mosquitoes were also carried out by Ward *et al.* (1960). They irradiated gametocytes of *P. gallinaceum in vivo* at dosages between 500 and 20 000 r. The oocysts which developed in the mosquitoes thus irradiated grew more slowly and exhibited abnormal development and increased mortality in proportion to the dosage. At 1000 r there was a significant decrease in mean oocyst size. Mortality in the oocysts attributable to the action of dominant lethals was 60% at 4000 r and 95% at 20 000 r. In oocysts developing from gametocytes which received 8000 r or more, the sporozoites appeared to be non-infective. When immature stages of the mosquitoes were irradiated (the larvae at 500–1,500 r; the pupae at 3000–5000 r) and the F_1 progeny from the mosquitoes which emerged from them were fed on non-irradiated parasites these mosquitoes had a 2–6-fold increase in susceptibility to infection as compared with unexposed mosquitoes.

They found at least two types of delayed death following irradiation. There was a great reduction in mean oocyst count. This can probably be attributed to the action of dominant lethal mutations. Since Bano (1959) has demonstrated that post zygotic meiosis occurs 53–55 h after an infected meal it seems probable that the irradiated zygotes were able to survive until division and that death followed as a result of chromosomal aberrations between 2 and 3 days after irradiation. Although these authors found no effect of X-irradiation upon the susceptibility of the mosquito to *P. gallinaceum* it should be noted that the dosages which they used were below the dosages at which Terzian

(1953) had a significant increase in the innate resistance of the mosquitoes to the same malarial parasite.

4. *Cytology and Genetics of the Parasites*

On the basis of observations made by the phase contrast microscope on living erythrocytic parasites Wolcott (1957) described what he believed to be chromosomes in two species of avian malaria (*P. lophurae* and *P. relictum*) and in *P. floridense* of lizards, *P. berghei* of rodents; and *P. knowlesi*. The structures which he described as chromosomes were two in number and dot-like in morphology in the two avian parasites. He did not offer proof that these organelles were chromosomes. As Huff *et al.* (1960a) have indicated from their studies of exoerythrocytic stages of *P. gallinaceum* and *P. fallax* a similar organelle is easily seen in all stages of development of these parasites. They observed in time-lapse studies nuclear divisions in which a spindle was observed but chromosomes were not visible in connection with the spindle fibers. They believed that the structures similar to the ones considered by Wolcott to be chromosomes were nucleoli. These structures were similar in size and in their relationship to the nucleus to structures in fixed and stained material which had the characteristics of nucleoli (Huff and Coulston, 1944). Although not mentioned in their paper, Huff *et al.* (1960a) noted that these nucleoli were single in all stages of development except that they were sometimes double in the newly formed merozoites in the schizont. In nuclear division the nucleolus was the last thing to divide and this division did not resemble chromosome splitting. It is apparent from this wide diversion of views that this subject needs more study before clarification will be achieved.

Bano (1959) has reviewed the earlier literature on meiosis in *Plasmodium* and has reported on cytological studies made on the early oocysts of *Plasmodium gallinaceum* and six species of *Plasmodium* of mammals. After obtaining unsatisfactory results with four different staining techniques upon sectioned material, a method involving making smears from crushed midguts was employed which made possible the satisfactory study of the young, entire oocysts. According to Bano's observations the ookinetes and oocysts up to 55 h of age were uninucleate. The sequence of events in the meiotic division, which started after 55 h, began with the disappearance of the nuclear membrane. It will be noted that according to cinematographic studies of Huff *et al.* (1960a), on this parasite in tissue culture the nuclear membrane remained intact in all mitotic divisions observed in the schizogonic exoerythrocytic stages. The prophase which was described by Bano involved the formation of a stumpy "bow-shaped" spireme which became condensed, segmented and resulted in four diploid chromosomes at mid-prophase, two of these being small and dot-like whereas the other two were larger and "J" shaped. In metaphase homologous chromosomes paired. In early anaphase the two homologous groups of haploid chromosomes were observed, each being composed of one large and one small chromosome. Telophase resulted in the binucleate condition with intact nuclear membranes. In contrast to the haploid chromosome number of 2, Bano reported the number as 4 for *P. cynomolgi* and *P. inui*, and 3 for *P. gonderi*; the number was 2 in *P. knowlesi, P. berghei*, and *P. vivax.*

Since susceptibility of some mosquitoes to avian malaria is known to be hereditary, it is important to know whether there is any correlation between this characteristic and its resistance to DDT and other residual insecticides. Mohan (1955, 1960) has shown that two strains of *Culex fatigans* — one DDT-resistant and the other DDT-susceptible — were equally susceptible to *P. relictum*. The exogenous development of the parasite occurred in the normal manner in mosquitoes highly resistant to DDT even when the mosquitoes were exposed to DDT deposits 24 or 48 h after the blood meal. The sporozoite infection rates were the same in treated and untreated groups of mosquitoes. It was concluded that DDT had no effect upon the capacity of *C. fatigans* for transmitting *P. relictum* and that the insecticide itself had no adverse effect on the parasite.

One of the most interesting phases in modern malariology was carried out by Dr. Joseph Greenberg and his associates in the period just preceding the time covered by this review. This work dealt with attempts to study the genetics in *P. gallinaceum* through markers produced by various experimental laboratory procedures, and to utilize these genetic studies in an effort to understand the chemotherapy of therapeutic agents, expecially drug resistance. A succinct summary of these findings up to 1955 was given by Greenberg (1955). Some papers were subsequently published, one of which will be here reviewed (1956). Because of the importance of this work a short summary will be given of the earlier work before reviewing the latter (1956). From the "normal" or SP strain which was characterized by (a) the development of fixed tissue infections soon after inoculation of sporozoites; (b) a parasitemia appearing about the 7th day after inoculation and consisting of both asexual stages and gametocytes; (c) a shift in the exoerythrocytic infection to endothelial cells; and (d) fatal termination due primarily to massive infections of the capillary endothelial cells but probably assisted by the heavy parasitemia, two aberrant strains developed. One of these, called the M strain, was completely benign and the tissue forms were either absent or very few in number in both blood- or sporozoite-induced infections. The other, BI, strain was a lethal strain

characterized by the absence of normal erythrocytic schizonts or gametocytes. Death occurred from the late exoerythrocytic infection before
development of a true parasitemia. From the rare erythrocytic parasites infections could be established and passed by blood. These eventually produced small numbers of gametocytes. However when passed
through mosquitoes the strain again was sterile. These strains were
considered as putative "mutants" of the SP strain; their characteristics being heritable and mutable. The two mutant strains were transferred to the same animal and large numbers of mosquitoes fed upon
the latter. The sporozoites from these mosquitoes were pooled and
inoculated into chicks. These chicks had gametocytes in their blood and
also died of exoerythrocytic infections; hence the infections possessed
one characteristic of each parent strain; lethality from the BI and
transferability by mosquitoes from the M. On second and subsequent
mosquito passages none of the infected chicks died of exoerythrocytic
infections. Their infections were indistinguishable from the M strain. At
this point several possible explanations existed: (1) lethality and non-
transferability could have been dominant and closely linked; (2) no
hybridization could have occurred, and the BI strain dropped out
because of its non-transferability; or (3) the characteristics were due to
cytoplasmic inheritance rather than dependent upon genes. In the
meantime a BI strain had been made resistant to sixty-four times the
amount of pyrimethamine necessary to stop the infection in non-
resistant parasites. The above experiment was repeated substituting
the resistant BI strain for the non-resistant one used in it. Infections
produced from mosquitoes infected from birds with this combination
of strains were again all benign. However, because of the added marker
(pyrimethamine resistance) it was possible to recognize parasites from
sporozoite-induced infections as coming from the BI strain. They had
retained their benign characteristic as well as resistance to the drug.
Although at this point it would appear that hybridization had occurred
there were some possible alternate explanations. Another experiment
was tried using a pyrimethamine-resistant M strain (benign) and a
pyrimethamine-sensitive SP strain. The result was an infection partially
and irregularly lethal, and drug resistant which subsequently yielded
to a benign infection after approximately ten passages.

In his subsequent publication Greenberg (1956) reported upon two
experiments. In the first, a BI strain with an 800-fold resistance to
pyrimethamine was mixed with the SP strain as in the previous experiments. In the mosquito passaged strains where no selection was
made for pyrimethamine resistance the drug resistance disappeared and
the mortality averaged 90% over eight to nine transfers. Where selection was made for pyrimethamine resistance after the first mosquito

passage drug resistance persisted and the average mortality was 33%. In the second experiment the combination was a BI strain with sixty-four-fold resistance to pyrimethamine and thirty-two-fold resistance to metachloridine and the normal SP strain. In the transfers from this mixture metachloridine resistance could not be demonstrated after eight transfers during which selection was made for pyrimethamine resistance. Although there seems to be little doubt that Greenberg demonstrated hybridization among some of these variant strains an exact genetic analysis is not possible. It was a great loss to malariology, protozoology, and genetics that with this valuable armamentarium of variant strains in his possession and standing on the threshold of possible unravelling of the complexities of the genetics of drug resistance Greenberg found it necessary to terminate his studies and that no one was prepared to take over the work and make use of the strains which he had so painstakingly acquired.

5. *Growth of Exogenous Stages* in vivo *and* in vitro

In an earlier publication Weathersby (1952) had shown that viable sporozoites could be obtained from *Aedes aegypti* into the hemocoeles of which had been introduced all stages in the exogenous cycle of *Plasmodium gallinaceum* (gametocytes, oocysts of various ages, and sporozoites). In order to clarify the location and development of the oocysts he (1954) made serial sections of mosquitoes into which blood of a chicken infected with *P. gallinaceum* had been injected. The mosquitoes were killed and fixed 7 or 8 days following the injections. A portion of the lot was allowed to live until the 12th day and then dissected and their salivary glands examined. In one lot seven of the seventeen which were injected had sporozoites in their salivary glands. In the fixed and sectioned mosquitoes normal looking oocysts were found in all three of the body divisions but more than half were in the thorax. They were seen attached to fat bodies, in and on striated muscle of the thorax, on the ventral nerve ganglion, on tracheae, adjacent to the integument, on the ventral diverticulum and on malpighian tubules. Some were free in the hemacoele, none was seen on the midgut but one was found on the foregut. Weathersby thus proved beyond any doubt that passage of the zygote through and development on the stomach wall were not essential. Having demonstrated the ability of the various exogenous stages of *Plasmodium gallinaceum* to develop into viable sporozoites in *Aedes aegypti* Weathersby (1960b) repeated these experiments with *P. fallax* and *A. albopictus*. Of 476 individual mosquitoes which survived the inoculation of these various stages sixty *A. albopictus* were capable of transmitting the infection to turkey poults. This successful repetition on another parasite-host combination of his former experiment proves that he was not dealing with unique conditions and indicates the probability that most parasites may be able to develop in susceptible mosquitoes without previous contact with the alimentary tract of the latter. Furthermore, the inability of *P. fallax* to develop in the normally refractory host *Culex pipiens*, which he demonstrated by the same techniques, indicates that the factors involved in mosquito susceptibility or insusceptibility do not reside in the stomach wall, but are systemic. Although the growth of the exogenous stages of these two parasites in the hemocoeles of the mosquito hosts was brought about experimentally by parenteral injection it is very interesting that Garnham *et al.* (1961) have shown that the hemocoele is the natural site of development of *Hepatocystis* (=*Plasmodium*) *kochi* of monkeys in *Culicoides adersi.*

Having successfully demonstrated that normal completion of the sporogonic stages of two species of avian malaria could occur in mosquitoes following the introduction of gametocytes or oocysts into the hemocoel Weathersby (1960a) proceeded to show that the injection of small pieces of the brain from chick embryos heavily infected with exoerythrocytic stages of *P. gallinaceum* was followed by capability of the injected mosquitoes to produce infection in chicks through biting the latter. Since infection in chicks could be produced by bites from mosquitoes as early as 3 days following the injection of the mosquitoes with the infected brain, it may safely be concluded that the infections in the mosquitoes were not from gametocytes in the inoculum because a minimum of 8 days was necessary under similar environmental conditions for development of sporozoites from gametocytes. Some of the infections in chicks resulted as early as 2 days (and as late as 20 days) following bites of the mosquitoes. This would indicate that the exoerythrocytic stages were probably capable of producing a form which could enter the salivary glands and then to enter erythrocytes immediately whereas it is well known that erythrocytic infection cannot be produced from sporozoites in less than 4 days.

The uneven distribution of oocysts on the stomachs of infected mosquitoes noted by earlier investigators led Stohler (1957) to make a more thorough study of the relationship of the peritrophic membrane of the midgut of mosquitoes in relation to the penetration of the malarial zygote through the wall prior to the growth of the oocysts. He demonstrated that in *Aedes aegypti* the peritropic membrane is always regenerated after each blood meal and is later discharged along with the undigested contents of the stomach. When a blood meal has been ingested the chitin and protein containing substances secreted by the midgut epithelium solidifies and envelops the engorged blood. In electron micrographs of the peritropic membrane a "dispersion texture" was observed which changed its character during the time required for digestion of the blood meal. The membrane is penetrable by the zygote at any place. However, its penetrability decreases with time and is impenetrable by the zygotes after 30 h. He reports that the ookinete penetrates the gut wall intercellularly. He offers circumstantial evidence for the occurrence of a post-zygotic meiosis.

For a number of years Dr. Gordon H. Ball has been attempting to grow the exogenous stages of *Plasmodium relictum in vitro*. He and Chao (1960) have reported upon successful cultivation in a series of steps from the gametocytes in the lumen of *Culex tarsalis*, the ookinete and the oocyst to the sporozoite. References to papers on earlier steps in this endeavor are given in their paper. Complete development of one entire cycle has not yet been obtained in the same culture. The composition of the medium used is too complex to be given in detail here but in general it contains a basic salt solution buffered with phosphates and bicarbonates, glucose, amino acids, B vitamins, purines and pyrimidines, chick serum and chick embryo extract. The pH was adjusted to 6.8 and the vessels containing the cultures were gassed with a mixture of 5% CO_2 and 95% air and rocked seven times a minute. They were maintained at 22–25°C. As yet, no infections in birds have resulted from injecting the oocysts containing sporozoites which have developed *in vitro*.

6. Gametogony and Gametocyte Infectivity

The literature on gametogenesis in Haemosporidiidea which had been published up to 1954 was well reviewed by Bishop (1955). She gave particular attention to the genus *Plasmodium*. Although her review should be read in its entirety by persons interested especially in this subject, her general conclusions based upon the literature up to that time will be briefly noted here. She emphasized the incompleteness of our knowledge of the nuclear changes occurring in gametogenesis and fertilization and the factors controlling gametocyte production. She suggested the possibility of the occurrence of a post-zygotic meiosis in *Plasmodium*. She reviewed evidence which in some species of *Leucocytozoon* and *Haemoproteus* indicated that the physiological state of the host was an important factor in the production of gametocytes. Other factors affecting the numbers of gametocytes formed were (1) type of host; (2) method of transmission; (3) small doses of pamaquin and primaquine; and (4) the action of sulfadiazine, proguanil or 2:4 di-amino-6: 7-di-isopropylpteridine in producing resistance to these substances in *P. gallinaceum*. At that time no correlation had been demonstrated in species of *Plasmodium* between acquired immunity and gametocyte formation although some passive transfer of an adverse effect on infectivity of gametocytes to mosquito by serum taken at the peak of parasitemia in birds heavily infected with *P. gallinaceum* had been noted.

The factors which control the release of gametocytes from erythrocytes and exflagellation of the microgametocytes have been sought since Ross' studies late in the 19th century. The various theories and experimental studies of these problems were reviewed by Bishop and McConnachie (1956) who reported on their own attempts to determine what these factors are in *P. gallinaceum* infection in chicks. From a variety of experiments they found that pH of the medium containing the infected erythrocytes was not the only factor concerned in release of gametocytes and exflagellation. In infected blood exposed to air or N_2 or in isotonic alkaline Tris buffer with pH of 8.0, normal development occurred but it was partially inhibited in this same buffer at pH below 7.38. When Diamox (2 acetylamino-1, 3, 4-thiadiazole-5-sulphonamide; a powerful inhibitor of carbonic anhydrase) was given intravenously to infected birds, the blood from the birds drawn 45 min later and exposed to air was a suitable medium for normal emergence of gametocytes and exflagellation in spite of the fact that the pH was lower than that of freshly drawn blood. Normal emergence and development of gametocytes was inhibited in washed parasitized erythrocytes suspended in isotonic buffer of pH 7.78 or 8.20 but this effect was reversed when the infected red cells were resuspended in plasma. They interpreted these results to mean that there is a factor present in plasma which is necessary for normal development of the gametocytes.

These same authors (1960) continued their investigations on the conditions necessary for release of gametocytes from erythrocytes and the exflagellation of the microgametocyte. Since they had previously found evidence that there was a factor in chicken plasma necessary to emergence of gametocytes and subsequent exflagellation they attempted to determine whether this effect was specific. When infected erythrocytes were washed and placed in normal chick plasma or serum, normal Seitz-filtered horse serum, heat (56°C) inactivated Seitz-filtered horse serum, and saline they found that emergence and exflagellation in both types of horse serum equalled if not exceeded that in chick serum and that the gametocytes so treated were capable of developing into oocysts in *Aedes aegypti*. Emergence and exflagellation were rare in saline. Results similar to those found from the use of horse serum were found in rabbit plasma. Hence the favorable effect of the fluid portion of blood was not specific to chickens. They compared hyperimmune with normal chick plasma and found no significant difference in the time of onset or frequency of exflagellation and concluded that any inhibitory action of immune plasma must either affect the maturation of macrogametocytes or some later stage in their development. While this may be the case for the *in vitro* experiments it would not rule out the possibility of a deleterious action on an earlier stage of the active immunity *in vivo* shown by Huff *et al.*, 1958. Since they had previously shown that isotonic sodium chloride was a poor medium for the *in vitro* emergence of gametocytes and exflagellation they next undertook a comprehensive study of the ions necessary for normal development *in vitro*. They found that a solution containing NaCl, KCl, CaCl₂, Na₂ HPO₂, MgSO₄, NaHCO₃ and Tris buffer, isotonic to bird blood and at pH 8 the development of the gametocytes was comparable to that in horse serum or chick plasma or serum. Inhibition was effected by the omission of Na or HCO₃ ions but not by Mg, K, Ca, SO₄ or HPO₄ ions. Within the range of inorganic salts tested, Na, HCO₃, and Cl ions constituted the minimal requirement for *in vitro* exflagellation.

In attempting to analyze the influence exerted by the vertebrate host on ability of the gametocyte to produce oocysts in the mosquito, Huff and Marchbank (1955) extended their study to include seven combinations of parasites, avian hosts and mosquitoes. These included *P. gallinaceum*, *P. fallax*, and *P. cathemerium*; chicks, pigeons, guinea fowl, turkeys, and canaries; *Aedes aegypti*, *A. albopictus*, *Culex pipiens*, and *C. tarsalis*. They found that in twenty-two infections the peak of oocyst production consistently preceded the peak of parasitemia by 1 to 4 days which indicated that there was a precipitate fall in oocyst numbers during the period when the number of gametocytes was still increasing. The patterns of oocyst production during the course of infection in the vertebrate host were similar in the three species of parasites studied with the exception that in *P. cathemerium* infections in canaries there was a recovery in the ability of gametocytes to produce oocysts 3 days after the beginning of the decline. In one instance in which the experiment was carried for a longer period of time a second peak of oocyst production occurred even though there was no concurrent change in numbers of gametocytes in the blood. The two species of mosquitoes, *Culex pipiens* and *C. tarsalis*, were fed upon the same canaries infected with *P. cathemerium* and the oocysts resulting from the feedings were counted. The numbers of oocysts were greater in *C. tarsalis* than in *C. pipiens* on each of the days that feedings were made on the two infected birds but there was a close parallelism in oocyst numbers during the course of infections in the two birds. This indicated a sensitive response of the gametocytes to some kind of influence of the avian host regardless of the species of mosquito in which the tests were made. The behavior of *P. fallax* in widely different hosts was reflected in the quality of the gametocytes produced. Patterns of change in oocyst numbers were very much alike in individual turkeys but very variable in different pigeons. The quality of the gametocytes was poor in chicks (when numbers of oocysts were compared with numbers of gametocytes ingested), but was very good in guinea fowl. Fairly good infections were produced in *Aedes albopictus* even when gametocytes were not seen in blood smears on 5 of the 8 days on which they fed. Oocyst size did not vary with fluctuations in degree of parasitemia or number of oocysts per mosquito; an indication that any adverse effect on gametocytes by the avian host did not persist in the resulting oocysts. No changes in rate of reproduction in the asexual stages paralleling the changes in infectiousness of gametocytes were reflected in the mean numbers of merozoites per schizont.

Attempts were made (Huff *et al.*, 1958) to analyze the factors involved in the phenomenon so generally found in the work reported above. Since the changes in the quality of infectivity of gametocytes were so closely associated with the course of parasitemia in the avian host attempts were made to test whether the adverse effect was produced by a deficiency in the host as the result of the progressive development of the infection or to some immune mechanism which came into play during the infection. To test the first possibility the following substances were administered during the course of infections but without any observed effect: uninfected whole blood, coenzyme A, ferrous sulfate, sodium glutathione, calcium pantothenate, and sucrose. Other experiments performed to test this same possibility were: (1) daily bleeding of the hosts during the course of their infection, and (2) pigeons were first inoculated with *P. relictum* (1P strain) followed 3 days later by the inoculation of *P. fallax*, then *A. albopictus* were fed daily on the pigeons (this mosquito was not susceptible to infection with the *relictum* strain but was highly susceptible to *P. fallax*). Neither of these experiments indicated any adverse effect on the gametocytes as compared to controls. Passive transfer of serum from hyperimmunized birds did not indicate any adverse effect on the gametocytes. Four experiments (three with *P. gallinaceum* in chickens and one with *fallax* in turkeys) were carried out by means of active immunization with killed parasites prior to the infecting inoculation. In all of them there was an early fall in infectivity of gametocytes as compared with the controls. In all of these experiments the infectivity of gametocytes for mosquitoes was expressed as the quotient of oocysts produced as numerator with the gametocyte count in the blood at the time of feeding as denominator. Hence this index was independent of the height of parasitemia. The results could be better explained on the hypothesis that active immunity is a major factor in decreasing the index of infectivity of gametocytes than the hypothesis that a depletion in the host is responsible.

A strain of *Plasmodium relictum* isolated from pigeons by Coatney in 1938 has since that time been studied by a number of investigators with some puzzling results in reference to its capabilities for infecting pigeons and canaries in both erythrocytic and exoerythrocytic stages and its transmissiblity by trophozoites and sporozoites. Huff *et al.* (1959) recorded the history of this strain (1P) and their own experiments on this and another similar strain (1B) isolated by Becker *et al.* (1956). They found that these two strains were easily passed serially from pigeon to pigeon by infected blood. A previously observed qualitative difference in the infectiousness of gametocytes of strain 1P in pigeons and of the strain after adaptation to canaries (1P1) was found to be instead, only a quantitative difference in their infectivity for mosquitoes. Previously no species of mosquito had been found which was capable of being infected with strain 1P (i.e. in pigeons). However, *Culex tarsalis* proved to be highly susceptible to gametocytes of both strains 1B and 1P (in pigeons). *Culex pipiens* was also found to be slightly susceptible to gametocytes of strain 1P. Sporozoites of strain 1P1 (from canaries) produced only five transient parasitemias and three subpatent infections in seventy-two pigeons (belonging to twenty-four varieties, plus mongrels and pigeon-dove hybrids) whereas sporozoites from 1P1 (i.e. in canaries) were readily produced in *C. pipiens*. Although strain 1B was more infectious to *C. pipiens* and *C. tarsalis* than 1P their known characteristics indicated that both strains probably were *P. relictum matutinum* (Huff). From analysis of the complex relations among the strains and substrains, their vertebrate hosts, and their insect vectors a hypothesis was proposed that (1) various species of mosquitoes have different susceptibilities, (2) the gametocytes of various species of avian hosts are infectious to different degrees and (3) that the probability of a mosquito of a given species being infected from a given species of parasite depends upon the degree of overlap between the susceptibility of the mosquito and the infectiousness of the gametocytes in the pertinent avian host. Such a hypothesis would explain the discrepancies noted in much of the previous experimental work; for example, why the strain 1P was formerly believed to have been changed by residence in the pigeon in respect to mosquitoes and subsequently shown to be capable of being transmitted when the proper mosquito was found. The authors believe that the susceptibilities of the mosquitoes to the two strains in pigeons is so low that it is questionable whether these strains could persist in an environment containing only these mosquitoes unless other avian hosts were present in which the gametocytes would be more infectious for the mosquitoes.

Working with the 1P1–1 strain of *P. relictum* Schinazi and Ball (1956) were able to pass it by blood inoculation from canaries to pigeons and canaries and vice versa with resulting heavy infections in all passages. In canaries this strain was capable of infecting *Culex tarsalis*, *C. pipiens*, *C. stigmatosoma* and *C. quinquefasciatus* but they did not indicate whether they had attempted to infect any of these mosquitoes from pigeons which had been infected with the strain.

7. *Periodicity of Asexual Reproduction*

Using a strain of *P. relictum* isolated in 1952 from a titmouse, *Pasus major*, in the vicinity of Moscow, Demina (1959) reported upon segmentation times of that parasite of the time of sleeping and of being awake of the host and of delayed development of the inoculated parasites by refrigeration. The reported findings were largely confirmations of findings made by American workers two and three decades ago on *P. cathemerium*. The strain of *relictum* used, interestingly enough, has a periodicity exactly opposite to that type of *P. relictum matutinum* reported from the American robin (Huff, 1937), that is, the Moscow strain exhibited crepuscular periodicity (similar to that of *P. cathemerium*) whereas the robin strain has a matutinal periodicity of segmentation.

Another strain of *matutinum* was isolated by Corradetti *et al.* (1960) from *Turdas iliacus* caught in Tuscany and studied in canaries. The period of maximum segmentation in their strain differed from those of the American strains and of that reported by Demina (1959) in occurring approximately at noon. Differences between *P. praecox* (=*relictum*) and *P. relictum* var. *matutinum* were considered by these authors as being sufficient to raise this variety *matutinum* to specific status, *P. matutinum* Huff, 1937.

In attempting to reduce to a minimum the extrinsic forces acting upon malarial parasites having strict synchronism of asexual reproduction McGhee (1958) studied the behavior of *P. cathemerium* (which in the canary has one of the greatest degrees of synchronism) in duck and chick embryos. Since body temperature of the host has been formerly thought to be a strong influence on this synchronism the experiments done upon embryos confined to a constant temperature in an incubator tested this belief. McGhee found it possible to adapt *P. cathemerium* to continuous passage in duck embryos with relative ease but was unable to adapt it to the chick embryo. He was able to demonstrate synchronism in one cycle of reproduction in the duck embryo during the evening hours but although he was able to carry on sampling of the blood in some embryos as late as 8 P.M. of the following date he found no peak of segmentation of the schizonts. The persistence of some synchronism in a host at constant temperature even for one segmentation period would indicate that some degree of genetic control must be inherent in the organism but that some physiologic condition in the host must also be necessary for a regular synchronism of reproduction. The existence of different strains of *P. relictum* having peaks of parasitemia 12h apart in animals on a normal day-night schedule (cited above) is additional proof of this genetic factor, whereas, the ability to reverse the time of synchronism of a given parasite by reversing its time of sleeping and waking show the importance of the physiological changes in the host.

The precise synchronism of asexual reproduction of *P. cathemerium* which has been the subject of investigation for more than three decades was studied by McGhee (1959) by a new approach. He transferred the infection from canaries to duck embryos and subjected the latter to incubator temperatures of 37° and 30° C respectively. At 30° there was a slower development of the infection and a lower peak parasitemia than at 37°. Subjection to 30° for 2 days and return of the embryos to 37° resulted in a delay of development of parasitemia at the lower temperature but with a return of the embryos to 37° a return to the normal pattern of development occurred. The effect of keeping embryos at lower temperature on the synchronism of schizogenic cycle was studied. Although synchronism was demonstrated during the first cycle of development in embryos at 30° the embryos died before the second parasite cycle was concluded. Since it is known from earlier work that a period of about 3 days is required to change the pattern of periodicity in canaries through alterations of their sleeping times it would appear that little significance can be attributed to the persistence of synchronism for one asexual cycle in embryos kept at temperatures lower than 37°. Therefore the earlier theory of Stauber (1939) that body temperature is probably the chief factor in regulating the periodism of the asexual cycle is not necessarily invalidated.

Temperature studies on chicks infected with *P. gallinaceum* and the effects upon the infection of lowered temperature of host and parasite were made by Nye (1961). She found the asexual development to be 36 h long and fairly synchronous. The length of the asexual development was not affected when the bird was inoculated three times consecutively at 12-h intervals. As in earlier studies of this kind in birds she found no pyrexia resulting from the synchronism of reproduction of the parasites. On the contrary there was a drop in body temperature corresponding to the height of parasitemia. The question arises whether this lowered temperature may have been effected by a possible diminution in the activity of the host on account of its high parasitemia. When infected birds were cooled to 30°C by immersion in water for 6 h the period of development of the parasite was lengthened and this effect was more pronounced when the cooling was done at the time of maximum numbers of young trophozoites in the blood. Cooling of the host did not destroy the ability of the parasite to infect mosquitoes nor to produce exoerythrocytic stages.

8. *Natural Immunity and Susceptibility of the Mosquito Host*

In another section of this review we have already discussed the work done upon the problems surrounding the mechanisms which contribute to the susceptibility or non-susceptibility of the vertebrate host to malarial parasites. The following discussion dealing with the similar problem in the invertebrate will indicate that certain approaches are open in this field that cannot be applied to the former.

Although the papers dealing with chemotherapy of avian malaria are not included it seems pertinent to the purposes of this review to make brief note of the work of Terzian (1955). Inhibition of normal development of *P. gallinaceum* in *Aedes aegypti* which had been fed upon sulfadiazine, chlortetracycline, oxytetracycline or chloroguanide was observed. His descriptions of the morphological changes in the surviving oocysts are too lengthy to record here. They are accompanied by excellent photomicrographs to which the reader is referred. Because of differences in the morphological changes produced by each of the drugs he suggests the possibility of individual specific mechanisms of action of the various compounds.

Another characteristic influencing the innate immunity of mosquitoes to malarial infection, namely the age of the mosquito, was investigated by Terzian *et al.* (1956). By matching groups of mosquitoes from an original lot of mosquitoes with newly hatched groups so that both were fed upon the same infected bird they were able to rule out all differences except age of the mosquitoes. In four such sets made at 1, 2, 3 and 4 day intervals there was a steady decline in the number of oocysts in the aging mosquitoes. This effect of aging was nullified, however, when the older mosquitoes were given blood meals (on uninfected birds) at least 9 days prior to the infecting meal. Similarly mosquitoes which were fed infusions of raisins for 4 weeks prior to the infecting meal were as susceptible to infection as young mosquitoes. Interestingly enough, solutions of chick and human plasma, hemoglobin, lysed red cells or combined plasma and lysed red cells were not capable of restoring the susceptibility of aging mosquitoes. The authors attributed the changes in host susceptibility to infection to the addition or depletion of specific physiological or metabolic factors which function in low concentration, and suggested that the differences of the effects produced between whole blood and separated blood elements might possibly be due to some labile component in whole blood, probably associated with intact cells, which undergoes qualitative change when cells are lysed or the blood elements are mechanically separated. Thus the delicate biological assay provided by the use of aging mosquitoes as tested by their susceptibility to malarial parasites yielded information thus far undetected by hematologists.

In the same year that Terzian *et al.* (1956) demonstrated the effect of supplementary feedings of blood by mosquitoes already infected with *P. gallinaceum* Ray *et al.* (1956b) made somewhat similar findings on the same combination of mosquito and parasite. From a lot of mosquitoes which had already had infective blood meals they fed three separate groups of the mosquitoes on normal fowl, guinea-pig and rabbit. On the basis of number and size of the oocysts observed upon dissection of the mosquitoes at 24-h intervals these authors concluded that there was a more rapid growth of oocysts in mosquitoes fed on normal chicken blood and mammalian blood as compared with the control groups maintained in 4% glucose. They also found that at 120h the group which had received supplemental chicken blood contained oocysts in which sporozoite formation had occurred whereas the oocysts fed upon the mammalian blood were well advanced but had not formed sporozoites. They provisionally concluded that there was some factor in the homologous blood which had a stimulating effect upon the sporogonous development of *P. gallinaceum.*

In a second experiment Ghosh and Ray (1957b) fed mosquitoes upon infected chickens and then divided them into three lots. One lot was maintained on 4% glucose solution as a control, a second lot was fed on a non-infected fowl 48 h after their infective meal and the third lot was fed on a guinea-pig 72 h after their infective blood meal. Dissections were made at 24-h intervals from each of the lots and the oocysts were counted and measured. Up to the 96th h there was no significant difference in the sizes of the oocysts in the control group, nor were there any significant differences in mean size of the oocysts in the three groups up to the 120th h. After the 144th h, however, the oocysts were significantly larger in the two groups given supplemental blood feeding as compared with those in the control group kept on glucose solution. They found no significant differences in oocyst size in the two groups fed on the blood of chicken and of guinea-pig. It may possibly be that the disparity in results relative to the effect of the different kinds of blood could be explained by the manner in which the data were treated. In dealing with oocyst size Huff (1940) showed that the variance *between* oocysts of different mosquitoes was greater than the variance of oocysts *within* mosquitoes. The importance of taking into account this variability in individual mosquitoes was clearly shown in a paper by Huff *et al.* (1958) discussed elsewhere in this review. Any comparison in size of two populations of oocysts must rule out the variability due to the individual mosquito by the technique of obtaining mean values of ocyst size within each mosquito and using them as values from which new mean is obtained.

In addition to the effects of certain biochemical, biological and physical factors which affect the physiological status of the mosquito *Aedes aegypti* as manifested in its susceptibility to *P. gallinaceum* (shown in the earlier work of Terzian) Terzian and Stahler (1960) were able to show that appropriate concentrations of certain bases, acids, and salts in the laboratory diet of the adult mosquito produce alterations in the susceptibility of the mosquito to malarial infection. Solutions of NaOH or KOH in 0.1 M concentrations, or of 0.02 M HCl; 0.1 M H$_3$PO$_4$ or 0.02 M H$_3$ Cit when present in the diet of the mosquitoes resulted in increased susceptibility to infection. However, salts of these acids and bases, and the chlorides of Ca and Mg in 0.1 M concentrations produced the opposite effect, that is, they increased the resistance to infection. Furthermore Na$_3$PO$_4$, K$_3$PO$_4$, and MgCl$_2$ according to the concentrations used appeared to be capable of altering the susceptibility in either direction. Thus, 0.005 M concentrations of Na$_3$PO$_4$ or K$_3$PO$_4$ produced a lowered susceptibility, whereas 0.1 M concentrations of these substances increased the susceptibility; also a 0.01 M concentration of MgCl$_2$ decreased whereas a 0.4 M concentration increased susceptibility. One further result, which could not have been expected, was that the administration in the diet of the adult mosquitoes of combined NaH$_2$PO$_4$ (0.1 M) and oxytetracycline (0.0025 M) produced no greater reduction in susceptibility than was produced by the former alone; and conversely, KH$_2$PO$_4$ (0.1M) combined with oxytetracycline (0.0025 M) did not produce any greater reduction in susceptibility than was produced by the latter alone. In other words one might think of the NaH$_2$PO$_4$ as blocking the potential effect of the oxytetracycline in the former instance, and of the oxytetracycline as blocking the potential effect of KH$_2$PO$_4$ in the latter case. The authors suggest the possible explanation that once a compound has combined with a metabolic site in the mechanism of susceptibility of the mosquito the resulting complex may be comparatively refractory to further reaction with another compound possessing a similar physiological effect.

9. *Effects on Parasites of other Microbial Agents*

a. Viruses. There have been very few observations of the effect of viruses or other microbiological agents upon malarial parasites. It is, therefore, particularly interesting that Trager (1959b) was able to demonstrate such an effect of a new spleen necrosis virus (which was fatal to ducks) upon *Plasmodium lophurae* when the latter was present in ducks infected with the virus. The virus could be readily separated from the malarial parasites. It can, therefore, be assumed that its deleterious effects on the parasites were indirect; possibly through deprivation of the parasite of some essential nutrient such as a folic acid coenzyme. In unpublished observations the reviewer had observed a deleterious action of fowl pox virus upon *P. cathemerium* when it was present in canaries infected with this parasite. Attempts to separate parasites from the virus were unsuccessful. The deleterious effects were exhibited by the loss of ability of the strain to produce gametocytes and the loss of synchronism of asexual reproduction (see Huff, 1958, p. 68). Ornithosis was shown by Jacobs (1957) to affect the resistance of ducklings to *P. lophurae*. When the virus was administered 6–14 days prior to the inoculation of the malarial infected blood there occurred a marked resistance which was associated with an increase of the reticulo-endothelial elements in the enlarged liver and spleen resulting from the ornithosis infection.

An investigation was carried out by Barnett (1956) upon the possibility that *Plasmodium relictum* which occurs in birds serving as hosts of western equine encephalitis virus might itself become infected with the virus and possibly be a factor in its spread. He found no evidence supporting such a hypothesis. In fact concurrent infection of canaries with the malarial parasite and the encephalitis virus gave evidence that there was significant suppression of the virus titers in the birds. However, the presence of *P. relictum* did not appear to alter the ability of the mosquito to transmit the virus.

b. Bacteria and yeasts. A possible effect of other micro-organisms in the gut of *Culex fatigans* upon the ability of *Plasmodium relictum* to infect the mosquitoes was noted by Micks and Ferguson (1961). Female mosquitoes given a mixture of dihydrostreptomycin (0.8%), chloramphenicol (0.49%) and sugar water (2%) for 5–12 days prior to blood meals from canaries infected with *P. relictum* and for 2–7 days after the blood meal were found to be comparatively free of micro-organisms. They found that such mosquitoes had higher incidence as well as larger numbers of oocysts per individual than the control group. The presence of undigested blood in the treated mosquitoes but not in the controls was interpreted as a possible interference to the digestion of the blood by killing the normal microbiological flora in the gut.

c. Coccidia. Al-Dabagh (1961c) studied the effects of concomitant coccidial parasites and malarial parasites on chicks. He demonstrated that infection with *Eimeria acervulina* and *E. mitis* caused a recrudescence in chicks with chronic infections of *Plasmodium juxtanucleare*. *E. acervulina* infection during the prepatent period of infection with *P. juxtanucleare* caused the latter to reach higher levels of parasitemia than in control animals, but did not affect the length of prepatent or patent periods nor increase the mortality among the infected chicks. In chicks with latent infections with *P. gallinaceum*, concomitant infection with *E. acervulina* induced severe, fatal relapse.

10. *Action of Low Temperatures on the Parasites*

Considerable earlier work has been published upon the effects of low temperatures on the malarial parasites of birds and of mammals. This work was reviewed and additional experiments have been reported by Molinari (1961). He used concentrations of glycerol from 0 to 25.0% but found that 5% was the preferred amount. The parasitized blood was diluted with one-fourth its volume of 2% sodium citrate and an equal volume of 10% glycerol. The solutions in Pyrex ampoules were placed in a deep freeze box maintained at −70°C. When removed for testing the ampoules were warmed by contact with the hand or in a water bath of 40°C. Blood infected with *P. gallinaceum* was kept in this manner for 3, 6 and 12 months and produced in chicks infections with prepatent periods unchanged from those produced by the samples before freezing. The morphological characters of the parasites and red cells appeared to be in good condition when stained with Giemsa. It is hoped that these experiments will be extended to longer periods of time in order to determine the limits of safety for keeping the parasites at low temperatures.

B. CULTIVATION

Cultivation of various stages of avian malarial parasites is both a goal and a means of revealing physiological and biochemical information on the parasites. Cultivation of exogenous stages has been reviewed under the section on Parasitology. For the endogenous stages three lines of attack are possible: (1) intracellular growth of exoerythrocytic stages; (2) intracellular growth of erythrocytic stages; and (3) survival studies on extracellular erythrocytic parasites. Because it seems best to treat the problems relating to exoerythrocytic stages in a separate section the work done on their *in vitro* cultivation will be postponed for discussion along with other problems relating to exoerythrocytic stages. Moreover, since the survival of erythrocytic stages in the extracellular condition is chiefly a means for studying the physiological and biochemical requirements of the parasite the work done in this field will be considered under the section on Physiology and Cytochemistry. Hence we shall restrict to this section a review of the work done on attempts to grow the erythrocyte-parasite complex *in vitro*. Manwell and his coworkers have concerned themselves with this phase of the cultivation problem.

Using *P. hexamerium* Glenn and Manwell (1956) tested the addition to the Harvard medium (Ball *et al.*, 1945) of pigeon and turkey plasma and vitamin B_{12}, folic acid and a porcine liver coenzyme concentrate. *In vitro* growth and reproduction were increased by the addition of turkey but not by pigeon plasma. The other supplements enhanced growth and reproduction in all cases when added singly or in combination to the basic medium. Similar experiments with *P. elongatum* were not as successful. Survival but not reproduction was noted after 72 h. There is an indication that the parasites require access to cells other than erythrocytes for multiplication.

Spandorf and Manwell (1960) attempted for the first time to determine the effect of various modifications of the Harvard medium on the *in vitro* development of *P. circumflexum* and *P. vaughani*, using *P. hexamerium* as a base of reference. For controls the Harvard medium was used with addition of folic acid and vitamin B_{12}. It was supplemented singly or in combination with coenzyme A, ATP, thioctic acid and K-malate (0.01 M; 0.005 M). The criteria for improvement were (1) increase in numbers of parasites; (2) staining characteristics and normality of appearance₃ and (3) ability of the parasites to infect ducklings or canaries. The Harvard medium supplemented with coenzyme A, ATP, thiotic acid and K-malate (0.005 M) provided for *P. hexamerium* a growth index of 3.7 after 72 h of incubation. This same medium provided a growth index of 2.2 for *P. circumflexum* after 48 h. This index was increased to 3.5 by the addition of porcine liver coenzyme concentrate and K-malate (0.0005 M) although individual growth indices as high as 7.9 were obtained. *P. vaughani* failed to grow in these media but their survival was proven by the production in canaries of infections with short prepatent periods.

Further improvements in technique particularly in the preparation of the Harvard Medium were reported by Nydegger and Manwell (1962) on the cultivation of *P. hexamerium*. They modified this medium by combining the organic constituents into five basic stock solutions and sterilized these solutions with Pyrex fritted glass filters. They also reduced the malate concentration to 0.0002 M. With this medium they were able to culture *P. hexamerium in vitro* up to 96 h. By subcultures made at 72-h intervals they were able to extend the culture to 9 days without enrichment of the medium with serum or red cell extracts.

C. PHYSIOLOGY AND CYTOCHEMISTRY

1. *Physiology*

Study of the physiology of obligate intracellular parasites such as the malarial parasites presents many difficulties. In spite of these difficulties an understanding of their physiology is important because of their

highly specialized nature. Their very obligate nature indicates their
lack of certain synthetic mechanisms. Studies made upon the parasite-
host cell complex are difficult to evaluate since the infected host cell
is altered by the presence of the parasite and hence one cannot assume
that a study of this complex as compared with uninfected cells will
reveal the real requirements of the parasite. Dr. William Trager has
for two decades been an advocate of the study of the parasite after its
removal from the host cell. He has published a continued series of
papers on this approach. Only his papers falling within the approximate 5-year period selected for this review will be considered here.
However, references to his earlier works are given in his recent papers,
particularly Trager (1957). A review of his methods of preparing extracellular parasites, preparation and maintenance of cultures, preparation
of the culture medium, and for determination of parasite development
of *P. lophurae* was published in 1955. He reported in that paper the
improvement of survival of the parasites by the addition to the medium
of three coenzymes, cozymase, adenosine-triphosphate and coenzyme
A. He also found that addition of sufficient red cell extract to bring the
medium up to full strength gave better survival of the parasites than
the one-sixth strength previously used. However, double-strength cell
extract was unsatisfactory. Clarke (1952) had previously shown that
such an extract was of importance in the maintenance of *Plasmodium
gallinaceum in vitro.*

Trager (1958) demonstrated the favorable action of folinic acid (as
leucovorin) upon the extracellular survival of *P. lophurae* when added
to cultures containing the fully supplemented erythrocytic extract and
inoculated with a crude hemolyzed parasite suspension. Folic acid at a
concentration of 0.005 μg per ml was also added. The favorable effect
on *P. lophurae* was not observed in experiments in which the concentration of folic acid was 0.8 to 1.2 μg (but such an effect was observed
on *P. falciparum*). He also demonstrated that certain yeast protein
preparations and a non-dialyzable fraction of duck erythrocyte extract
(hemoglobin-free) could partially replace the erythrocyte extract in
favoring early extracellular development of *P. lophurae*. He suggested
the possibility that the parasite may require a coenzyme of folic acid
whereas *para*-aminobenzoic acid and folic acid influence its growth
within the living cell; and that the favorable effect of yeast protein and
of non-dialyzable fractions of red cell extract indicate that the parasite
may require growth factors of high molecular weight. (See Rudzinska
and Trager, 1957.)

Further light was thrown on the role of folic and folinic acid in the
metabolism of *P. lophurae* in Trager's (1959a) studies on the comparative amounts of these substances in erythrocytes of normal 2-month-

old ducks and of ducks infected with this parasite. Folic acid was 20- to 50-fold higher in the infected than in uninfected erythrocytes and leucovorin was 5- to 20-fold higher. He showed by micro-biological assay that of the 12×10^{-9} mμg of folic acid and 2 to 4×10^{-9} mμg of leucovorin in the infected erythrocyte, 2 to 4×10^{-9} mμg of folic acid and 0.5 to 1.5×10^{-9} mμg of leucovorin were contained in the malarial parasite itself. In other words only 1/5 to 1/3 of the increased amounts of the two growth factors were in the parasites, leaving presumably 2/3 to 4/5 of the increased amounts in the cytoplasm of the infected erythrocytes. This is evidence in favor of an alteration in the erythrocyte by virtue of the presence of the parasite and that this alteration was favorable to the parasite.

The next step taken by Trager (1961) in analysis of the increased amounts of folic and folinic acid contents of duck erythrocytes infected with *P. lophurae* was through the use of antimalarial drugs and drug-resistant strains of this parasite. Most of the formerly noted increase in folic and folinic acid which occurs in infected erythrocytes of the duck (N, or normal strain) was prevented by the treatment with sulfadiazine. It can be assumed that this drug interfered with folic and folinic acid synthesis, as it is known to do in bacteria, and hence inhibited the growth of the parasites. However, this same effect was observed in a strain (SR) of this parasite which was resistant to sulfadiazine. The dose of drug which brought out this effect was such as to produce no effect on the infection. The SR strain was then treated with pyrimethamine to which it was also resistant with the result that the increase in folinic acid was inhibited but the increase in folic acid was not inhibited. Again, because the SR strain was pyrimethamine-resistant the parasites continued to grow. These results suggest the hypothesis that these drugs interfere with the mechanism for folinic acid synthesis in the host erythrocyte and that the resistance of the parasites to the two drugs may possibly depend upon a decreased requirement by the parasite for the products of the reactions in the host cell inhibited by them.

An interesting physiological effect of parapyruvic acid on both intra- and extracellular parasites of *P. lophurae in vitro* was observed by Trager and Singer (1955). Since this substance did not act as an antimalarial agent *in vivo* it is not excluded, along with most papers dealing with chemotherapy, from consideration here. When parapyruvate was added in concentrations of 25 μg/ml for extracellular parasites *in vitro* there was inhibition of respiration in mitochondria which appeared to depend upon competition between this compound and alpha-ketoglutarate for alpha-ketoglutaric acid oxidase. They pointed out that parapyruvate may have also produced some of its deleterious action on the tricarboxylic acid cycle in the oxidative metabolism of the parasites through an interference with the utilization of alpha-ketoglutarate. It is presumed that the action of this compound, although capable of penetrating the infected erythrocyte and acting directly upon the parasite, was altered *in vivo* before it could reach the infected erythrocytes.

A detailed review of the biochemistry of malarial parasites which includes a discussion of their metabolic pathways and nutritional requirements was given by Moulder (1962).

An improvement in the methods for maintaining extracellular *P. lophurae in vitro* used by Trager (1957, 1958) was described by Trager and Jernberg (1961). Old culture fluids were automatically removed and fresh media supplied by a special flask and mechanical equipment. The extracellular parasites were attached as a scum to a thin plasma clot lining the flask wall and the flasks were rocked by a motor driven platform. A time switch activated a solenoid which tipped the flasks thereby emptying them of the old culture fluid. Other solenoids opened clamps permitting the flow of new medium through a side arm. The supply of fresh medium was refrigerated until the time of entry into the flasks which were kept in a constant temperature cabinet at 40°C. By this apparatus they were able to obtain good survival of the parasites for 5 days and infectivity for 6 days. The physiology of an intracellular parasite such as that of an avian malaria is only one facet of the extremely fascinating phenomenon of intracellular parasitism and symbiosis in general. An excellent discussion of this general field has been given by Trager (1960).

The parasitologist is not only interested in the physiology of the parasite itself but in the complex inter-relations between host and parasite. In the case of vitamins it was shown by the early work of Trager and others that the B vitamins had a favorable effect upon the growth of malarial parasites free from their host cell. Investigations of Rama Rao and Sirsi (1956) involved the part played by thiamine, riboflavin, and *para*-aminobenzoic acid in infections of chicks with *P. gallinaceum*. They demonstrated that thiamine depletion of the blood occurs during the acute phase of the infection, beginning in prepatent and extending to the period of exoerythrocytic development. This thiamine depletion affects both the parasite and host adversely bringing about a decreased multiplication of the former and earlier death of the latter. Administration of low dosages of this vitamin to the depleted host retarded the multiplication of the parasites and prolonged the survival of the host, whereas high dosages assisted the growth of the parasites so that the earlier and higher parasitemia brought about earlier death of the host. They found that riboflavin blood levels increased slightly during the prepatent period of infection and decreased during the acute parasitemia, the net result being that parasitemia was reduced and the severity of the infection was lessened. When deficient animals received supplementary riboflavin the growth and multiplication of the parasites were stimulated with the result that a higher parasitemia was produced and an earlier death of the host resulted. They found that infection in chicks with *P. gallinaceum* also brought about an increase in the blood level of *para*-aminobenzoic acid during the prepatent period and that the level fell as the parasitemia increased. The giving of supplemental PABA in large doses reduced the prepatent period and increased the severity of the infection. All of their results can be explained by assuming that these three vitamins are essential to the host-parasite complex but it does not necessarily follow, as indicated by these authors, that the vitamins, as such, are required by the parasites themselves.

Because so little is known about the physiology of the group of avian parasites such as *Plasmodium vaughani*, *P. rouxi*, *P. hexamerium*, and other similar forms, Khabir and Manwell (1955) chose to study glucose consumption in *P. hexamerium*. This species produces good infections in ducklings whereas it is difficult to obtain sufficiently high parasitemias in the other members of this group to permit this kind of study. They found the rates of glucose consumption in uninfected reticulocytes and mature erythrocytes to be 3.66×10^{-1} mg per 10^9 and 7.58×10^{-2} mg per 10^9 μ^2 of parasite area respectively; whereas the corresponding value for parasitized erythrocytes was 1.42×10^{-11} mg per 10^7 μ^2. They calculated consumption for an "average parasite", having a surface area of 24.8 μ^2, as 3.53×10^{-11} mg glucose/h — about five times as much as the uninfected red cell. They found a lower rate in this species of questionable significance when compared with the rates in *P. relictum* and *P. gallinaceum*.

Since previous investigations upon glucose consumption by erythrocytic parasites of malaria had given no clue whether gametocytes were metabolically active Manwell and Loeffler (1961) determined glucose consumption upon mature erythrocytes, reticulocytes, and erythrocytes of *Columba livia* infected with *Haemoproteus columbae*. Based upon values in terms of surface area their findings indicate that the parasite-host cell complex consumed glucose about a hundred times as fast as uninfected mature erythrocytes and about twenty-five times as fast as uninfected reticulocytes. There was some evidence that gametogenesis (which occurs in drawn blood) does not play an important part in increasing glucose consumption except when excessive numbers of the parasites have left their host cells. Comparison of the rates of glucose consumption of *Haemoproteus* with those of *Plasmodium gallinaceum*, *P. relictum*, and *P. hexamerium* indicates that they are of

C

the same order of magnitude and, therefore, that gametocytes are metabolically active.

Unlike the findings reported on the effects of starvation of mammalian hosts to their malarial parasites (*P. berghei* and *P. knowlesi*) the report of Dutta *et al.* (1956) showed that starvation of chickens did not halt the normal course of parasitemia in *P. gallinaceum* infections. This finding is indication of another possible difference between the physiology of avian and mammalian malarial parasites.

Treating infection of chicks with *P. gallinaceum* as a stress phenomenon, Taylor *et al.* (1956) investigated the commonly accepted physiological accompaniments of stress: namely, adrenal hypertrophy, depletion of adrenal ascorbic acid and depletion of adrenal cholesterol. They found in the infected birds adrenal hypertrophy, lowered total cholesterol and less adrenal cholesterol ester but no decrease in the adrenal ascorbic acid. They interpreted their findings as showing a lack of interrelation between the metabolism of ascorbic acid and of cholesterol in birds. These observations strengthened the belief based on the work of other authors that birds and mammals react differently to stress.

Because other workers had shown that the parasitic infections caused by *Babesia rodhaini* and *P. berghei* are decreased when the hosts were maintained on a diet rich in cod-liver oil and that this effect was not present when large amounts of vitamin E were administered orally, Taylor (1958) tried out similar regimens of diet, properly controlled, on *Plasmodium gallinaceum* infection in chicks. Her results were essentially the same as those obtained on *P. berghei* except not so marked in degree. The hypothesis advanced to explain her results was that the unsaturated fatty acids of cod-liver oil created a pro-oxidant state unfavorable to the parasites and that the anti-oxidant action of vitamin E nullified this effect.

2. *Cytochemistry*

Studies on cytochemistry as an aid to the biochemistry and physiology of malarial parasites has been relatively neglected. The following observations constitute contributions to this subject.

Ray *et al.* (1955) reported cytochemical observations on the gametocytes of *Haemoproteus columbae*. The nucleus showed a negative reaction for DNA by Feulgen's nuclear reaction and Unna-Pappenheim stain. However, as is true in the nucleus of *Plasmodium*, a slightly positive Feulgen appeared in material treated for 30 min in alkaline alcohol prior to hydrolysis. The authors suggest that this pretreatment by removing the hemozoin pigment may remove certain inhibitory factors from the nucleus thus rendering it Feulgen-positive after acid hydrolysis at 60°C. Presence of RNA in the nucleus was indicated by positive Unna-Pappenheim stain which also revealed deeply pyronino-philic particles scattered in the cytoplasm. The periodic acid Schiff reaction for polysaccharides was negative; however, the same minute granules in the cytoplasm which were pyroninophilic were positive to Hale's method for localization of the hyaluronic acid type of poly-saccharide. Gomori's revised technique for alkaline phosphatase activity was negative.

Ghosh and Ray (1957a) found a faint, extensive sudanophilic area in ookinetes of *P. gallinaceum* 24 h after feeding. In the 48-h oocysts they observed irregularly scattered sudanophilic dots and rods and that these bodies increased in size and intensity of the action of Sudan black with increased age of the oocysts. At maturity of the oocysts the in-crease in size and intensity of staining reaction had continued. They indicated that the lipid material observed probably was a source of energy in the metabolism of the oocyst.

Lipid material was found in the oocysts of *Plasmodium gallinaceum* as small sudanophil granules. These appeared to increase in size with the growth of the parasite. Diffuse sudanophil material appeared at a later stage. Phospholipid occurred at a certain stage of the oocyst but later disappeared. Some Sudan-black material was observed in exoery-throcytic stages but the erythrocytic stages did not react with any of the lipid stains (DasGupta, 1960a). Glycogen was absent in the oocysts and other stages of *P. gallinaceum*. A positive reaction for poly-saccharides was obtained in the wall of oocysts (DasGupta, 1960b). By the use of the calcium-cobalt method DasGupta (1961) found that the alkaline phosphatase reaction in *P. gallinaceum* was almost negative in ookinetes, moderately strong in the oocysts, weak in exoerythrocytic schizonts but strong in exoerythrocytic merozoites.

D. EXOERYTHROCYTIC STAGES

1. *Historical*

Aside from the work done on chemotherapy of avian malaria the greatest amount of effort and attention in the past three decades has been devoted to the exoerythrocytic stages. The discovery of these stages revolutionized most of the thinking concerning malariology. It is not surprising that research and interest in these stages continue to be active although, like all research in malariology, it too is receiving less attention in recent years.

Fortunately the history of the work on exoerythrocytic stages has been well documented with reviews from 1940 until the period covered by the present review. By consulting the following reviews the reader will not only be able to follow the course of development in this field but will be able to build a very complete bibliography: Porter and Huff (1940); Kikuth and Mudrow (1940); Corradetti (1943); Huff (1949); Mudrow-Reichenow (1952); Garnham (1954); Bray (1957); and Raffaele (1959).

2. New Reports of Exoerythrocytic Stages

A tentative report was given (Huff, 1956) on exoerythrocytic stages of *Plasmodium nucleophilum* seen in a few old sections of spleen from a canary infected with this species. On the basis of the very small amount of material it was considered likely that these exoerythrocytic stages resemble most nearly those described by Muniz *et al.* (1951) in *P. huffi*. They occurred predominantly in lymphocytes, the mature schizonts were spherical in shape, produced some enlargement in the host cell, and had a larger number of merozoites than are found in *P. elongatum*. Although this incomplete information would indicate that there is another category of exoerythrocytic stage nearer to elongatum-type than to other known ones, more complete study is needed of both this species and *P. huffi* (if the two are not identical).

Demina (1956) reported the presence of abundant exoerythrocytic stages of a new strain (S) of *P. relictum* isolated from siskins and linnets which showed considerable promise for solving the type of problems hitherto chiefly studied in *P. gallinaceum*.

3. Cultivation

Cultivation of *P. elongatum* exoerythrocytic stages in tissue culture of mixed liver and bone marrow cells from infected ducklings was reported by Weiss and Manwell (1960). All stages of the exoerythrocytic development were demonstrated in the cultures. However, these authors were unable to carry the cultures for longer than 72 h. Zasukhin and Vasina (1956) were able to repeat the cultivation of exoerythrocytic stages of *P. gallinaceum* from sporozoites as previously reported by Dubin *et al.* (1949, 1950) and Laird *et al.* (1950). The type of cell in which exoerythrocytic stages of avian malaria may develop in cell culture is difficult to determine. However, Dubin (1954) presented good histological evidence from fixed and stained preparations from tissue cultures of *P. gallinaceum* that the exoerythrocytic stages in all stages of growth may be found in hepatic and pulmonary epithelium.

Although there are several earlier reports of the cultivation of exoerythrocytic stages of *P. gallinaceum* continuous and serial subculturing was first reported by de Oliveira and Meyer (1955). They were successful in cultivating this parasite for one year by the alteration of the use of plasma clot and fluid medium in roller tubes. Fresh tissue was added at the time of each transfer to the hanging drop. At the end of the year the infections were of high grade and readily produced, when inoculated into chicks, first an exoerythrocytic infection and then parasitemia. They were unsuccessful in obtaining infection of erythrocytes introduced into cultures rich in exoerythrocytic stages. They also found that after a 24 h incubation of tissue cultures they could store them at room temperature for as long as 23 days and then return them to roller tubes without losing the infection. Remarkable success in long-term tissue culture infected with *P. gallinaceum* was reported by Meyer and de Oliveira Musacchio (1958). By alternately growing the cultures in roller-tube and hanging drop with plasma clot they were able to subculture without interruption the exoerythrocytic stages of this parasite for 4 years. At intervals the viability was checked by inoculations of the infected cultures into chicks. For 1 year they observed no change in virulence. In one strain thus recovered, however, they (de Oliveira Musacchio and Meyer, 1958) reported a decline in virulence which permitted the survival of the chicks which were infected. No exoerythrocytic stages were observed in the chicks infected with this strain.

Although numerous authors had previously reported the growth in tissue culture of various species of avian malaria (see review by Pipkin and Jensen, 1958) development of methods for routine study of the living exoerythrocytic stages in monolayers by phase contrast optics and time-lapse cinematography was first reported by Huff *et al.* (1960a). These authors adapted strains of *P. gallinaceum* and *P. fallax* to serial passage in chick embryos from which they established primary cultures of the infected embryo tissues. The parasites in these cultures were observed in all stages of development at high magnifications, were photographed by still camera, and time-lapse moving pictures were made both from temporary mounts under coverglass and in perfusion chambers. (A full-length moving picture of one cycle of development of the exoerythrocytic stages was produced and presented before the VIIth International Congress of Microbiology in Stockholm and at the VIth International Congresses of Tropical Medicine and Malaria in Lisbon in 1958). Confirmation of almost all previous observations on fixed and stained material was made except: (1) that a motile filament on one end of the free merozoite was seen in the living material; (2) the cytoplasmic clefts of large schizonts were not observed in the living material and (3) the vacuole-like spaces previously observed around the parasites in fixed material were absent in the living material. Emergence of merozoites from mature schizonts, their progressive, spiralling motility and their entry into host cells, both actively and passively were observed. A form of nuclear division in the parasites was seen in the motion pictures which resembled that known in certain other protozoa in which the nuclear membrane remains intact until the moment of splitting into the two nuclei. The various stages in schizogony were observed including cytokinesis and final arrangement of the separate merozoites around the residual bodies to produce an effect resembling cytomery. Three different methods of merozoite alignment were described and large variations in the size and numbers of merozoites were recorded. More massive infections were observed in the host cells *in vitro* than *in vivo* and the only observed cytopathic effects upon the host cells were seen in such heavily infected cells. Active phagocytosis of free merozoites and repeated unsuccessful attempts to engulf an entire mature schizont were observed. Exoerythrocytic stages of *P. fallax* and of *P. gallinaceum* were similar in morphology and behavior except for the greater curvature in the merozoites and the smaller number of merozoites per schizont in the former than in the latter. Mitochondria were observed and photographed in various stages of the parasite. Their presence in *P. gallinaceum* had been previously reported by Ray *et al.* (1956a). Huff *et al.* (1960a) expressed confidence that the methods employed in their studies offer great opportunities for better understanding of the behavior of parasites, host cells and their interactions.

4. *Host Cell Preferences*

One of the most tantalizing problems still unsolved in the relationships between avian malarial parasites and their host cells is the manner by which changes are wrought in the selectivity on the part of the parasites for different cell types. An extensive series of studies was made (Huff, 1957) on the organ and tissue distribution of exoerythrocytic stages of seven species of parasites (*P. cathemerium, circumflexum, elongatum, fallax, gallinaceum, lophurae,* and *relictum*), on nine species of birds (canaries, chickens, ducks, gosling embryos, partridges (*Alectoris graeca chukar*), pheasants (*Phasianus colchicus*), pigeons, quail (*Colinus virginianus*), and turkeys. His results are rather difficult to summarize and the reader is, therefore, referred to the original report for many of the details which cannot be mentioned here. Since chickens and turkeys are both susceptible to *P. gallinaceum* and *P. fallax* they presented one of the best sets of combinations for analysis of the effect of species of host and of parasite upon the distribution of exoerythrocytic stages in the various tissues. Infections in chickens and turkeys by *P. gallinaceum* and *P. fallax* respectively, which represented examples of the highest infections in the host, were characterized as follows: (1) exoerythrocytic stages were prevalent and widely distributed in the early portion (3–9 days) of sporozoite-induced infections and disappeared in the late portion (10–19 days); (2) these stages were scarce during the early portion of blood-induced infections but prevalent and widely distributed in the latter portion. In the converse combinations (chickens and turkeys infected respectively with *P. fallax* and *P. gallinaceum*) the distribution of these stages in sporozoite-induced infections of *P. gallinaceum* in turkeys was approximately like that of the blood-induced infections mentioned under (2) above. In the remaining combinations (blood-induced infections of *P. gallinaceum* in turkeys and both blood- and sporozoite-induced infections of *P. fallax* in chickens) sparse and sometimes degenerate parasites were found in both early and late portions of the infections. The results of blood-induced infections were similar in *P. lophurae* and *P. fallax* in turkeys and in both instances the exoerythrocytic stages appeared in great numbers regularly on the 12th or 13th day following inoculation regardless of the size of the inoculum given. In nine combinations of host, parasite and stage inoculated, no exoerythrocytic stages were found even though parasitemia resulted in all. In the remaining combinations representing the less susceptible hosts to the parasites concerned, exoerythrocytic stages were found only rarely, showed a preference for the spleen and were more likely to occur early than late in the infection. He concluded from these results that: (1) exoerythrocytic stages (of the gallinaceum-type) are less likely to occur in blood- than in sporozoite-induced infections; (2) these stages occur earlier in sporozoite- than in blood-induced infections; (3) patterns of exoerythrocytic occurrence and distribution are not characteristic of host species or of parasite species but are always determined by both; (4) no clear relationship exists between degree of exoerythrocytic infection and (a) size of inoculum in blood-induced infections or (b) degree of parasitemia in infections produced by either inoculation of sporozoites or infected blood; (5) in the cases in which exoerythrocytic infection following inoculation of infected blood was severe and generalized the most important factor determining its onset is the length of the period of infection of the host, and (6) the types of cells invaded by *P. elongatum* are so different from those occupied by the other species of parasites as to make the generalizations drawn here not applicable.

Further attempts to analyze the nature of the change mentioned above in the time of onset of heavy exoerythrocytic infection in certain blood-induced infections were made by the same author (Huff, 1959a). Testing whether the depleting action of the infection on the host might have a nonspecific effect in altering the time of occurrence of the onset of heavy and generalized exoerythocytic infection he first inoculated chicken with *P. fallax* and followed it by an inoculation of *P. gallinaceum*. A similar experiment was performed by administering *P. lophurae* first, followed by *P. gallinaceum*. There was no evidence in either experiment that the first infection had any effect on the exoerythrocytic infection of *P. gallinaceum* as compared to that obtained in animals previously uninfected. Since *P. lophurae* was known to produce some transferable immunity two attempts were made to alter the course of of its exoerythrocytic infection by the administration of hyperimmune serum to animals with *P. lophurae* infections. No alteration occurred compared to the results in animals which did not receive immune serum. No effect upon the pattern of development of *P. gallinaceum* infections resulted from the inoculation of sporozoites which had been incubated with the specific immune serum. Turkeys which received seven successive daily inoculations of killed erythrocytic stages of *P. fallax* previous to the inoculation of live parasites and were killed and their tissues examined from the 3rd to the 10th post-inoculation day revealed no evidence that the active immunization had altered the pattern of exoerythrocytic development. Although the factors responsible for the observed shifts in localization of exoerythrocytic stages during the course of infection were not revealed by his experiments the writer concluded that changes which occur in host-cell selectivity tend to persist in the parasite until some other factor intervenes. One additional fact relating to the previous report (Huff, 1957) was added. He studied the type of exoerythrocytic infection of *P. fallax* in turkeys inoculated with primary tissue cultures heavily infected with exoerythrocytic stages from chick embryos and found that the resulting infections corresponded closely to infections of this species induced by sporozoites.

E. FINE STRUCTURE

The propriety of including a discussion of fine structure of malarial parasites in a review dealing primarily with experimental studies may justifiably be raised. The use of the electron microscope is comparatively recent and the period of its application to the study of malarial parasites falls within the period covered by this review. Although the element of experiment is small in this field, it is believed that the results obtained may be appropriately discussed here because of the close relationship between fine structure and function.

1. *Asexual stages*

   The study of the fine structure of asexual erythrocytic stages of avian malaria has until now been confined to *P. lophurae*. Rudzinska and Trager (1956, 1957, 1961) have shown that these organisms contain all of the major components found in other animal cells although some of them are poorly represented. A thin plasma membrane (100 Å thick), which appears to be double, covers the body of the parasite and lies in close contact to the cytoplasm of the host. The dense bodies within the parasite consist of large spherical bodies (of over

0.5μ diameter) which are probably lipids, and smaller (170 mμ) elongated granules of pigment in the residual body. A thin membrane (100 Å thick) limits the residual body which appears to have a homogeneous matrix. They believe that the residual body represents a repository for wastes of a watery nature containing solid remnants of the parent cell. This view is strengthened by the observations of the reviewer and his collaborators on living exoerythrocytic stages which reveal that active Brownian movement occurs mainly in the residual body. This Brownian movement is evidence of low viscosity. Rudzinska and Trager (1957) first reported conclusive evidence for phagotropy in *P. lophurae*. Their studies indicated that an invagination from the cytoplasm of the host cell is formed which contains hemoglobin and that digestion proceeds in the food vacuole formed by the closing of the invagination. The mitochondria of *P. lophurae* are oval or irregular in shape and 350–600 mμ in their shorter diameter; and are surrounded by a double membrane. Microvilli on the inner linings appear to be homologous to the cristae mitochondriales of higher forms and are similar in this respect to other protozoa. Small portions of what appears to be endoplasmic reticulum are present in the cytoplasm. The nucleus has a higher density than the cytoplasm and is surrounded by a double membrane. The latter appears to be penetrated by pores. Small, denser bodies found within the nucleus, are without limiting membranes and are composed of fine fibrils. These bodies are labelled nucleoli in the photomicrographs but some uncertainty about their actual identity is expressed in the text.

Rudzinska and Trager (1961) were able to show that the cytoplasm of schizonts undergoing division plays a more important part than generally supposed. They showed that cytokinesis is initiated before the final nuclear division has been completed. They noted an increase in the number of mitochondria in the cytoplasm of the parasite. Distinct zones appear in the cytoplasm; one type being dense and containing almost all of the cytoplasmic organelles (mitochondria, endoplasmic recticulum, and Palade's small particles), whereas the other type consists of a ground substance of low density and contains few Palade's particles. They conclude that at the time of merozoite formation all organelles, including the ribonucleo-protein particles, move toward the nuclei leaving a watery cytoplasm behind. Presumably the organelles become distributed among the merozoites so that each merozoite obtains some of each kind of organelle. The question might here be raised whether this distribution is always equitably effected. It is not inconceivable that some merozoites may fail to obtain some organelle such as a mitochondrion which is necessary to life and that these merozoites are destined to perish.

C*

Rudzinska and Trager (1961) found that the nucleus in the young trophozoite appeared to be homogeneous except for the presence of particles about 300 Å in diameter, which were denser, and sometimes lined up in parallel. The character of the nuclei did not appear to change until just before the last nuclear division. At that time there was an accumulation of condensed materials at the periphery of the nucleus which they assumed might be chromatin. They admitted, however, that this assumption could not be confirmed by the Feulgen reaction. They confirmed the observation made by Huff *et al.* (1960a) by cinematographic studies on exoerythrocytic studies that the nuclear membrane remains intact during division. Important changes in the endoplasmic reticulum were observed during the growth of the parasite. It is meager in the young trophozoite but increases in amount in the larger trophozoite and long tubules become more numerous. The membranes become more densely covered with ribonucleo-protein particles and the matrix of the tubules increases in density. They observed connections between the endoplasmic reticulum and the nuclear envelope and a similarity in density of the homogeneous substance in both structures which suggested exchange of materials between the cytoplasm and nucleus. These observations on the role of the cytoplasm in schizogony which becomes more readily seen during cytokinesis are important in confirming the long-held hypothesis that the nature of the cytoplasm is very complex and that it has intimate relations with the nucleus in malarial parasites as in other cells.

2. *Gametocytes*

In electron micrographs of *P. cathemerium* Duncan *et al.* (1959) were able to distinguish and differentiate gametocytes from other erythrocytic stages. The gametocytes were distinguished by limiting membranes of three dense lines whereas these membranes on the asexual stages consisted of only two thin, dense lines. The mitochondria were usually smaller and contained a matrix of much higher density than those of the asexual stages. In some of the gametocytes vesicles of different sizes, which were associated with laminated fine membranes, were thought to represent a somewhat simplified Golgi complex. The parasites in which these structures occurred were tentatively identified as male gametocytes. Evidence of phagotropy was seen in the gametocyte. They reported nucleoli in all stages of the parasites.

3. *Ookinetes*

The first fine structure studies of the ookinete were reported by Garnham *et al.* (1962). Their studies were made upon *Haemamoeba gallinacea* (*P. gallinaceum*) in *Aedes aegypti queenslandensis* and *P. cynomologi bastianelli* in *Anopheles stephensi*. The authors found only very slight differences between the fine structure of the two species. The ookinete of the former was enclosed in a membrane consisting of two layers the total width of which was 50 mμ; the outer layer being corrugated and the inner smooth, with a space between the two. The inner layer at the anterior end of the organism was more dense and appeared to be split like "the mouth of a shark". At least fifty-five longitudinal, peripheral fibrils were seen just inside the envelope. They were hollow and extended throughout the length of the ookinete. The anterior end was comparatively simple; containing some solid bodies of spherical or oval shape. The nucleus had a patchy, granular structure without a visible membrane and contained a nucleolus. The cytoplasm contained relatively large "crystaloids", mitochondria, small bodies, usually near the envelope and tentatively referred to as lysosomes, some "fenestrated buttons", and pigment granules in irregular black masses in vacuoles which were limited by membranes. The "crystaloids" were in masses measuring up to 1 μ in width and appeared as irregular spheres of about 35 mμ diameter. Their crystalline patterns suggested aggregates of virus particles. The mitochondria appeared as circles or tubes within an outer envelope. Penetration of the gut wall of the mosquito was observed. At first the ookinete lay close to and parallel to the peritrophic membrane. After passing through the latter it pushed aside the brush border of the host's mucosal cells at which time the anterior end came close to the membrane of a host cell. The latter lost its definition at the point of closest approach of the ookinete. The ookinete came to occupy an intracellular position in the mucosal cell. After passing through the cytoplasm of the mucosal cell the ookinete came up against the external border of the cell and the basement membrane. Observations were not made beyond this stage.

4. Exoerythrocytic stages

So far the only fine structure studies on exoerythrocytic stages of avian malaria have been done by Meyer and de Oliveira Musacchio (1960 a,b). They have published what they, themselves, term preliminary studies on the exoerythrocytic stages of *P. gallinaceum* grown in tissue culture of cardiac muscle of chick embryo. Certain similarities as well as differences can be noted between their observations and those of Rudzinska and Trager. In making these comparisons it must be emphasized that the species being studied as well as the host cell were different with the two sets of investigators. The points of similarity in the two studies are (1) the greater electron density of the merozoites than in the schizonts; (2) the presence of an endoplasmic reticulum; (3) the general appearance of the nucleus and nuclear membrane; and (4) the similarity of the structures tentatively identified by Rudzinska and Trager as a nucleolus and designated "oval body" by Meyer and de Oliveira Musacchio. The differences are that Meyer and de Oliveira Musacchio observed neither mitochondria nor evidence of phagotropy whereas both were seen in *P. lophurae* by Rudzinska and Trager. Meyer and de Oliveira Musacchio described a ring-like opening in cross sections of the pole of the merozoite. This structure gradually disappeared when the merozoite re-entered a new cell and started to grow. Although motility and the presence of a polar filament were observed by Huff *et al.* (1960a) in merozoites of *P. gallinaceum* and *P. fallax* by phase contrast optics, Meyer and de Oliveira Musacchio were unable to see any evidence in electron micrographs of such filaments in free merozoites or merozoites inside the segmenters[1] of the former species. In view of the preliminary nature of the studies of the Brazilian investigators it would be premature to state that their failure to record the type of cytoplasmic activity which occurs before the final nuclear division in the schizont noted by Rudzinska and Trager or other differences is valid.

5. *Oocysts*

The first fine structure studies on any of the exogenous stages of avian malarial parasites were made by Duncan *et al.* (1960). They studied the oocysts of *P. cathemerium* from 3 to 10 days old on the stomachs of *Culex fatigans*. The 3-day oocysts appeared to be in the stomach wall and to be dense and fairly uniform in appearance. In some of the oocysts of this age there were well-defined nuclei and nucleoli and the oocysts were separated from the host cells by a thick homogeneous capsule. Since none of the illustrations of the 3-day oocysts are at magnifications greater than × 8,000 one may well raise the question whether separate components of the membrane would be resolved at these magnifications. The 5-day oocysts were larger, contained smaller and more numerous nuclei, mitochondria, and a vacuole containing malarial pigment. Sporozoite development had begun in the 7- and 8-day-old oocysts. At this stage a large central vacuole appeared which presumably represents the residual body and probably is formed in much the same manner as the corresponding structure in the schizont. The membrane surrounding the oocysts became progressively thinner with the increase in size of the oocysts and had apparently disappeared in those oocysts which were discharging their sporozoites. Endoplasmic reticulum and associated Palade's particles of ribonucleo-protein were prominent in the older oocysts. Filamentous branched mitochondria

---

[1] "Segmenters" are ripe schizonts. (Ed.)

were present in the unsegmented cytoplasm, this being the first demonstration of such mitochondria in a malarial parasite either by electron or by phase microscopy. Minute rings and dots of very high electron density, sometimes very abundant, remain unidentified. The capsule of the oocyst was believed by the authors possibly to be a product of the mosquito. They based this belief upon the appearance of blending of the parasite membrane and the outer "elastic" layer of the stomach wall with no discernable separation of the two. As suggested by Trager (in a personal communication) it would appear to the reviewer that the capsule must have a dual origin and consists of a merging of the oocyst wall with a membrane from the stomach of the host. In this respect it should be recalled that normal appearing oocysts were produced in the hemocoeles of mosquitoes without any contact with the stomach (Weathersby 1952, 1954 and 1960b).

6. *Sporozoites*

Duncan *et al.* (1960) made some observations on the sporozoites both those in the process of developing and the mature ones. They reported them as possessing very prominent limiting membranes consisting of two dark lines separated by less dense material. The sporozoites contained nuclei, mitochondria, endoplasmic reticulum, Palade granules and rod-like bodies of moderate and uniform density about 4 μ in length. In none of the sections of oocysts undergoing sporogony which were examined was any evidence of mitosis observed.

A more detailed and complete study of the fine structure of the sporozoite of *P. gallinaceum* was made by Garnham *et al.* (1960). They were able to obtain excellent longitudinal and transverse sections of sporozoites in the salivary glands of *Aedes aegypti queenslandensis*. The outer coat was 250 Å thick and consisted of two layers, the outer of which appeared to be longitudinally corrugated. At the anterior end of the sporozoite a cup-like organelle was visible, the base of which appeared to be connected with fibrils and organelles to be described below. The cup was about 120 mμ deep and 140 mμ in diameter. The nucleus was uniformly granular with what appeared to be a single membrane enclosing it. Although not mentioned by them a structure resembling a nucleolus appears in their figure 7. They made a careful study of a pair of structures similar to those seen by Duncan *et al.* (1960) in *P. cathemerium* sporozoites. They referred to this as a "paired organelle" 1.4 μ long and with diameters varying from 38–120 × 111–371 mμ. Each lobe had a well-defined edge and the interior was dark. In cross section it occupied the inner portion of the sporozoite and its end came within 0.6 μ of the nucleus. They noted a superficial resemblance of the "paired organelle" with the toxonemes of *Toxoplasma* which, however, exceed them in number. They called attention to their similarity to a gland. Twelve deeply staining fibrils were observed around the periphery of the organism which were 190 Å in diameter and apparently hollow. In cross sections they were not seen beyond the ends of the paired organelle. They estimate that about a hundred mitochondria are found in each sporozoite which is in sharp contrast to the small number in merozoites. Some internal structure could be seen in these mitochondria. They did not observe an endoplasmic reticulum.

From this small number of studies on the fine structure of malarial parasites an excellent beginning has been made toward a better understanding of their internal organization, and its relationship to the physiological processes which occur in them. Obviously many questions yet remain to be answered, foremost among which is the nature of the hereditary material and its behavior during nuclear division.

F. IMMUNOLOGY

1. Role of the Spleen and Reticulo-endothelial System

In the period of time covered by this review there has been, perhaps, a disproportionate decrease of work done on immunity and histopathology of avian malaria. The work of the Taliaferros (W. H. and L. G., 1955) would appear as a culmination of an era of intense effort in this field. They reported on the reactions of the connective tissue in chickens to infections with *P. gallinaceum* and *P. lophurae:* the former was both blood- and sporozoite-induced, the latter was blood-induced, but in the case of each species primary infections and superinfections were studied. Inasmuch as this work was to a large extent confirmatory and an extension of previous work by the Taliaferros (together with Cannon, Mulligan and Bloom) on various other species of animal malarias, the reader interested in informing himself on the general subject should consult the various references cited in their paper (Taliaferro and Taliaferro, 1955). Tissues were taken at closely spaced intervals from normal animals infected with each species of parasite and by the kinds of inoculums indicated above through the entire course of infections. Changes in the infected animals occurred chiefly in the spleen and to a less extent in the liver, bone marrow and bursa Fabricii. Other tissues exhibited little or no reaction.

The following activities were observed to rise and fall with the degree of parasitemia in initial and superinfections: (1) phagocytosis by macrophages in the spleen, liver and bone marrow of parasitized cells, free parasites and their debris, including malarial pigment; (2) the destruction of lymphocytes, other lymphoid cells, macrophages, and granulocytes; (3) the proliferation in lymphatic and myeloid tissues of lymphoid cells; (4) the great increase of abnormally large lymphocytes both by mobilization from reticular cells and by mitosis; (5) the development of plasma cells; and (6) the production of macrophages from reticular cells, lymphocytes, and monocytes. During the first part of initial infections a progressive depletion of lymphocytes of the spleen reached its maximum in terminal lethal infections and was accompanied by degeneration of many lymphocytes and the development of macrophages from others. A lymphoid hyperplasia compensated for this loss during the last acute rise in mild infections and during the developed infection in the persisting type of infection. This hyperplasia lasted for a month or more and its regression depended upon whether the infection subsided. The lymphoid hyperplasia consisted of a proliferation of lymphocytes, particularly one of the medium and larger ones, from reticular cells. Large lymphocytes frequently played a major role in the development of various connective tissue cells associated with immunity and repair. They developed into plasma cells which behaved as primitive free cells, migrating to various tissues. When animals were superinfected they underwent a lymphoid depletion sooner, and more rapidly returned to hyperplasia than in the initial infection. The changes in erythropoietic and myelopoietic centers were not as pronounced. The number of nodules in the spleen (counted per unit of area in the section) reflected very clearly the lymphoid activities observed. Thus the differences between sporozoite and blood-induced initial infections of *P. gallinaceum* were reflected in the earlier disappearance and reappearance of the nodules of the latter infections. A similar relationship was observed between initial blood induced and superinfections of both species.

An interesting point which needed to be clarified in the work reported by Taliaferro and Taliaferro (1955) was whether the great enlargement of the spleen in malarial infections represented a true increase in living tissue or merely an increase of the fluid content of this organ. This question was clearly answered by the studies of Moulder and Taliaferro (1955). Spleen slices from the infected chickens were found to have normal percent dry weights, protein contents, and rates of aerobic and anaerobic glucose metabolism throughout the entire course of infection. The same results were found in slices of liver, heart, lung and kidney. Thus, they unequivocally proved that the splenomegaly represented a true increase in living tissue having the same glucose metabolism as the cells in the uninfected spleen.

The lack of understanding of the role of the spleen in malarial infections is well shown in the results of splenectomy on the host prior to or after infection. Splenectomy of canaries either before or after inoculation with *P. rouxi* altered the rate of multiplication of the parasite but this was more limited than in other species of avian *Plasmodium* (Corradetti and Verolini, 1958 a,b). Al-Dabagh (1960) found that splenectomy caused marked recrudescence if carried out in chicks at the chronic stage of infection with *P. juxtanucleare*. Splenectomy also raised the mortality rate. No effect upon the course of infection, mortality rate or survival time of infected hosts was found to result from splenectomy if carried out prior to infection. Similar results of prior splenectomy have previously been shown by other authors in infections by *P. cathemerium*, *P. gallinaceum*, *P. lophurae* and *P. circumflexum*. No greater pathological changes in the viscera of chicks splenectomized while infected were observed than in those of non-splenectomized animals. The author believes that the loss of the portion of the lymphoid-macrophage system present in the spleen cannot account for all of the effects produced by splenectomy in malarial infection and that other functions (possibly antibody production) must account for some of the changes which occur in the host following splenectomy.

A comprehensive review of the functions of the spleen was given by Taliaferro (1956). Although his conclusions were based upon broader studies than those on birds infected with malaria his conclusions are pertinent to this review. He considered the phagocytic function of the spleen, its cytopoietic activity including the production of lymphoid cells and macrophages, its role in the production of specific antibodies and some of the regulatory actions on nonsplenic antibody-forming sites. Since the studies on antibody formation were to a large extent done upon hemolysins in rabbits it would seem inappropriate to attempt to review his conclusions in this field here but to refer the reader to the original article. Also pertinent to the subject of immunology of avian malaria (as well as to such subjects as the influence of hypoxia on infection) is the comprehensive review on the reticuloendothelial system by Goble and Singer (1960). This review covers more than avian malaria and provides a very extensive discussion of the older as well as the more recent literature.

The effects of intravenous inoculations of India ink into chickens upon the course of infection with *P. gallinaceum* were reported by Rahm and Kauffman (1959). Graded doses of India ink were administered at different times in the course of infection and quantitative assays and histological sections of different organs were made to determine the granulopoietic effect of the injected carbon. They reported that the temporary depression of the reticulo-endothelial system was more striking than the stimulatory effect. They believed this to be due to the functionally immature state of the reticulo-endothelial system in 30-day-old chicks and to the dual role of macrophages in the defense mechanism as well as host cells for the exoerythrocytic forms of *P. gallinaceum*. They found different degrees of storage of the ink in different organs and corresponding degrees of reticulo-endothelial system stimulation. The reader is referred to the more comprehensive studies of blockade in canaries and its effect upon natural and acquired infections with *P. cathemerium* and *P. relictum* by Gingrich (1941).

2. Humoral Immunity

The finding by McGhee (1960) that subcutaneous injections of duck embryo erythrocytes parasitized by *P. lophurae* into ducklings resulted in the almost complete eradication of polychromatophil erythroblasts led him to attempt to analyze the mechanism by which this effect was produced. Ducklings thus inoculated developed a considerable degree of anemia but low infections by the parasites. Since the results could not be explained by the presence of viral hemagglutinins he believed that they might be due to the existence of an auto-antibody which was produced in response to the parasite-erythrocyte combination. These auto-antibodies in turn acted against the uninfected polychromatophil erythroblasts. He believed that the presence of the parasite in the duck embryo cells was sufficient stimulus for production of strong antibodies against the host's own erythroblasts, and that the infectivity of the parasite for duckling cells was attenuated through residence in the embryo. The presence of a low grade infection along with marked anemia, therefore, revealed results that would be obscured in infections where there was high parasitemia. That this phenomenon is not peculiar to avian malarial infections was shown earlier in the same year by Zuckerman (1960a) for *P. berghei* in adult rats.

Ingram *et al.* (1961) demonstrated a high degree of fluorescence in chicken blood parasitized with *P. gallinaceum* by the fluorescent antibody technique. The antibodies were produced by inoculation of sporozoites into rabbits. Immunological specificity was indicated by the (1) lack of staining when slides were treated with conjugated normal serum; (2) inhibition of staining by prior exposure of the parasites to unconjugated homologous immune serum; (3) failure of the conjugated anti-malarial serum to stain after being adsorbed on a suspension of the organisms and (4) failure of prior application of non-immune serum to inhibit staining.

3. Miscellaneous Observations Related to Immunity

a. *Relation of merozoite numbers to immunity.* Some of the experiments reported in the work of Huff *et al.* (1958) yielded results on the significance of mean numbers of merozoites in mature schizonts during the course of infection. The decreases in merozoite numbers at the crisis of parasitemia observed by other authors were not confirmed in the experiments. On the other hand, there were significantly higher mean merozoite numbers in birds on adequate diets compared with birds on diets deficient in pantothenic acid. This raises the question whether the reduction in merozoite numbers which have been interpreted as the result of developing immunity may have been the result of poor nutritional conditions resulting in the infected animals, perhaps from loss of appetite during the period of highest parasitemia.

b. *Active immunization.* A relative, active immunization of chickens against infection with *P. gallinaceum* was reported by Deschiens *et al.* (1956) who also briefly reviewed the earlier experiments of other authors to produce this state against other avian malarial parasites. They administered separate injections of living B.C.G. and killed parasites of *P. gallinaceum* intraperitoneally followed by injection of a mixture of living B.C.G., of killed parasites, and of paraffin oil. Evidence of a relative, active immunity was the very feeble parasitemia of short duration in birds so treated and then inoculated with living parasites as compared with the severe or fatal infections resulting in the untreated controls. The duration of the relative immunity was believed to last at least for 2 to 3 months and was distinguished from premunition which lasts as long as any living parasites persist in the host but which also disappears after the disappearance of parasites in the premunized host. Protection was not obtained by injection of killed parasites alone or of living B.C.G. in paraffin oil.

c. *Relapse.* An interesting observation on relapse was reported by Raffaele (1955). In one experiment in which he inoculated a canary with sporozoites of *P. gallinaceum* the canary, even though its blood was negative prior to inoculation, relapsed from an infection of *P. cathemerium* on the 7th post-inoculation day and died on the 13th day. At death it had an intense parasitemia and upon autopsy numerous exoerythrocytic stages were found in the liver, brain and spleen. While it is possible that the relapse was a coincidence, it would appear to be important to determine experimentally whether the inoculation in a bird of sporozoites of a species of malaria to which it is not susceptible would provoke a relapse of a latent infection. Since such happenings must occur frequently in nature it might possibly be an important factor in natural relapse.

G. PATHOLOGY

A contribution to the physiological pathology of malaria was made by Ramaswamy (1956) who found that the spleens of chicks infected with *P. gallinaceum* contained about five times the amount of hydroxyproline as found in the normal spleen. By means of paper chromatography he separated the components of the hydroxy-proline band and found the amino-acid to be allohydroxy-L-proline complex. He suggests the possibility that this substance may be toxic to cells and therefore be a factor in the pathogenesis of malaria. He indicates the need of more research to elucidate this matter.

Sherman and Hull (1960b) examined the hemoglobin of chicks during the course of infection with *P. lophurae* for qualitative changes. They found no significant differences either in the faster moving or the slower moving electrophoretic components of the hemoglobin between infected and uninfected birds when samples were taken previous to, at the peak of, and after the peak of parasitemia. Their results indicate no detectable degradation of the hemoglobin outside the parasite itself and that synthesis of normal hemoglobin occurs in about the same proportions in infected as in uninfected animals even though the former show increased anemia and reticulocytosis.

A more intensive study of the alterations of the serum of chicks infected with *P. lophurae* by means of electrophoresis was made by Sherman and Hull (1960a). The α-globulin and β-lipoprotein fractions appeared erratically and in insignificant amounts in both infected and uninfected animals. The albumin fraction varied extensively during the early stage in the infections but decreased significantly by the 4th day and continued to decrease to day 7. During the acute rise and at the crisis of parasitemia the α-globulins varied widely but were significantly different from the initial level. There were wide differences from host to host in the α-globulin and γ-lipoprotein during crisis which indicated individual differences in respect to their physiological variability — a situation not observable in pooled serum. On the 5th day of infection the rise in α-globulin became statistically significant and persisted about one day. On the other hand the α-lipoprotein showed no significant rise until the 8th day. The β-globulin showed little variability from host to host but was significantly increased on the 4th day and remained high up to the 8th day of infection (which was well into the latent period). The only component which underwent alterations in relative mobility was the γ-globulin which increased by the 4th day and was decreased to the original rate by the 7th day. This study is particularly valuable since it was made upon an infection in which acquired immunity develops fairly rapidly and in which the observations can be carried into the period of latency. The authors consider that their results are consistent with the earlier beliefs and finding of an opsonin and also with the suggestion made by Taliaferro (1941) that two types of immunological entities may be involved in malarial infection. Since the γ-globulin appears to have undergone a qualitative change during its increase on the 4th and 5th days of infection and disappears as the concentration decreases there is the suggestion that γ-globulin contains an antibody (agglutin or opsonin) which becoming bound to the parasite is removed from the blood stream by the disposal of the parasite-erythrocyte combination by the host. Moreover, the rise in β-globulin on the 4th day and persisting into the latent period might be due to the parasiticidal or reproduction-inhibiting antibodies or a combination of the two.

A fast-moving lipoprotein demonstrated electrophoretically in the serum of pigeons infected with *P. relictum* by Schinazi (1957) seemed to be correlated with the erythroblastosis produced by the infection and may possibly result from nonspecific causes.

Biochemical studies of the effect of *P. gallinaceum* infection on the amino acids of the chick were reported by Rama Rao and Sirsi (1958). They found an increase in nearly all of the amino acids in the erythrocytes during the prepatent to the period of peak parasitemia and attributed this increase to rapid hydrolysis of the globin fractions of the hemoglobin to its amino acid components. In the blood plasma they reported a gradual decrease of amino acids in the prepatent period continuing up to the peak of parasitemia. They believed this to be a reflection of the interference of the infection with protein metabolism as revealed by the presence of histopathological lesions of the liver, by biochemical analysis of the blood proteins, the utilization of some of the amino acids in the host nutrition and for antibody production, and to the increased demands of the parasite for its growth and multiplication. They reported an increase of the free and a diminution of certain of the bound acids in whole blood during the peak of parasitemia. In the hydrolysate of the whole blood leucine, phenylalanine, valine, methionine, glycine, lysine, and cystine are reduced by about half during the incubation period but isoleucine and methionine alone reach higher levels in the acute stage than in the initial concentration. In the liver phenylalanine, tyrosine, and aspartic acid decreased with the progress of the infection while all other amino acids decreased in the incubation period then increased during parasitemia. There was also a decrease in most of the free amino acids in the brain tissue.

Because he had found that the numbers of myocardial mast cells in African patients were much higher than in Europeans, Fernex (1959) conducted studies on experimental infections of *Plasmodium gallinaceum* and *P. cynomolgi* in chickens and monkeys. Two lots of chickens infected with sporozoites of *P. gallinaceum* and a control lot were studied. One of the lots with malarial infections was also given intravenous injections of Chinese ink in an attempt to blockade the reticuloendothelial system. Although the numbers of mast cells in the left ventricle varied considerably in the different animals there was no clear evidence that either malarial infection alone or with blockade affected the number of mast cells.

Involvement of the central nervous system was observed in ten of 148 chicks infected with *P. juxtanucleare* by Al-Dabagh (1961b). Both in the paralyzed chicks and in some which died of chronic malarial infection without exhibiting paralysis pathological changes consisting of gliosis and granulomata-like lesions were observed. Since efforts were made to rule out the possibility that Toxoplasma, viral and bacterial disease were the causes the author concluded that the lesions were probably the result of the action of the malarial parasite itself or of its by-products on the central nervous system.

Lesions on the eyelids of hosts of various types of malarial infection have been observed many times. These reports are reviewed by Al-Dabagh (1961a) and further studies are recorded on these lesions in chicks infected with *Plasmodium gallinaceum*. The first symptom is marked hyper-sensitivity to light observed as early as the 6th or 7th day in blood-induced infections (13th day in sporozoite-induced infections). Severe lachrymation accompanies or follows this symptom. Then an inflammatory lesion develops especially on the lower lid and to a lesser extent on the upper, but does not affect the nictitating membrane. Chicks surviving until the 9th or 10th day of infection show degenerative and necrotic changes in the lesions, the feathers on the lids are lost and the eyelids often stick together and eventually may slough off. The author considers these lesions to be identical to those occurring in pantothenic acid deficiency in chicks except that they develop more rapidly than the latter. He believes it likely that they result from competition between the malarial parasites and the host for pantothenic acid. Eyelid lesions had been previously observed by Becker *et al.* (1949) and by Harding (1955) in *P. lophurae* infections in chickens.

IV. RESEARCH ON HAEMOPROTEUS

Aside from the papers by Manwell and Loeffler (1961) on glucose consumption in the gametocytes of *Haemoproteus columbae* and by Ray *et al.* (1955) on the cytochemistry of gametocytes of this species (both of which are discussed elsewhere in this review) the only work done on this genus is concerned with its transmission.

Tarshis (1955) successfully transmitted *H. lophortyx* from quail to quail by bite of *Stilometopa impressa*. Prepatent periods of 44, 60, 103, 151 and 162 days were observed (5 pos. out of 26 laboratory reared). Four positive transmissions were made with naturally infected *S. impressa* (prepatent periods were 20, 20, 21 and 44 days). All attempts to obtain fly-bite transmission with *Lynchia hirsuta* were negative. Sporogonic stages of *H. lophortyx* were not found in either species of fly whether reared in the laboratory and fed on infected quail or in flies taken from trapped, infected quail. Three out of twenty tissue transplants of lung were successful (prepatent periods were 11, 21, and 21 days).

Baker (1957) found that sporogonous development of *Haemoproteus columbae* could occur in *Ornithomyia avicularia* and indicated in the title to his paper that this fly is a new vector in spite of his failure to infect pigeons by bite or by injection of the macerated fly. This seems to be a dangerous assumption in view of the known unsuccessful experiences at transmission of *P. berghei* by means of mosquitoes in which complete schizogony occurs.

Although surveys and descriptions of species are not treated in detail in this review the two volumes by Mohammed (1958) deserve to be called to the reader's attention because they contain reviews of recent literature on *Plasmodium* and *Haemoproteus*, records of species of these two genera in Egyptian birds and experimental studies on several of the species. His description of the sporogonous development of *Haemoproteus columbae* in *Pseudolynchia canariensis* is particularly pertinent to the discussion of transmission of *Haemoproteus* above.

It is unfortunate that in the history of the transmission of disease success in the demonstration of one means of transmission has often been followed by the dogmatic assumption that this can be the *only* means of transmission. This is exemplified by the long-held belief that *Aedes aegypti* was the only possible vector of yellow fever. Once it was known that a Hippoboscid fly could transmit *Haemoproteus* or a species of *Simulium* could transmit *Leucocytozoon* thinking crystallized into the tacit assumption that these insects were uniquely able to transmit the respective parasites. Old idols have been tumbled by the finding that species of *Culicoides* could transmit certain species of both *Haemoproteus* and *Leucocytozoon*. Fallis and co-workers in Canada have been the first iconoclasts in this exciting series of studies. Fallis and Wood (1957) first demonstrated that unidentified species (possibly *piliferus*) of *Culicoides* could transmit *Haemoproteus nettionis* to ducks. Ookinetes and structures identified as oocysts and sporozoites were found in midges that were sectioned. Demonstration of parasites was made in the blood of ducks 14–21 days after inoculation and the gametocytes required 4–6 days to mature. This represents not only the first proof that a *Culicoides* could act as a vector of *Haemoproteus* but was the first recorded transmission of any *Haemoproteus* of ducks. Bennett and Fallis (1960) surveyed 3000 birds in Algonquin Park, Canada and found that *Leucocytozoon* occurred in 60% and *Haemoproteus* in 26% of them. From their observations on incidence of infections and the levels of parasitemia when considered with the occurrence and feeding habits of the ornithophilic flies they suggested the possibility that *Culicoides* may transmit *Haemoproteus* in this area. Fallis and Bennett (1960) described and illustrated the sporogonic cycle of a new species *H. canachites* of spruce grouse (*Canachitis canadensis* L.) in *Culicoides spagnumensis* and produced infections experimentally in ruffed grouse (*Bonasa umbellus* L.) by injection of the sporozoites from the infected midges. They described the sporogonic stages of this species as being similar to those of *H. nettionis*. Fallis and Bennett (1961 a,b) traced the earlier events surrounding the discovery of the part played by *C. spagnumensis* in transmitting *Haemoproteus* in the spruce grouse and showed that *Haemoproteus* sp. of the crow could be transmitted by *C. crespuscularis* and *C. stibobezzioides* in Canada. They also incriminated *C. stibobezzioides* in the transmission of an unidentified species of *Haemoproteus* in a purple finch. Because of these discoveries Fallis and Wood raised the following questions: (1) If a hippoboscid fly could be found that would feed on ducks will it be capable of transmitting *H. nettionis*? (2) Will *Culicoides* serve as vectors of *Haemoproteus* known to be transmitted by hippoboscids? Fallis and Bennett (1961b) suggested on the basis of their discoveries that the three genera: *Plasmodium, Haemoproteus*, and *Leucocytozoon* should be placed in separate families but that the last two should probably be in the same order. The reviewer thinks that the state of our knowledge is too rudimentary, as yet, to draw up a satisfactory classification. He believes, however, that the findings just discussed support the belief that the earlier evolution of these parasites occurred in dipteran hosts and that later evolution occurred after they became parasites of vertebrates also.

V. Research on Leucocytozoon

A. SCHIZOGONY AND TYPE OF HOST CELL

In a study of the megaloschizonts of *L. simondi* in ducklings Cowan (1955) arrived at opinions concerning the manner of development of these stages and the nature of the central body quite at variance with the earlier studies of Ivanic (1937), Huff (1942), and Wingstrand (1947, 1948). He considered the central body as an integral portion of the parasite from which bud off sections which develop into cytomeres, rather than as the greatly enlarged nucleus of the host cell. His evidence is fragmentary when compared with that of Wingstrand (1948), which, however, was obtained from a study of *L. sakharoffi* (see his fig. 3). The latter author exhibits a nice series of stages in the growth of the megaloschizont and its host cell. The nucleus of the latter undergoes progressive hypertrophy until it becomes the "central body" within the mature megaloschizont. Figure 8 of Cowan's paper exhibits a hitherto undescribed condition in which sectors surrounding the central body are in different stages of development. Whether this is actually the case or whether the different sectors represent separate parasites of a multiple infection is not, as yet, satisfactorily resolved.

More evidence on the types of host cells infected by gametocytes of *L. simondi* has been presented by Savage and Isa (1959). By comparing the percentage of white cells in the blood of a normal duck with one heavily infected by gametocytes they were able to show a definite selectivity of the young gametocytes for monocytes and macrophages. They found a very low infection in lymphocytes and indicate that these cells may not be capable of assuming the size and shape of typical gametocyte host cells. The reviewer would like to remark that invaded lymphocytes may be stimulated very soon after invasion to abnormally rapid development and distortion so that they are no longer recognizable as lymphocytes. The same type of hypertrophy occurs in cells harboring asexual stages so that their identification is impossible soon after they are invaded by the young parasites.

B. PATHOLOGY

Although some mention has been made in the older literature of the gross pathology of *Leucocytozoon* infections, only recently has attention been paid to its histopathology. Newberne (1955) examined the histopathology of *L. smithii* in turkeys. He found no histological evidence of local host tissue reaction to gametocytes but noted moderate increase of focal and diffusely distributed lymphocytes in the liver. The focal areas of infiltration were periportal and intralobular and the diffuse infiltration was in the sinusoids and hepatic cell cords. Kupffer cells were swollen with phagocytized cellular debris and amorphous brown pigment particles. He found some macrophage proliferation and pigment deposition in the spleen of one animal. Megaloschizonts were not found in any of the infected turkeys. Hepatic schizonts were present but there was no evidence of local host tissue reaction to them. In the same year Richey and Ware (1955) reported finding hepatic schizonts in the liver of a turkey experimentally infected with sporozoites from *Simulium slossonae*. Later, Newberne (1957) studied the histopathology of *L. smithii* infections in ducks in which he demonstrated both hepatic and megaloschizonts; the latter were found in liver, spleen, heart, lungs, brain, kidneys, intestine and bone marrow. Newberne noted all stages of development of megaloschizonts but was unable to determine the type of cell invaded because of the distortion and hypertrophy produced in the cell by the parasite. A significant observation was the association of these schizonts with the Schweigger-Seidel sheaths of the spleen. Local host tissue reaction to megaloschizonts was observed only in brain and lungs and no tissue reaction was evident from hepatic schizonts or gametocytes. In the birds dying from acute fulminating infections there was marked damage to the liver and enlargement of the spleen from congestion and macrophage proliferation. He attributes the alterations in liver and spleen to massive red cell destruction and anemia. One is led to speculate whether there is an auto-immune antibody taking part in massive red cell destruction as discussed in the section on immunology of *Plasmodium*. Cowan (1957) likewise reported the reactions against megaloschizonts of *L. simondi* in ducks. He described five types of change: (1) possible encapsulation which he admits may not be a host reaction; (2) destruction by phagocytes, in all infected tissue except the brain, at the time after the parasite had reached its maximum size; (3) necrosis of the megaloschizont; (4) combined phagocytosis and necrosis and (5) destruction by inflammatory cells. The reader would do well to examine this paper in the original particularly in order to study the photomicrographs of the types of change described. These papers represent pioneering excursions into a field which would appear to be extremely complex and deserving of much more detailed study.

The coexistence of *Leucocytozoon* infections in turkeys with fowl cholera (*Pasteurella multocida*) in one instance and with leukosis in another led Simpson *et al.* (1956) to conjecture that infection with *L. smithii* might act as a stress factor which complicates certain diseases of turkeys. Animals dying of leukosis, as verified by hematological and histological findings, were also heavily infected with *L. smithii*. After the losses from leukosis had declined a sampling of the blood of surviving birds revealed either a very low or no infection by *Leucocytozoon*. In the instance in which the turkeys suffered from simultaneous infections of fowl cholera and *Leucocytozoon* infection there was little beneficial effect from the use of antibiotics (penicillin, dihydrostreptomycin, and terramycin). The authors did no experimental work under controlled conditions to establish their theory on a firm basis. However, their observations would indicate the need for further work along this line.

Byrd (1959) found few symptoms that could be attributed to *Leucocytozoon smithii* in turkeys and considered the parasite to be an innocuous organism in native wild and pen-raised turkeys in the Piedmont region of Virginia in which his studies were conducted. An outbreak of *Leucocytozoon* disease in chickens on farms in the outskirts of Taipei, Taiwan was reported by Liu (1958). More than 300 chickens were lost from 1500 hatched. Sixteen of the dead and diseased were necropsied. The comb, wattle, visible membranes, subcutaneous tissues and muscles were paler than normal; the blood was watery, hemorrhages were seen in the lungs, liver and kidneys; the spleen was enlarged and covered with white spots. White spots 0.5 – 4.0 mm in diameter were seen on the epicardium, endocardium and myocardium. The mature gametocytes were mostly of the round type but in one animal there were elongate forms. Histopathological findings included liver necrosis and infiltrations of the lymphatics, hyaline degeneration of the sheathed arteries of the spleen, lung hemorrhage and infiltration of the alveolar septal cells. Megaloschizonts were found in the kidneys, lung, heart, pancreas and arachnoida; they were all encapsulated by a wall of reticular fibers. No mention was made of hepatic schizonts.

C. DIFFERENCES IN HOST RESPONSE

Identification and systematic relationships between species of *Haemoproteus* and of *Leucocytozoon* occurring in different species of birds present difficult problems because of the conditions (1) that schizogony is confined to the internal organs and (2) that gametocytes are often very similar in appearance. Behavior of species of these genera in different hosts present then another characteristic which may be studied in attempting to facilitate identification. Briggs (1960) studied the behavior of *Leucocytozoon simondi* in Peking (*Anas platyrhynchos*) and Muscovy ducklings (*Cairina moschata*) by allowing uninfected groups of each to be bitten by naturally infected blackflies. Both hosts became infected, but Muscovies had consistently lower gametocytemias than Pekings, developed their parasitemias later and had smaller percentages of elongate gametocytes. Mortality was lower in rate and deaths were delayed in Muscovies when compared with Peking ducklings. Difference between gametocytemias in the two species might possibly have been the result of the fact that blackflies may feed more readily on Pekings. Although not conclusive these studies point the way to better knowledge of parasite-host relationships and possible significance of the difference in appearance of one species of parasite in different species of hosts.

D. TRANSMISSION

1. *Natural and Artificial Transmission to Goslings*

Leucocytozoon simondi which occurs so commonly in ducks was transmitted by Fallis *et al.* (1954) to goslings. Tissues from a duck infected with this species were inoculated intraperitoneally into goslings, duck, turkeys, pheasants, chickens, and ruffed grouse. Infection resulted only in the ducks and goslings. Similar experiments were carried out with tissues of a crow infected with *L. sakharoffi* inoculated into grouse, pigeon, duck and chicken. No infection resulted in any of these birds. Two goslings were exposed alongside ducks infected with *L. simondi*. Parasites resembling *L. simondi* appeared in the blood of both goslings 9 days later. The vector was not identified.

2. New Transmissions by Simulium

Fallis *et al.* (1956) demonstrated that *Simulium croxtoni, S. euryadminiculum*, and *S. rugglesi* are suitable hosts of *L. simondi*. Oocysts were observed on the stomach wall of *S. rugglesi* which contained small numbers of sporozoites. Their observations suggest the possibility that sporogony may be completed in 3–4 days. Experimental transmission was successful by injecting into ducks the ground-up specimens of *S. rugglesi* intraperitoneally.

Wild-caught specimens of *S. slossonae* when macerated and injected experimentally into 10-week-old turkeys gave rise to *Leucocytozoon* infections (Jones and Richey, 1956). The bite of only one fly collected while feeding on an infected turkey was also capable of producing an infection in a turkey.

Fallis and Bennett (1958) found *Simulium aureum* and *S. latipes* to be capable of developing infective sporozoites of *L. bonasae* when the latter were inoculated into grouse. Parasitemia in grouse which obtained their infections in this manner, or naturally, was low and no gross signs of disease were observed in the infected birds. Byrd (1959) experimentally transmitted *L. smithii* to turkeys from infected *Prosimulium hirtipes* in Virginia.

3. Transmission by Culicoides

Outbreaks of leucocytozoon disease in the prefectures of Aichi, Saitama, Gumma, Yamanashi and the Tokyo districts of Japan were studied by Akiba (1960). He experimented with *Dermanyssus gallinae*, *Culex pipiens pallens*, and *Culicoides arakawae* as possible vectors of *Leucocytozoon caulleryi*. He was able to demonstrate ookinetes, oocysts, and sporozoites in specimens of *C. arakawae* fed upon infected chickens and was able to produce infections in chickens in about 14 days following the injection of a suspension of the sporozoites. The various stages in sporogony were presented in photomicrographs. It is interesting that within the period of a few years *Culicoides* has been incriminated in the transmission of both *Haemoproteus* and *Leucocytozoon*. It would appear to be important now to determine whether *Simulium* may be capable of transmitting species of *Haemoproteus*. Fallis and Bennett (1961a) have summarized the various types of disease for which Ceratopogonidae have been suspected of or shown to be capable of transmitting.

4. Sporogony

Fallis and Bennett (1961b) have given us a careful report on the comparative sporogonous stages of *Leucocytozoon* and *Haemoproteus*. Their paper is well illustrated and contains so much detail that it should be read in its entirety. Some generalization can, however, be made. Sporogony is more rapid in both genera than in *Plasmodium*, being completed in from 5 to 7 days. Oocysts are small in each genus in their orthorrhaphous hosts as compared with the oocysts of *Plasmodium* in mosquitoes or of *Haemoproteus* in hippoboscids. The sporozoites are few in number; those of *Haemoproteus* in ceratopogonids have both ends pointed; those of *Haemoproteus* in hippoboscids and those of *Leucocytozoon* in simuliids have one end less pointed. Residual bodies are present in the oocysts of each.

VI. PRESENT STATUS OF RESEARCH IN AVIAN MALARIA

As previously indicated, the volume of experimental work on malaria has decreased since World War II. It is not possible to say precisely whether this was due entirely to the decreased military urgency for solutions to the problems of control and treatment of the disease or to what extent the recent movement toward eradication of malaria brought along with it a lack of interest in working upon a disease presumed to be approaching extinction. Although work on avian malaria (as well as the malarias of other laboratory animals) has also decreased in amount it is apparent from the work reviewed here that great progress is still being made toward the solution of the more basic problems of malariology. It is idle to speculate upon the probable course of development which would have been followed without the impetus of World War II. The reviewer chooses to believe that there has been for a long time a nucleus of investigators challenged by the complex problems presented by the many facets of malarial research who would have continued their efforts even if the human aspects of it had not been so greatly emphasized by a war.

Speculation aside, the recent past has seen real advances in the physiology of the erythrocytic stages, improvements in the methods of studying exoerythrocytic stages and the growth of the sporogonous stages; improved techniques for serological and immunological studies; startling discoveries in the transmission of *Haemoproteus* and *Leucocytozoon* and the inception of the study of microstructure which in turn offers guideposts toward better understanding of how these microorganisms function in their various stages and environments.

VII. AREAS FOR FUTURE DEVELOPMENT

Research on avian malaria, as pointed out by the reviewer (Huff, 1959b), offers to microbiologists, biochemists, physiologists and many other scientists tools for solving many of their problems and this will continue to be true regardless of whether human malaria is eradicated. Moreover, the growing feeling that eradication of malaria is just around the corner has given a great majority of people the idea that malarial research is no longer necessary. Since malaria is *not* yet eradicated our tools for controlling it are rusting away leaving us unprepared for combàtting an unexpected return of this great scourge. In this respect research on animal malarias not only provides us with a means for solving problems of basic importance to many fields of biology but keeps alive the interest of a small nucleus of investigators in a disease which may be with us for longer than is generally believed.

Obligate parasites like malarial parasites present unique problems in physiology. The solution of these problems is not likely to come from the study of non-parasitic forms. The intracellular parasite which is a cell itself lives within another cell upon which it is dependent. The physiological interactions of these two cells present problems which are very challenging. Little is known about the genetics and cytology of malarial parasites. What is the chemical nature of the bearer of the inheritance of these organisms? What is the mechanism involved in nuclear division? What determines the choice of host cell which is made by the parasite and why does this choice change during the course of infection? What really are the systematic relationships among the great numbers of species of malarial parasites and how did they evolve from common ancestors? These are only a few of the unanswered questions which are posed by this group of microorganisms. They are not peculiar to avian malaria but many of them can be answered through the continued study of avian malaria.

REFERENCES

Akiba, K. (1960). *Jap. J. vet. Sci.* **22**, 309–17.
Al-Dabagh, M. A. (1960). *Trans. R. Soc. trop. Med. Hyg.* **54**, 400–5.
Al-Dabagh, M. A. (1961a). *Trans. R. Soc. trop. Med. Hyg.* **55**, 351–4.
Al-Dabagh, M. A. (1961b). *J. comp. Path.* **71**, 217–21.
Al-Dabagh, M. A. (1961c). *Parasitology* **51**, 257–61.
Algire, G. H., Weaver, J. M. and Prehn, R. T. (1954). *J. nat. Cancer Inst.* **15**, 493–507.
Baker, J. R. (1957). *J. Protozool.* **4**, 204–8.
Ball, E. G., Anfinsen, C. B., Geiman, Q. M., McKee, R. W. and Ormsbee, R. A. (1945). *Science* **101**. 542.
Ball, G. H. and Chao, J. (1960). *Exp. Parasit.* **9**, 47–55.
Bano, L. (1959). *Parasitology* **49**, 559–85.
Barnett, H. C. (1956). *Amer. J. trop. Med. Hyg.* **5**, 99–109.
Becker, E. R., Brodine, C. E. and Marousek, A. E. (1949). *J. infect. Dis.* **85**, 230–8.
Becker, E. R., Hollander, W. F. and Pattillo, W. H. (1956). *J. Parasit.* **42**, 474–8.
Bennett, G. F. and Fallis, A. M. (1960). *Canad. J. Res. (Zool.)* **38**, 261–73.
Bishop, A. (1955). *Parasitology* **45**, 163–85.
Bishop, A. and McConnachie, E. W. (1956). *Parasitology* **46**, 192–215.
Bishop, A. and McConnachie, E. W. (1960). *Parasitology* **50**, 431–48.
Bray, R. S. (1957). *Lond. Sch. Hyg. trop. Med.*, Mem. **12**, 192 pp. H. K. Lewis, London.
Briggs, N. T. (1960). *Proc. helm. Soc. Wash.* **27**, 151–6.

Byrd, M. A. (1959). *J. Wildlife Mgmt.* **23**, 145–56.

Clarke, D. H. (1952). *J. exp. Med.* **96**, 451–63.

Corradetti, A. (1943). *Arch. Protistenk.* **96**, 235–87.

Corradetti, A. and Verolini, F. (1958a). *Riv. Parassit.* **19**, 21–28.

Corradetti, A. and Verolini, F. (1958b). *R. C. Ist. sup. Sanit.* **21**, 529–38.

Corradetti, A., Neri, I. and Scarrza, M. (1960). *Parassit.* **2**, 333–43.

Cowan, A. B. (1955). *J. Protozool.* **2**, 158–67.

Cowan, A. B. (1957). *J. inf. Dis.* **100**, 82–7.

DasGupta, B. (1960a). *Parasitology* **50**, 501–8.

DasGupta, B. (1960b). *Parasitology* **50**, 509–14.

DasGupta, B. (1961). *Mém. Soc. zool. tchécosl.* **25**, 16–21.

Demina, N. A. (1956). *Med. Parasit., Moscow* **25**, 48–53.

Demina, N. A. (1959). *Riv. Malariol.* **38**, 27–44.

Deschiens, R., Pick, F. and Sarauw, U. (1956). *Bull. Soc. Pat. exot.* **49**, 353–65.

Dubin, I. N. (1954). *Exp. Parasit.* **3**, 425–32.

Dubin, I. N., Laird, R. L. and Drinnon, V. P. (1949). *J. nat. Malar. Soc.* **8**, 175–80.

Dubin, I. N., Laird, R. L. and Drinnon, V. P. (1950). *J. nat. Malar. Soc.* **9**, 119–217.

Duncan, D., Eades, J., Julian, S. R. and Micks, D. W. (1960). *J. Protozool.* **7**, 18–26.

Duncan, D., Street, J., Julian, S. R. and Micks, D. W. (1959). *Tex. Rep. Biol. Med.* **17**, 314–22.

Dutta, B. N., Chaudhuri, R. N., Ray, H. N. (1956). *Bull. Calcutta Sch. trop. Med.* **4**, 171–2.

Fallis, A. M. and Bennett, G. F. (1958). *Canad. J. Res. (Zool.)* **36**, 533–9.

Fallis, A. M. and Bennett, G. F. (1960). *Canad. J. Res. (Zool.)* **38**, 455–64.

Fallis, A. M. and Bennett, G. F. (1961a). *Mosquito News* **21**(1), 21–8.

Fallis, A. M. and Bennett, G. F. (1961b). *Canad. J. Res. (Zool.)* **39**, 215–28.

Fallis, A. M. and Wood, D. M. (1957). *Canad. J. Res. (Zool.)* **35**, 425–35.

Fallis, A. M., Pearson, J. C., and Bennett, G. F. (1954). *Canad. J. Res. (Zool.)* **32**, 120–4.

Fallis, A. M. Anderson, R. C. and Bennett, G. F. (1956). *Canad. J. Res. (Zool.)* **34**, 389–404.

Fernex, M. (1959). *Acta trop.* **16**, 362–5.

Garnham, P. C. C. (1954). *Ann. Rev. Microbiol.* **8**, 153–66.

Garnham, P. C. C., Bird, R. G., and Baker, J. R. (1960). *Trans. R. Soc. trop. Med. Hyg.* **54**, 274–8.

Garnham, P. C. C., Heisch, R. B. and Minter, D. M. (1961). *Trans. R. Soc. trop. Med. Hyg.* **55**, 497–502.

Garnham, P. C. C., Bird, R. G. and Baker, J. R. (1962). *Trans. R. Soc. trop. Med. Hyg.* **56**, 116–20.

Geigy, R. and Freyvogel, T. (1954). *Acta trop.* **11**, 167–71.

Ghosh, T. N. and Ray, H. N. (1957a). *Bull. Calcutta Sch. trop Med.* **4**, 178.

Ghosh, T. N. and Ray, H. N. (1957b). *Bull. Calcutta Sch. trop. Med.* **5**, 17–18.

Gingrich, W. D. (1941). *J. infect. Dis.* **68**, 37–45.

Glenn, S. and Manwell, R. D. (1956). *Exp. Parasitol.* **5** (1), 22–33.

Goble, F. C. and Singer, I. (1960). *Ann. N. Y. Acad. Sci.* **88**, 149–71.

Greenberg, J. (1955). *Trop. Med. Hyg. News* **4**, 6–14.

Greenberg, J. (1956). *Exp. Parasit.* **5**, 359–70.

Harding, D. E. (1955). *Proc. Iowa Acad. Sci.* **62**, 543–9.

Hewitt, R. (1940). *Amer. J. Hyg.* Monog. Ser. 15, 222 pp. Johns Hopkins Press.

Huff, C. G. (1937). *J. Parasit.* **23**, 400–4.

Huff, C. G. (1940). *Amer. J. Hyg.* **32**C, 71–80.

Huff, C. G. (1942). *J. infect. Dis.* **71**, 18–32.

Huff, C. G. (1949). *In* "Malariology" (M. F. Boyd, ed.), Vol. I. pp. 54–64. W. B. Saunders, Philadelphia.

Huff, C. G. (1956). *J. Parasit.* **42**, 612.

Huff, C. G. (1957). *Exp. Parasit.* **6**, 143–62.

Huff, C. G. (1958). *Rice Inst. Pamphl.* **45**, 55–79.

Huff, C. G. (1959a). *Exp. Parasit.* **8**, 163–70.

Huff, C. G. (1959b). *Riv. Parassit.* **20**, 289–92.

Huff, C. G. and Coulston, F. (1944). *J. inf. Dis.* **75**, 231–49.

Huff, C. G. and Marchbank, D. F. (1955). *Exp. Parasit.* **4**, 256–70.

Huff, C. G., Marchbank, D. F. and Shiroishi, T. (1958). *Exp. Parasit.* **7**, 399–417.

Huff, C. G., Marchbank, D. F. and Shiroishi, T. (1959). *J. Protozool.* **6**, 46–51.

Huff, C. G., Pipkin, A. C., Weathersby, A. B. and Jensen, D. V. (1960a). *J. Biophys. Biochem. Cytol.* **7**, 93–102.

Huff, C. G., Weathersby, A. B., Pipkin, A. C. and Algire, C. H. (1960b). *Exp. Parasit.* **9**, 98–104.

Hughes, F. W. and Tatum, A. L. (1955). *J. infect. Dis.* **97**, 231–7.

Hull, R. W. (1958). *J. Parasit.* **44** (4, sect. 2), 22.

Ingram, R. L., Orken, L. E., Jr. and Jumper, J. R. (1961). *Proc. Soc. exp. Biol., N. Y.* **106**, 52–4.

Ivanic, M. (1937). *Arch. Protist.* **89**, 16–44.

Jacobs, H. R. (1957). *Proc. Soc. exp. Biol., N.Y.* **95**, 372–3.

Jones, C. M. and Richey, D. J. (1956). *J. econ. Ent.* **49**, 121–3.

Jordan, H. B. (1957). *J. Parasit.* **43**, 395–408.

Khabir, P. A. and Manwell, R. D. (1955). *J. Parasit.* **41**, 595–603.

Kikuth, W. and Mudrow, L. (1940). *Riv. Malariologia* **19**, 1–15.

Laird, R. L., Dubin, I. N. and Drinnon, V. P. (1950). *J. nat. Malar. Soc.* **9**, 128–31.

Liu, Si-Kwang (1958). *Mem. Coll. Agri. Nat. Taiwan Univ.* **5**, 74–80 (In Chinese and English).

McGhee, R. B. (1951). *J. inf. Dis.* **88**, 86–97.

McGhee, R. B. (1956). *J. Protozool.* **3**, 122–6.

McGhee, R. B. (1957). *J. inf. Dis.* **100**, 92–6.

McGhee, R. B. (1958). *J. Parasit.* **44**, 153–60.

McGhee, R. B. (1959). *J. Protozool.* **6**, 84–8.

McGhee, R. B. (1960). *J. inf. Dis.* **107**, 410–18 (Also *J. Protozool.* **7** (suppl): 7 *abs.* 1960).

Manwell, R. D. (1933). *Amer. J. trop. Med.* **13**, 97–112.

Manwell, R. D. and Loeffler, C. A. (1961). *J. Parasit.* **47**, 285–90.

Manwell, R. D. and Robinson, F. O. (1962). *Amer. J. Hyg.* **75**, 69–73.

Manwell, R. D., Weiss, M. L. and Spandorf, A. A. (1957). *Exp. Parasit.* **6** (4), 358–66.

Meyer, H. and de Oliveira Musacchio, M. (1958). *Sixth Intern. Cong. trop. Med. Malar., Instit. Med. trop.*, Lisbon, 293–4 (abstract).

Meyer, H. and de Oliveira Musacchio, M. (1960a). *J. Protozool.* **7**, 222–8.

Meyer, H. and de Oliveira Musacchio, M. (1960b). *Ann. Acad. bras. Sci.* **32**, 91–4.

Micks, D. W. and Ferguson, M. J. (1961). *J. Insect Path.* **3**, 244–8.

Mohammed, A. H. H. (1958). "Systematic and Experimental Studies on Protozoal blood parasites of Egyptian birds." Cairo University Press. Vol. I, 165; Vol. II, 169–298.

Mohan, B. N. (1955). *Indian J. Malar.* **9**, 287–96.

Mohan, B. N. (1960). *Indian J. Malar.* **14**, 179–85.

Molinari, V. (1961). *J. trop. Med. (Hyg.)* **64**, 225–32.

Moulder, J. W. (1962). "The biochemistry of intracellular parasitism". 172 pp. Univ. of Chicago Press.

Moulder, J. W. and Taliaferro, W. H. (1955). *J. infect. Dis.* **97**, 137–42.

Mudrow-Reichenow, L. (1952). *Ergebn. Hyg. Bakt.* **27**, 420–511.

Muniz, J., Soares, R. and Batista, S. (1951). *Rev. bras. Malariol.* **3**, 339–56 (In English, pp. 357–62).

Newberne, J. W. (1955). *Amer. J. vet. Res.* **16**, 593–7.

Newberne, J. W. (1957). *Amer. J. vet. Res.* **18**, 191–9.

Nydegger, L. and Manwell, R. D. (1962). *J. Parasit.* **48**, 142–7.

Nye, P. A. (1961). *Exp. Parasit.* **11**, 77–89.

de Oliveira Musacchio, M. and Meyer, H. (1955). *Parasitology* **45**, 1–4.

de Oliveira Musacchio, M. and Meyer, H. (1958). *O. Hospital* **53**, 379–82.

Pipkin, A. C. and Jensen, D. V. (1958). *Exp. Parasit.* **7**, 491–530.

Polizzi Sciarrone, M. (1957). *Rendc. Ist. sup. Sanit.* **20**, 267–71 (English summary).

Porter, R. J. and Huff, C. G. (1940). *Amer. J. trop. Med.* **20**, 869–88.

Raffaele, G. (1955). *Riv. Malariol.* **34**, 215–30.

Raffaele, G. (1959). *Riv. Malariol.* **38**, 159–96.

Rahm, U. von and Kauffman, M. (1959). *Acta trop.* **16**, 302–30.

Rama Rao, R. and Sirsi, M. (1956). *J. Indian Inst. Sci.* **38** (Part I.), 108–14; (Part II.), 186–9; (Part III.), 224–7.

Rama Rao, R. and Sirsi, M. (1958). *J. Indian Inst. Sci.* **40**, 23–30.

Ramaswamy, A. S. (1956). *J. Indian Inst. Sci.* **38**, 62–72.

Ray, H. N., DasGupta, B., Sen, H. G. and Dutta, B. N. (1955). *Bull. Calcutta Sch. trop. Med.* **3**, 170–1.

Ray, H. N., DasGupta B. and Sen Gupta, P. C. (1956a). *Bull. Calcutta Sch. trop. Med.* **4**, 20.

Ray, H. N., Ghosh, T. N. and Smith, R. O. A. (1956b). *Bull. Calcutta Sch. trop. Med.* **4**, 159.

Richey, D. J. and Ware, R. E. (1955). *Cornell Vet.* **45**, 642–3.

Rudzinska, M. A. and Trager, W. (1956). *J. Parasitol.* **42**, (4) Sect. 2: 36–7 (abs).

Rudzinska, M. A. and Trager, W. (1957). *J. Protozool.* **4**, 190–9.

Rudzinska, M. A. and Trager, W. (1961). *J. Protozool.* **8**, 307–22.

Savage, A. and Isa, J. M. (1959). *Canad. J. Res. (Zool.)* **37**, 1123–6.

Schinazi, L. A. (1957). *Science* **125**, 695–7.

Schinazi, L. A. and Ball, G. H. (1956). *Exp. Parasit.* **5**, 541–50.

Sherman, I. W. and Hull, R. W. (1960a). *J. Protozool.* **7**, 171–6.

Sherman, I. W. and Hull, R. W. (1960b). *J. Parasitol.* **46**, 765–7.

Simpson, C. F., Anthony, D. W. and Young, F. (1956). *J. Amer. vet. med. Ass.* **129**, 573–6.

Spandorf, A. A. and Manwell, R. D. (1960). *Exp. Parasit.* **10**, 287–92.

Stauber, L. A. (1939). *J. Parasitol.* **25**, 95–116.

Stohler, H. (1957). *Acta trop.* **14**, 302–52.

Taliaferro, W. H. (1941). In "Protozoa in Biological Research." (Calkins, G. N. and Summers, F. M. ed.), pp. 830–54. Columbia Univ. Press, N. Y.

Taliaferro, W. H. (1956). *Amer. J. trop. Med. Hyg.* **5**, 391–410.

Taliaferro, W. H. and Taliaferro, L. G. (1955). *J. infect. Dis.* **97**, 99–136.

Tarshis, I. B. (1955). *Exp. Parasit.* **4**, 464–92.

Taylor, A. E. R. (1958), *Ann. trop. Med. Parasit.* **52**, 139–44.

Taylor, D. J., Greenberg, J., Josephson, E. S. and Nadel, E. M. (1956). *Acta endocr.* **22**, 173–8.

Terzian, L. A. (1953). *J. Immunol.* **71**, 202–6.

Terzian, L. A. (1955). *J. cell and comp. Physiol.* **46**, 279–300.

Terzian, L. A. (1961). *Exp. Parasit.* **11**, 102–10.

Terzian, L. A. and Stahler, N. (1960). *J. inf. Dis.* **106**, 45–52.

Terzian, L. A., Stahler, N. and Irreverre, F. (1956). *J. Immunol.* **76**, 308–13.

Trager, W. (1955). *In* "Eleventh Conference on Protein Metabolism", pp. 3–14. Rutgers University Press.
Trager, W. (1957). *Acta trop.* **14**, 289–301.
Trager, W. (1958). *J. exp. Med.* **108**, 753–72.
Trager, W. (1959a). *Exp. Parasit.* **8**, 265–73.
Trager, W. (1959b). *Proc. Soc. exp. Biol., N. Y.* **101**, 578–82.
Trager, W. (1960). *In* "The Cell" (J. Bracket and A. E. Mirsky, eds.) Vol. IV, pp. 151–213.
Trager, W. (1961). *Exp. Parasit.* **11**, 298–304.
Trager, W. and Jernberg, N. A. (1961). *Proc. Soc. exp. Biol., N. Y.* **108**, 175–8.
Trager, W. and Singer, I. (1955). *Proc. Soc. exp. Biol., N. Y.* **90**, 539–42.
Ward, R. A., Bell, L. H. and Schneider, R. L. (1960). *Exp. Parasit.* **10**, 324–32.
Weathersby, A. B. (1952). *J. inf. Dis.* **91**, 198–205.
Weathersby, A. B. (1954). *Exp. Parasit.* **3**, 538–43.
Weathersby, A. B. (1960a). *Exp. Parasit.* **9**, 334–7.
Weathersby, A. B. (1960b). *Exp. Parasit.* **10**, 211–3.
Weiss, M. L. and Manwell, R. D. (1960). *J. Protozool.* **7**, 342–6.
Wingstrand, K. G. (1947). *K. svenska VetenskAkad. Handl.* Series 3, **24** (5), 1–31.
Wingstrand, K. G. (1948). *K. svenska VetenskAkad. Handl.* Series 3, **24** (8), 1–17.
Wolcott, G. B. (1957). *J. Protozool.* **4**, 48–51.
Zasukhin, D. N. and Vasina, S. G. (1956). *Zool. Zhurnal* **35**, 1450–3.
Zuckerman, A. (1960a). *Nature, Lond.* **185**, 189–90.
Zuckerman, A. (1960b). *J. inf. Dis.* **107**, 133–48.

Coccidia and Coccidiosis
in the Domestic Fowl and Turkey

C. HORTON-SMITH and P. L. LONG

Houghton Poultry Research Station, Houghton,
Huntingdon, England

I. Introduction 68
II. The Pathology and the Life Cycles of the Species of *Eimeria* in Fowls 86
    A. The Pathogenicity of *E. acervulina* 68
    B. The Pathogenicity and Life Cycle of *E. brunetti* 69
    C. The Life Cycle of *E. maxima* 70
    D. The Life Cycle and Pathology of *E. mitis* 73
    E. The Life Cycles of *E. necatrix* and *E. tenella* 74
III. The Pathology and the Life Cycles of the Species of Eimeria occurring in Turkeys.. 76
    A. The Life History of *E. adenoeides* 76
    B. The Life History and Pathogenicity of *E. meleagridis* 76
    C. The Life History and Pathogenicity of *E. meleagrimitis* 78
IV. Oocyst Production of Different Species 82
V. Cytochemical Observations on Stages of the Coccidial Life Cycle 83
    A. Desoxyribonucleic Acid (DNA) 83
    B. Ribonucleic Acid (RNA) 84
    C. Proteins 85
    D. Lipids 85
    E. Carbohydrates 85
    F. Protein-carbohydrate Complex 88
    G. Mucopolysaccharides 90
    H. Enzyme activity 91
VI. Immunity to Coccidiosis 91
    A. The Phase of the Life Cycle Inducing the Immune Response 91
    B. The Immunization of Chickens and the Immunizing Power of Different
       Species of Coccidia 92
    C. The Fate of Sporozoites and Second Generation Merozoites of *E. tenella* in
       Fully Immune Chickens 93
    D. The Duration of Immunity to Coccidiosis in the Absence of Reinfection 95
    E. The Transference of Resistance to *E. tenella* from one Caecum to the Other in
       Individual Fowls 96
    F. Detection of Precipitating Antibodies and Tests for the Specificity of the
       Reactions 97
    G. Precipitating Antibodies Associated with Immunity to Four Species of *Eimeria*
       in Fowls 98
    H. Electrophoretic Studies 100
    I. Detection of Lysins in the Sera of *E. tenella*-Immune Fowls 100
    J. Attempts to Demonstrate Antibodies in Caecal Tissue of *E. tenella*-Immune
       Fowls 101
    K. Attempts to Induce a Passive Immunity to *E. tenella* Infections 102
    L. Cellular Responses 103
    References 104

I. Introduction

Within recent years attention has been given to the re-examination of the pathology of coccidiosis and the life-cycles of the Eimeriidae occurring in fowls and turkeys and, especially, of those species associated with disease in the avian host. The cytochemical characters of the various stages of the life-cycle have also been considered. The *Eimeria* are particularly well suited to the application of cytochemical methods on account of their relatively large size and easy identification in host tissues. Immunity plays an important part in the epidemiology and chemotherapy of the disease (coccidiosis) associated with coccidial infestations and much work has been done in attempts to determine the mechanism by which immunity develops and to extend our knowledge of this complicated phenomenon. This review will confine itself to the consideration of these aspects of recent researches.

II. The Pathology and the Life Cycles of the Species of *Eimeria* in Fowls

Within recent years the life cycles of *Eimeria maxima* Tyzzer, 1929, *E. mitis* Tyzzer, 1929, *E. necatrix* Johnson, 1930, and *E. tenella* Railliet and Lucet, 1891 have been re-examined. A full account of the development of *E. brunetti* Levine, 1942, has also been published as well as a reconsideration of the pathogenicity of *E. acervulina* Tyzzer, 1929.

A. THE PATHOGENICITY OF *E. acervulina*

It is interesting to recall that Tyzzer (1929) in his description of this species regarded it as responsible for a chronic condition which caused extreme wasting of the fowl. Later (1932), he failed to induce any severe pathogenesis and concluded that its pathogenicity was unproved. A number of authors, including Johnson (1931), have all considered this species to be of some pathogenicity. Watery droppings, suppression of weight gain and a temporary drop in egg production have been mentioned. Dickinson and Schofield (1939) obtained 20% mortality in Single Comb White Leghorn chicks which had received a single dose of about thirty-five million sporulated oocysts of *E. acervulina*, deaths occurring in the sixth, twelfth and fourteenth days of the infection. Brackett and Bliznick (1950) failed to kill chickens with any size of inoculum of oocysts, and Cuckler *et al.* (1956) referred to this species as pathogenic but non-lethal. Morehouse and McGuire (1958) used New Hampshire chickens aged from 4 – 10 weeks as hosts in experiments with *E. acervulina*. These authors showed that birds were severely affected by large doses of sporulated oocysts of *E. acervulina*, single or multiple infective doses of 5 million or more sporulated oocysts sometimes killing 75% of the experimental birds and they concluded that deaths from this form of intestinal coccidiosis may well occur under farm conditions. *E. acervulina* is now known to cause a mild pathological condition similar to that described by Tyzzer (1929) and a severe inflammatory condition of the mucosa of the intestine. Morehouse and McGuire have repeatedly produced both these conditions by varying the magnitude of the infective dose of a single pure culture of sporulated oocysts of *E. acervulina*. Horton-Smith and Long (1959) produced deaths in Rhode Island Red x White Leghorn chickens aged 8 days, by giving them three doses of 5, 3 and 2 million sporulated oocysts of a British strain of *E. acervulina* respectively on 3 successive days. Some years ago *E. acervulina* was regarded as an economically unimportant parasite of chickens in Britain but over the last few years it has assumed an increased importance and its incidence as a pathogen is now widespread. Al-Dabagh (1961) observed a synergistic effect of *E. acervulina* and *E. mitis* on the parasites *Plasmodium juxtanucleare* and *P. gallinaceum*. He found that oocyst production which had ceased in *E. acervulina* infected chickens started again after infecting the chickens with *P. gallinaceum*. In view of the self-limiting life-cycle of coccidia the renewed oocyst production is difficult to understand in the absence of reinfection.

B. THE PATHOGENICITY AND LIFE CYCLE OF *E. brunetti*

This species was named in 1942 by Levine, who described the oocysts as egg-shaped or oval and larger than those of any other species occurring in the fowl with the exception of *E. maxima*. The dimensions of the oocysts of *E. brunetti* varied from 20.7 to 30.3 μ in length with an average of 26.8 μ in length and a width ranging from 18.1 to 24.2 μ and averaging 21.7 μ. At this point it would be as well to indicate that oocysts characters alone have only limited value in differentiating species of *Eimeria*. Becker *et al.* (1956) in their biometrical study of the oocyst of *E. brunetti* concluded that there are dangers in distinguishing species on oocyst measurements and, especially so, when the oocysts lack other obvious morphological or physiological characters which can be used to separate them. Various factors influence the shape of oocysts, and Fish (1931) showed that the oocysts of *E. tenella* became longer and broader as the infection developed but that the ratio between the two dimensions (shape index) remained more or less constant. Cheissin (1947) noted that the size of the oocysts of *E. magna* from rabbits decreased when the size of the inocula of oocysts was increased. There was an increase in size of oocysts towards the end of the patent period. Variations in size of oocysts might vary from rabbit to rabbit. According to Levine the sporulation time is from 24 to 48 h when the oocysts are stored in $1\frac{1}{2}\%$ potassium dichromate at 30°C. The prepatent period lasts about 5 days following the feeding of sporulated oocysts which is 1 day shorter than the prepatent period of *E. maxima*. A thickening of the gut wall and the formation of a pinkish or blood-tinged catarrhal exudate occur as a result of moderate infections. Levine also describes red transverse streaks which run down into the the mucosa of the lower intestine and rectum. In severe infections there is coagulation, necrosis and sloughing of the mucosa. Boles and Becker (1954) have given a detailed account of the development of *E. brunetti*. They noted that *E. brunetti* parasitized the epithelium of the villi at points in contact with or close to the basement membrane. The sporozoites penetrate and develop in the upper small intestine and later stages in the middle small intestine to the cloaca as well as the caeca. The first generation schizonts are large, with an average measurement of $30\mu \times 20\mu$ and contain about 200 merozoites. These schizonts are found along the sides of the villi of the whole intestine within 51 to 76 h of the infection. Smaller second generation schizonts with an average measurement of $29.6\,\mu \times 16.2\,\mu$ and containing fifty to sixty merozoites are found in the tips of the villi on the 95th h of the infection. A third type and small schizont was also seen on the 95th h. Larger microgametocytes and smaller macrogametocytes measuring $25.2 \times 22.2\,\mu$ and containing plastic granules were found on the basement membrane in the lower small intestine, rectum, caeca and cloaca. This species is extending its incidence in Britain and the United States and is now proving of economic importance. Photomicrographs of second generation schizonts (small type) and sexual phases of *E. brunetti* are shown in Fig. 1. The endigenous cycle is shown in Fig. 2.

C. THE LIFE CYCLE OF *E. maxima*

Long (1959) and Scholtyseck (1959) have published accounts of the life-cycle of this species. On the whole, Long's description of a British strain confirms the original account of *E. maxima* Tyzzer, 1929 as well as other reports by Johnson (1938), Edgar (1955) and Becker *et al.* (1956) who worked with American strains. Long's account differs from that of Tyzzer and closely agrees with that of Edgar in the matter of the length of the prepatent period which he found to be 121 h or one day less than the time given by Tyzzer. Long found that the sporulation of the oocyst was completed in 48 h at a temperature of 30°C, but that the minimum sporulation time, as confirmed by test dosing of chickens, was 30 h which, again, is very similar to the observations of Edgar. Long also noted that the maximum oocyst production occurred on the 6th and 8th days of the infection after which there was a sharp decline until all oocyst production ceased between the 10th and 11th days of the infection. He considered that these observations supported Tyzzer's

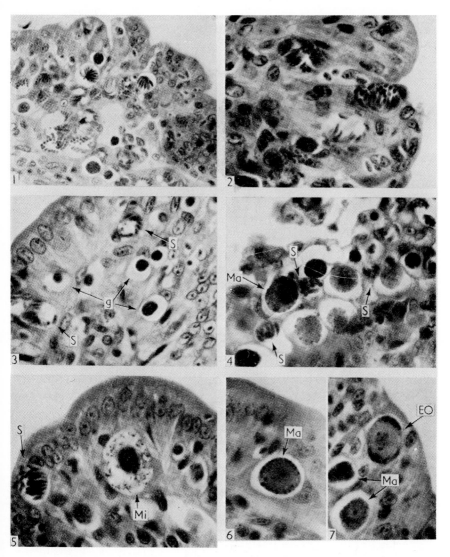

Fig. 1. Sections of the lower intestine of chickens infected with *Eimeria brunetti*. Stain haematoxylin and Eosin. 1, magnification × 700; 2–7, magnification × 100. 1. 96 h after infection showing large numbers of 2nd generation schizonts in a villus. 2. as 1, higher magnification. 3. 102 h after infection, villus. S=schizonts, g=young gametocytes. 4. 120 h after infection, villus. S=schizont, Ma=Macrogametocyte with prominent "plastic granules", many developing gametocytes also present. 5. 120 h after infection, villus, large mature microgametocytes (Mi) with gametes arranged peripherally and large nuclear mass in centre. Schizont (S) also present. 6. 120 h after infection, villus, large macrogametocyte (Ma). 7. 120 h after infection, villus, Macrogametocytes (Ma) and on early oocyst (EO) showing fusion of "plastic granules" to form the oocyst wall.

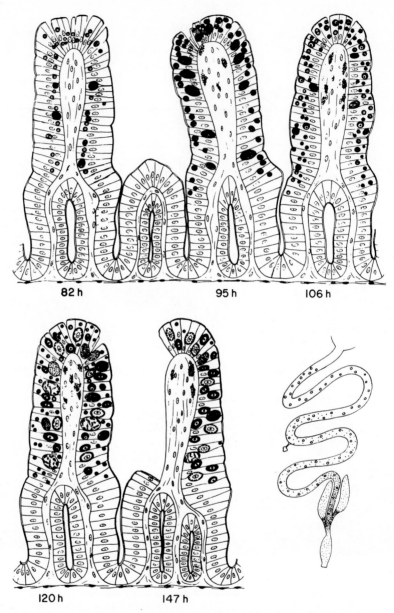

82 h   95 h   106 h

120 h   147 h

Fig. 2. (*Above*). A schematic drawing showing the position of parasites in the lower small intestine. At 82 h, merozoites that have just entered cells and multinucleated 2nd generation schizonts are observed, usually below the nucleus. At 95 h, multinucleated 2nd generation schizonts, mature 2nd generation schizonts and small sized schizonts with merozoites are observed. At 106 h merozoites that have just entered cells, young macrogametocytes, and a few multinucleated 2nd generation schizonts are observed. During all these hours, there is some sloughing of the epithelium.   (*Continued on facing page*) view that only one generation of schizogony occurred. Long also found that the number of oocysts produced by a given dose of oocysts increased with the age of the chicken although there was considerable variation from chicken to chicken. Scholtyseck (1959), on the other hand, believes that two asexual generations are formed. There appears to be no morphological differences between the first and second generation schizonts figured in Scholtyseck's paper. Long found that the schizonts contained only 8–16 merozoites and in view of the oocyst-production, he recorded approximately 9 000 000 oocysts derived from a dose of 500 sporulated oocysts, it seems likely that Scholtyseck is correct in his belief that two asexual generations occur.

Brackett and Bliznick (1950) killed fourteen out of forty young chickens by using an infective dose of 500 000 oocysts. There seems to be little doubt that *E. maxima* can be pathogenic under field conditions and can cause deaths in commercial flocks.

D. THE LIFE CYCLE AND PATHOLOGY OF *E. mitis*

Little work has been done on this species since Tyzzer described it briefly in 1929. Joyner (1958) published a more detailed account of *E. mitis* as it occurred in experimental infections. He found that the general morphological characteristics of the oocysts closely agreed with the description given by Tyzzer although they were slightly smaller in size. Joyner's measurements of 100 oocysts followed unimodal distribution with a mean length of 15.58 μ and breadth of 13.83 μ. Dimensions ranged from 11.5 μ to 20.7 μ and 10.35 μ to 18.4 μ. Sporulation was completed in 48 h at 15.5°C. Joyner, like Tyzzer, failed to identify the earlier stages of the life-cycle but he found free merozoites in the intestinal contents on the 4th day of the infection. Schizonts were demonstrated 67 h after infection. Mature schizonts were mostly situated superficially in the epithelium where they showed no tendency to aggregate but were evenly distributed. In contrast to Tyzzer, Joyner did not find that *E. mitis* developed in the greatest numbers in the upper portion of the small intestine, schizonts and merozoites first occurring in those parts of the intestine anterior to the yolk stalk but they were not restricted to this section of the intestine. The schizonts produced about 16 merozoites. Gametocytes, which developed by

---

(*Below*). A schematic drawing showing the position of parasites in the lower small intestine. At 120 h, mature and young macrogametocytes, microgametocytes, and developing oocysts are observed. At 147 h, all the sexual forms present at 120 h are observed, and there is a denudation of the epithelium which leaves only the basement membrane separating the tunica from the lumen.

The distribution of *E. brunetti* in the intestine. Circles indicate the first generation, and the black dots indicate the rest of the development. (From Boles and Becker, 1954. Reproduced by kind permission of the authors and the Iowa State College Journal of Science.)

about the 120th h of the infection, occurred throughout the intestine. The prepatent period of the infection was 101 h. Heavy infestations with this species retard growth of chickens.

E. THE LIFE CYCLES OF *E. necatrix* AND *E. tenella*

The life-cycle of *E. necatrix* was re-examined by Davies (1956). It has long been known that the major part of the schizogonous cycle occurs in the intestine and gametogony is restricted to the caeca. The account of the life-cycle given by Davies differs little from that of Tyzzer *et al.* (1932). The only differences Davies observed were in the length of the prepatent period which he found to be 6 days, in the sporulation time which was 21 h and in the dimensions of the oocysts which averaged $20.5\ \mu \times 16.8\ \mu$ with a range of $15.5\ \mu$ to $25.3\ \mu$ in length and $13.6\ \mu$ to $20.4\ \mu$ in breadth which closely approached the dimensions recorded by Edgar (1955). Davies does not describe the behaviour of the sporozoites preceding the formation of trophozoites. Van Doorninck and Becker (1957) studied the newly hatched sporozoites of *E. necatrix* and the way in which they reached the cells of the deep glands. Tyzzer *et al.* (1932) found that sporozoites were demonstrable in the epithelial cells of the gland fundi of chickens killed 1 h after being given sporulated oocysts. These authors believed that the sporozoite entered the intestinal gland by its lumen and then penetrated the epithelial cell. The same authors also stated that they found sporozoites of *E. praecox* in the epithelium or in the core of the villus 8 h after receiving sporulated oocysts. It was thought that no further development of the sporozoites occurred in the core. Boles and Becker (1954) figured sporozoites of *E. brunetti* invading the core of the villus and like Tyzzer *et al.* believed that no further development occurred in this site. Scholtyseck (1953) was of the opinion that the sporozoites of *E. tenella* leave the crypts of Lieberkühn and enter fibrocytes in the underlying connective tissue inside which cells they developed in the mucosa and submucosa. According to Van Doorninck and Becker, Grevan (1953) found the earliest stages of development of *E. tenella* in fibrocytes of the connective tissue of the mucosa. The observations of Van Doorninck and Becker (1957) suggest that the sporozoites of *E. necatrix* usually invade the lamina propria of the small intestine before entering the glandular epithelium and migrate towards the muscularis mucosae. During this migration most of the sporozoites are engulfed by macrophages which eventually invade the epithelial cells of the fundi of the intestinal glands. After invasion of the glandular epithelial cells the macrophages disintegrate and the sporozoites are released and become trophozoites. Challey and Burns (1959) describe a similar process in *E. tenella* in which the sporozoites do not reach the glandular epithelial cells by way of the gland lumina. They found that once the sporozoites have entered the lamina propria they are quickly engulfed by macrophages. Van Doorninck and Becker suggested that the transport of the sporozoites of *E. necatrix* by macrophages may be an attempt on the part of the host to excrete the parasite and also that when the sporozoite-bearing macrophages reach the cells of the intestinal glands the sporozoite's requirements for growth are satisfied and development ensues. As Challey and Burns point out further investigations are necessary to elucidate the problem of why the transporting macrophages are directed towards the glands and if the process is aimed at the elimination of the parasite why is movement of the macrophages stopped when the glandular epithelium is penetrated.

Landers (1960) made the interesting observation that oocysts of *E. nieschulzi* excysted when inoculated into the thigh musculature, the femoral and jugular veins and intraperitoneal cavity of the rat. Sharma and Reid (1962) succeeded in producing caecal infections by introducing *E. tenella* oocysts subcutaneously, intravenously, intraperitoneally or intramuscularly in chickens. When viable sporozoites were introduced by the same routes light infections were produced. These authors also state that infections have been induced by other species following subcutaneous inoculation but fail to name the species used. The method of excystation and transfer to the site of infection is not yet understood. Davies and Joyner (1962) obtained much the same results by parenteral inoculation of oocysts of *E. acervulina, E. maxima, E. necatrix* and *E. tenella*. In preliminary experiments the inoculation of second merozoites of *E. tenella* intraperitoneally produced gametogony and oocysts but failed to do so when injected by the intramuscular or subcutaneous routes. These authors suggest that the migration of invasive stages to their sites of development may be more important than previously believed. They also point out that schizogony resulting from the parenteral inoculation of oocysts of each species always occurs in the sites normally invaded by the species of coccidia used. This confirms the site-preference of these species and it would seem that migration away from the normal sites would only occur under exceptional circumstances in naturally infected birds. However, occasional reports have come to our notice which suggest that migration from the usual site of parasitism into the blood stream might occur. Recently, we have confirmed the findings of the above named authors with oocysts of *E. tenella* and *E. acervulina* inoculated intramuscularly and with *E. tenella* inoculated intravenously and in all cases large numbers of oocysts were produced by each species in the expected sites. We failed to recover oocysts of *E. tenella* from the caeca of chickens inoculated intraperitoneally and subcutaneously but found raised whitish spots (1 – 2 mm diameter) on the surface of the liver which contained sporulated oocysts. A chicken inoculated intramuscularly with *E. tenella* oocysts showed numerous oocysts in the caeca 7 days later. In addition, haemorrhagic spots (2 – 4 mm diameter) were found in the liver. The oocysts seen in the liver sections were in various stages of disintegration and it might be that the sporozoites and sporocysts are released and reach the intestine and caeca via the bile duct. It seems reasonable to assume that oocysts inoculated into the blood stream would be removed from the circulation by the liver in common with other foreign bodies. The fowl liver appears to be most effective in this function. Dobson (1957) compared this activity in various animals and found that the fowl liver was highly efficient, removing chromic phosphate from the circulation in 35 sec.

III. The Pathology and the Life Cycle of the Species of *Eimeria* occurring in Turkeys

Seven species of *Eimeria* have been reported from turkeys in the United States by Moore (1954) and Clarkson (1958, 1959a, 1959b) has described three of these, *E. adenoeides* Moore and Brown, 1951, *E. meleagrimitis* Tyzzer, 1927 and *E. meleagridis* Tyzzer, 1927, in British turkeys. Clarkson (1960) regards *E. adenoeides* and *E. meleagrimitis* as very pathogenic and states that heavy infections can cause 100% mortality in young turkey poults whereas *E. meleagridis* causes no deaths and no significant drop in weight gain.

A. THE LIFE HISTORY OF *E. adenoeides*

This species occurs in the lower small intestine, caeca and rectum. Clarkson (1958) described the life cycles of this species. The first generation schizont is large and usually lies below the host epithelial cell nucleus. The second generation schizont is smaller than the first and lies above the nucleus of the host epithelial cell. Drawings of stages in the life cycle of this species are shown in Fig. 3. The second generation merozoites develop into gametocytes in the tips of the villi as well as in the deep glands. This species is very pathogenic to young turkeys under 5 weeks of age but is much less so to older birds (Moore and Brown, 1951). Clarkson confirmed its pathogenicity to 3-weeks-old turkeys given 200 000 sporulated oocysts as well as the resistance of 11-weeks-old birds to doses of 3 million oocysts.

B. THE LIFE HISTORY AND PATHOGENICITY OF *E. meleagridis*

E. meleagridis was the first species to be described from the turkey (Tyzzer, 1927, 1929). Tyzzer discussed the morphology of the oocysts,

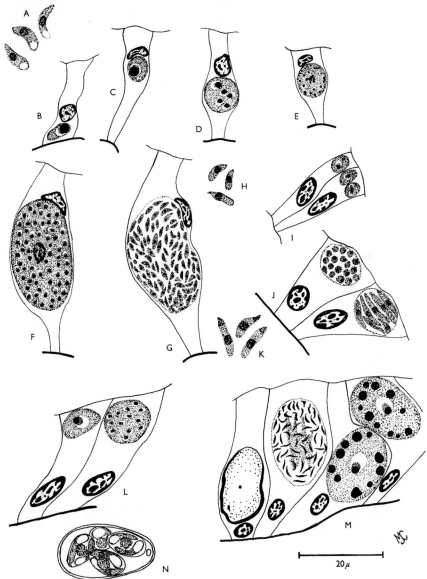

Fig. 3. Life cycle of *E. adenoeides*. A. sporozoites; B. sporozoite in cell, before becoming rounded off: 6 h; C. trophozoite; 6 h; D., E. developing schizont undergoing nuclear division: 12–36 h respectively; F. 1st stage schizont: 54 h; G. mature 1st stage schizont, containing merozoites 60 h; H. 1st stage merozoites: 72 h; I. developing 2nd stage schizonts: 84 h; J. mature 2nd stage schizonts containing merozoites: 108 h; K. 2nd stage merozoites; L. early macro- and microgametocytes: 120 h; M. macrogametes, mature microgametocyte showing irregular residual mass and microgametes, and oocyst: 144 h; N. sporulated oocyst showing sporocysts containing sporozoites and residual body.

A, H and K, Giemsa-stained smears. N, fresh preparation; remainder: sections stained with Heidenhain's iron haematoxylin (camera lucida × 2000). The thick line represents the base of the epithelial cells.

Figure after Clarkson, M. J. (1958), "Parasitology"; reproduced by kind permission of the author and the Cambridge University Press.

the sporulation time and prepatent period. The oocysts and large schizonts were mainly developed in the caeca and a residual body was seen in the schizont when the merozoites had developed. Morehouse (1949) believed that this species was pathogenic and he reported that it caused a mortality of 6.3%. In the original account of *E. adenoeides* (Moore and Brown, 1951) it was suggested that Morehouse may have been working with a mixed infection as the oocysts of *E. adenoeides* and *E. meleagridis* are indistinguishable and stated that *E. meleagridis* was non-pathogenic. Clarkson (1959a) in his re-examination of this species found that the life cycle was not confined to the caeca as suggested by previous investigators. He found merozoites in the small intestine in the neighbourhood of the rudimentary yolk stalk 54 h after infection with oocysts but when a bird was killed at the 120th h of the infection large numbers of oocysts were found in the caeca and one in the small intestine. The first schizogonous generation developed in the epithelial cells of the small intestine in the region in which the merozoites were found at the 54th h of the infection. Second generation schizogony and gametogony occur in the caeca with some spread of gametogony into the rectum and ileum. Twenty-four hours after initial infection trophozoites were seen in the epithelial cells of the small intestine each containing a large globule and single nucleus. Most of the first generation schizonts developed near the base of the villi but none occurred in the deep glands. Mature schizonts measuring $20\,\mu \times 15\,\mu$ were present at the 48th h of the infection and were more numerous at 60 h. The schizonts formed approximately 50–100 merozoites. Uninucleate trophozoites were found in the caeca at the 52nd h and many developing second schizonts were observed at 60 h. Second generation merozoites, eight to sixteen in number, were seen in the second generation schizonts on the 70–84 h of the infection. Developing gametocytes were found at the 91st h of the infection and were mature by the 198th h. The average prepatent period was 110 h with a range of 108–112 h. Stages in the life cycle of *E. meleagridis* as shown by Clarkson (1959a) are shown in Fig. 4. Clarkson's observations confirm the view that *E. meleagridis* is non-pathogenic to turkeys.

C. THE LIFE HISTORY AND PATHOGENICITY OF
E. meleagrimitis

Tyzzer (1927) briefly described this species and discussed the morphology of the oocysts and other stages of the cycle. Hawkins (1952) described the tissue changes and pathogenicity. He also recorded that this species could produce a 100% mortality in young turkeys. As so frequently occurs in studies of the coccidia, differences of opinion arise on the tissue stages of the cycle. Tyzzer did not deal with these aspects

in detail and only mentioned that small schizonts occur. Hawkins
described two small generations which differed little from one another in
their morphology and stated that they contained about twelve merozoites. He also mentions a third and larger schizont which occurred

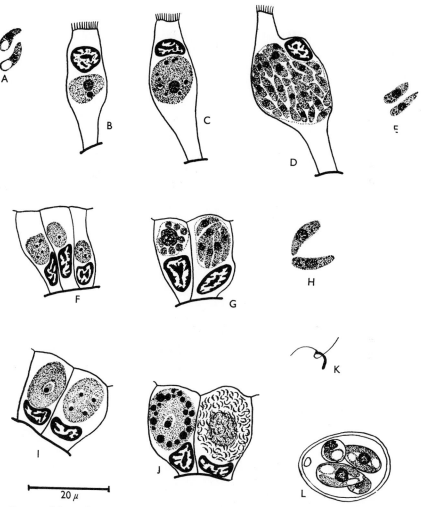

Fig. 4.   Life cycle of *E. meleagridis*. A. sporozoites; B. trophozoite: 12 h; C. developing
schizont: 36 h; D. mature 1st stage schizont: 48 h; E. 1st stage merozoites: 60 h; F. developing
2nd stage schizonts: 72 h; G. mature 2nd stage schizonts: 84 h; H. 2nd stage merozoites: 84 h;
I. early gametocytes: 96 h; J. macrogamete, microgametocyte showing residual mass and
microgametes: 108 h; K. microgamete: 108 h; L. sporulated oocyst.
   A, E, H and K Giemsa-stained smears. L, fresh preparation. Remainder: sections stained
with Heidenhain's iron haematoxylin (camera lucida, × 1600). The thick line represents the
base of the epithelial cells.
   Figure after Clarkson, M. J., (1959a) *Parasitology*; reproduced by kind permission of the
author and the Cambridge University Press.

alongside the sexual generation. Clarkson (1959b) found that three distinct asexual generations must be completed before gametogony is initiated. This observation was confirmed by Horton-Smith and Long (1961). Photomicrographs of the three schizont generations are shown in Fig. 5.

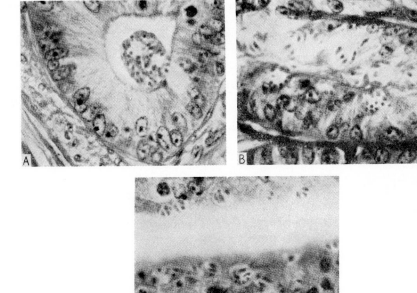

FIG. 5. Transverse sections of small intestine of turkey poults infected with *E. meleagrimitis*. Stained Picro-Mallory; magnification approximately × 875. A. 1st generation schizont in deep gland 49 h after infection; B. 2nd generation schizonts in deep gland 66 h after infection; C. 3rd generation schizonts in epithelium of the villi 96 h after infection.
From Horton-Smith and Long (1961), "Experimental Parasitology", New York: Academic Press.

Clarkson considers the differences existing between his description of the asexual cycle and that of Hawkins. Clarkson is of the opinion that the second and third generation schizonts of his species correspond closely to the first and second generations described by Hawkins who states that no stages were found in the glands, whereas Clarkson and Horton-Smith and Long frequently found groups of second-stage schizonts in these sites. Clarkson's first stage schizont matured by 48 h and occurred only in the glands. Clarkson points out that the first generation schizont can be distinguished by the presence of a refractile globule which has also been noted in *E. adenoeides* and other species.

The first generation is completed by the 48th h of the infection. The second generation schizont usually occurs in the glands and the third generation along the villi. The peak of first generation merozoites occurs

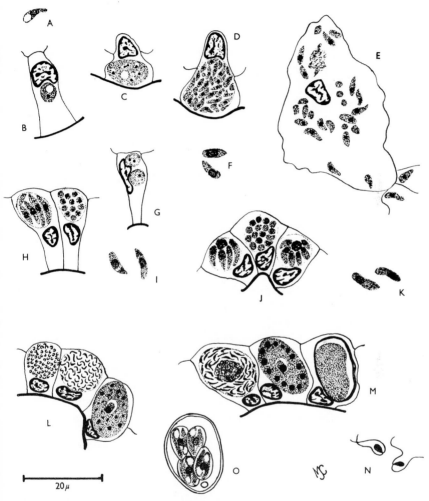

Fig. 6. Life Cycle of *E. meleagrimitis*. A. sporozoite; B. trophozoite: 24 h; C. developing schizont: 36 h; D. mature first stage schizont, pushing cell nucleus into gland lumen: 48 h; E. ruptured schizont in gland lumen, two merozoites having re-entered cells: 48 h; F. first stage merozoites; G. developing second stage schizonts: 60 h; H. mature second stage schizonts; I. second stage schizonts; J. mature third stage schizonts: 96 h; K. third stage merozoites; L. developing gametocytes: 109 h; M. macrogamete, oocyst and mature microgametocyte: 114 h; N. microgametes; O. sporulated oocyst.

A, F, I, K and N, Giemsa stained smears; O, fresh preparation; remainder from sections stained with Heidenhain's iron haematoxylin (camera lucida). The thick line represents the base of the epithelial cells.

Figure after Clarkson, M. J. (1958), *Parasitology*; reproduced by kind permission of the author and the Cambridge University Press.

E

at 48 h, that of the second generation merozoites at 66 h and the third generation at 96 h. There is no doubt at all that this species is one of the most pathogenic species in the turkey. Stages in the life cycle of *E. meleagrimitis* are shown in Fig. 6.

IV. Oocyst Production of Different Species

A knowledge of the potential oocyst production of different species of coccidia is of importance. Not only does it influence the development of the immunity in a flock but also has a direct bearing on possible economic losses. Brackett and Bliznick (1949) published data indicating the approximate total oocyst production arising from a single light infection with *E. tenella*. They found that for each oocyst given in a light infection approximately 100 000 oocysts will be produced. Brackett and Bliznick (1950) suggested that certain species of coccidia of chickens were better oocyst producers than others. The same authors (1952) believe that six factors at least affect the number of oocysts produced. These are (1) that each individual parasite has an inherent potential to reproduce in a non-immune host, (2) immunity developed by the host will interfere with the usual reproductive potential of the parasites (3) a "crowding" effect, as suggested by Tyzzer *et al.* (1932), in which fewer oocysts are produced because of the crowding of epithelial cells by coccidial stages, sloughing of patches of epithelium and the formation of caecal cores which prevent the discharge of oocysts as in *E. tenella*. These possibilities are, on the whole, theoretical and no quantitative data are available to support them. This factor might also be explained by immunity responses, (4) where there are competing species of coccidia in a host and even other infectious agents, the 'crowding' effect may afford some influence over the numbers of oocysts produced, (5) the nutrition of the host may also contribute some control and (6) differences in susceptibility to coccidial infections between different strains of host may also determine the extent of oocyst production. In their paper of 1952 Brackett and Bliznick considered the first three factors in connection with *E. tenella*, *E. necatrix*, *E. acervulina*, *E. maxima* and *E. brunetti*. Tyzzer *et al.* (1932) observed that more oocysts of *E. necatrix* were produced by light infections than by heavy infections and Brackett and Bliznick noted that increasing the size of the inoculum above a very low level failed to produce a corresponding increase in oocyst yield. They found, for example, that an inoculum of 200 sporulated oocysts of *E. necatrix* given to 2–3 week old chickens gave a yield of approximately 50 000 oocyst per oocyst inoculated. When an inoculum of 2000 oocysts of the same species was used the yield was only 2500 oocysts per oocyst inoculated. In the case of *E. tenella* an inoculum of fifty oocysts per oocyst inoculated, an inoculum of 250 oocysts gave 60 000 and one of 6250 oocysts gave only 10 000. An inoculum of fifty oocysts of *E. brunetti* given to 2–3 week old chickens yielded 108 000 oocysts whereas one of 1250 yielded 84 000 oocysts. An inoculum of 2000 oocysts of *E. acervulina* given to 3 week old chickens gave a return of from 35 000 to 72 000 oocysts per oocyst inoculated whereas an inoculum of 20 000 gave a return of only 7600 oocyst per oocyst inoculated (Brackett and Bliznick, 1950). In the same year it was recorded that an inoculum of 200 oocysts of *E. maxima* given to 3 week old birds yielded 11 000 oocysts per oocyst inoculated whereas 10 000 gave only 940.

In using mild infections produced by giving each bird fifty oocysts Brackett and Bliznick (1952) found that *E. tenella* and *E. brunetti* were about equally productive. Under given circumstances the greatest number of oocysts (in millions) produced per bird was approximately as follows: *E. acervulina* 430, *E. tenella* 65, *E. brunetti* 55, *E. maxima* 36, and *E. necatrix* 12. As already pointed out, several infections do not necessarily produce progressively large numbers of oocysts. These differences in oocyst potential are important in explaining the differences in the epidemiology of the various coccidial diseases. *E. tenella* for example, is a highly pathogenic species which produces large numbers of oocysts in the chickens' environment and soon cause caecal coccidiosis in susceptible chickens of a few weeks of age. *E. necatrix* is an equally virulent species but is a poor oocyst producer with the result that the associated disease is typically a disease of older chickens. On the other hand *E. acervulina* is a copious oocyst producer but is a less virulent species than *E. tenella* or *E. necatrix* so that enormous numbers of oocysts must be ingested before fowls become diseased. The development of immunity in birds exposed to these infections will reduce or even stop oocyst production as pre-oocyst stages are affected by the immune response of the host.

V. Cytochemical Observations on Stages of the Coccidial Life Cycle

Cytochemical work on coccidia has been largely carried out on *E. stiedae, E. magna, E. intestinalis* and *E. media* in the rabbit, to which references are made, and with *E. brunetti, E. acervulina, E. tenella, E. necatrix* and *E. maxima* in the fowl.

A. Desoxyribonucleic Acid (DNA)

Pattillo and Becker (1955), working with *E. brunetti* and *E. acervulina* in the fowl and Cheissin (1940 and 1959) with *Eimeria* species from the intestine of the rabbit, found DNA in the nuclei of all the stages examined, with the exception of the nucleus of macrogametocytes.

Sassuchin (1935) obtained negative results in the macrogametocytes and oocysts of *E. perforans*. Lillie (1947) obtained a weak positive reaction of zygote nuclei of *E. stiedae* by the Feulgen method. Cheissin considered that the negative Feulgen staining of the nucleus of the gametocytes was probably not due to the complete absence of DNA, but rather that the Feulgen reaction was probably not sensitive enough. Pattillo and Becker were of the same opinion, and quoted another author, Alfert (1950) who, in a study of oogenesis and cleavage in the mouse, suggested that in egg cells the Feulgen staining may be diluted below the concentration at which it is visible. In cytochemical studies at Houghton a weak Feulgen reaction of the macrogametocyte nucleus of *E. maxima* was obtained. Macrogametocytes of this species are large which probably assisted the observation. The Feulgen staining of the nuclei of other stages is exhibited by a ring of fine granules around the periphery of the nucleus (Cheissin 1957 and 1959). The Feulgen reactions of the nuclei are best seen in the schizonts and merozoites, the microgametocytes give strong reactions. Tsunoda and Itikawa (1955) obtained positive Feulgen reactions in the nuclei of most of the stages of *E. tenella*, but found that the nuclei of young schizonts were often Feulgen negative. Ray and Gill (1955) considered that the unsporulated oocysts are devoid of detectable amounts of DNA and concluded that the DNA contained in the sporozoites formed from similar oocysts must have been formed *de novo* during the process of sporulation.

B. RIBONUCLEIC ACID (RNA)

Roskin and Ginsburg (1944) found that the cytoplasm and karyosome of the unsporulated oocysts of *E. stiedae* stained strongly with pyronin by the methyl-green pyronin technique. They considered the reactions to be due to "zymonucleic acid" (RNA) because the staining could be prevented by pre-treatment with ribonuclease. Pattillo and Becker (1955) found RNA in the nucleus and cytoplasm of all stages of *E. brunetti* and *E. acervulina*. Cheissin (1957 and 1959) also demonstrated RNA in the cytoplasm and nucleus of all stages of *Eimeria magna* in the rabbit. He used toluidin blue or the methyl-green pyronin method and found he could prevent the reaction by pre-treatment with ribonuclease (Brachet, 1953). He found that the cytoplasm of the merozoites showed less RNA, but after invasion, and when growth occurred, more RNA was present. Studies, only published in part at present (Long and Rootes, 1959), confirmed Pattillo and Becker's findings with regard to RNA and that pre-treatment of the sections with ribonuclease prevented the staining reactions. Tsunoda and Itikawa (1955) also described RNA in the cytoplasm and karyosome of all stages of *E. tenella*, especially in the growing forms. Ray and Gill (1955) claimed that the so-called "plastic granules" of the macrogametocytes of *E. tenella* reacted for RNA when using toluidin blue stain and that the oocyst walls gave a weak reaction as well. These findings have not confirmed by other workers.

C. PROTEINS

Proteins other than the nuclear proteins are readily demonstrated in various stages of *Eimeria*. We have followed Pattillo and Becker (1955), using the mercuric bromophenol blue staining reaction to demonstrate protein. By this method the refractile globules of the sporozoites of *E. tenella* stained intensely, and the cytoplasm to a lesser degree. The refractile globules also stain with eosin and light green which are also good stains for non-nuclear proteins. Schizonts and merozoites of *E. tenella* and *E. necatrix* also react and there are areas of intense staining. Protein is also present in concentration in the cytoplasm of the macro-gametocytes and to a lesser degree in the microgametocyte. The "plastic granules" in the macrogametocytes and the walls of the oocyst stain intensely although the cytoplasm of the oocyst gives a weaker reaction. The refractile body of the oocyst and the stieda body of the sporocyst stain strongly. Pattillo and Becker subjected the oocysts to peptic digestion for 1 h which prevented the staining of all except the refractile globules of the sporozoites. These globules needed 16 h digestion to prevent staining. This digestion process proves beyond doubt the protein nature of the refractile globules.

D. LIPIDS

Pattillo and Becker demonstrated lipids, stained with Sudan Black 'B' in the cytoplasm of unsporulated oocysts and sporocysts of *E. brunetti* and *E. acervulina*. This material did not stain if the sections were pretreated with chloroform-methanol. Their findings were confirmed at Houghton in investigations of *E. maxima*, *E. tenella* and *E. necatrix*, which also showed that the asexual stages, microgametocytes and immature macrogametocytes were negative. Cheissin (1959) also found lipids in the late macrogametocytes and oocysts of *E. magna*, *E. intestinalis* and *E. media*. None of the workers has detected lipids in the walls of the oocysts.

E. CARBOHYDRATES

Giovannola (1934) found glycogen in insignificant amounts in sporozoites within the oocyst, in schizonts, microgametocytes and young macrogametocytes of *Eimeria falciformis* and *E. stiedae* and that the concentration increased in older macrogametocytes and oocysts.

Cheissin (1935), working with *Eimeria* species in rabbits, obtained negative results on the "plastic granules" with Best's carmine reaction.

Reliable detection of glycogen is now more easily performed using the periodic acid-Schiff technique with enzyme treated controls. Lillie (1947) obtained reactions in the cytoplasm of oocysts of *E. stiedae* which were removable by pre-treatment with diastase. Pattillo and Becker found a weak reaction in the merozoites of *E. acervulina*, but obtained negative results with the schizonts of both species. Cheissin (1959) found glycogen accumulated in almost all stages of rabbit *Eimeria*, but an insignificant amount was found in the microgametocytes. He also made the interesting observation that glycogen, rich in the macrogametocytes, unsporulated oocysts and sporulated oocysts, diminishes in stored sporulated oocysts. The sporozoites from oocysts stored for 18–20 months lose their glycogen completely. Wilson and Fairbairn (1961) in a study of the biochemistry of sporulation of *E. acervulina* concluded that carbohydrate provided energy for the early stages of sporulation. The energy needed for the final stages of sporulation and metabolism after sporulation was provided by the oxidation of lipids. They considered that the carbohydrate was resynthesized in the latest stages of sporulation.

We have obtained positive PAS results in mature schizonts and merozoites of *E. necatrix* and *E. tenella*, and this material did not stain when the sections were pre-treated with α-amylase. The positive reaction was localized near the nuclei of the merozoites, but was absent in immature second generation schizonts of both species. Pattillo and Becker (1955) failed to demonstrate glycogen in encysted sporozoites. Our more recent work shows that PAS positive material, removable by pre-treatment with α-amylase, is present in all invasive stages of *E. tenella*, and can be detected in the nuclear area of sporozoites harvested from the intestine of birds given large doses of oocysts. When the sporozoites had reached the deep glands of the caecal mucosa, no glycogen was detected and it was absent until the trophozoites formed the first generation schizonts, when the first generation merozoites gave a weak reaction in the area close to the nucleus. When the first generation invaded the glands of submucosa and rounded up they gave a positive reaction characterized by PAS staining of granules near the nucleus. This disappeared within a few hours and did not reappear until the second generation schizonts were mature when the cytoplasm of the contained merozoites gave moderate reactions. Freshly invaded merozoites and early growing gametocytes gave negative reactions. None was found in the microgametes. The macrogametocytes and oocysts contained easily detectable amounts in the cytoplasm. The results are summarized in Table I.

The PAS staining of the oocyst wall was α-amylase fast and therefore not due to glycogen and will be discussed later. Our findings do not agree with those of Edgar *et al.* (1944), who did not find glycogen in any

TABLE I

Reactions of different stages of the life-cycle of Eimeria tenella to the periodic acid-Schiff technique

Freshly hatched sporozoites	Trophozoites in the deep glands of the caeca	Multinucleate 1st generation schizonts	Mature 1st generation schizonts	Uninucleate 2nd generation schizonts	Multinucleate 2nd generation schizonts	Mature 2nd generation schizonts	Freshly invaded and partially grown gametocytes	Mature macrogametocytes	Mature microgametocytes
Large granules of PAS. + ve material around nuclear area and smaller amount sometimes seen near one of the poles	No reactions	No reactions	Very faint staining of the cytoplasm	Intensely stained mass in the cytoplasm	No reactions	Moderate reactions in the cytoplasm giving an overall staining	No reactions	Strong reactions in both cytoplasm and plastic granules	No reactions

stages preceding the developing macrogametocytes, and the amount of glycogen increased when these developed into oocysts. They failed to find any in asexual stages or in the microgametocytes. However, they did not employ the periodic acid-Schiff reaction, but used iodine techniques. It appears that their failure to find glycogen in the earlier stages of the life cycle may be due to the techniques employed at that time. Gill and Ray (1954a) using the PAS reaction examined all stages of *E. tenella* excepting first generation schizogony. They found only an insignificant amount in the sporozoites, although these were examined in the tissues and not in smears of freshly emerged sporozoites. The second generation schizonts and merozoites contained some glycogen and the macrogametocytes gave the best reaction. In addition, these authors described some reactions in the microgametocytes.

F. PROTEIN-CARBOHYDRATE COMPLEX

This complex, designated by Pattillo and Becker (1955), was found by them in the so-called "plastic granules" and oocyst walls of *E. brunetti* and *E. acervulina*. They considered it to be largely mucoprotein, neutral mucopolysaccharide or glycoprotein, because of the positive protein staining, the PAS positive reactions, the negative lipid reactions and because the "plastic granules" were not affected by diastase or hyaluronidase and did not exhibit metachromasia. Cheissin (1959) did not think acid mucopolysaccharides or lipids took part in the formation of the oocyst walls and spores. He found, as Pattillo and Becker found, that no stages contained mucopolysaccharides although Ray and Gill (1955) found them in *E. tenella*. With regard to the protein-carbohydrate complex described by Pattillo and Becker in the "plastic granules", our own findings (Long and Rootes, 1959, and Long *et al.*, 1961) are that the preservation of the "plastic granules" in paraffin sections of intestine depend on the fixative used before paraffin embedding and that certain fixatives failed to preserve them. The reactions following the use of different fixatives are given in Table II.

Because the granules are preserved in paraffin sections after fixation in fluids known to preserve lipids, and are readily removed after using other fixatives which are inferior for lipid preservation, it was hoped to show that the granules contained lipoprotein. The results, however, showed no firm reactions for lipids in the granules. The substance appears to be a polysaccharide bound to a basic protein and the fixation effects are unexplained at present.

The walls of the oocyst differ from the "plastic granules" in that they are preserved by all the fixatives employed. The reactions of the oocyst wall were the same as those of the "plastic granules" except that they gave a positive reaction to Baker's acid haematin. This persisted after

TABLE II

The Reactions of the "Plastic Granules" of the Gametocytes of Eimeria maxima to various Cytochemical procedure, following the use of different Fixatives

Fixative		Paraffin Sections											Frozen Sections			
	Mercuric Bromophenol blue	periodic acid-Schiff Reaction					Toluidin Blue	Light Green	Sat. Sol. Sudan Black in 70% alcohol	Methasol Fast Blue	Baker's acid Haematin	Sat. Sol. Sudan Black in 70% alcohol	Colloidal Sudan Black in Gelatine	Sudan III/IV in Herxheimers mixture	Colloidal Sudan III/IV (Govan)
		PAS alone	After α-amylase	After Hyaluronidase	After acetylation	Schiff's Reagent alone									
Formal Calcium	+	+	+	+	−	−	−	+	−	−	*	−	−	−	−
Buffered Formalin	+	+	+	+	−	−	−	+	−	−	−	−	−	−	−
Helly	+	+	+	+	−	−	−	+	−	(+)	*	−	*	−	−
Formal Calcium (Post-chromed)	+	+	+	+	−	−	−	+	−	(++)	−	−	−	−	−
Weak Bouin (Pyridine extracted)	−	−	−	−	−	−	−	−	−	−	−	−	−	−	−
Serra, Bouin and Heidenhain, Susa	−	−	−	−	−	−	−	−	−	−	−	* Not applicable			

* = The fixation method precluded the use of this staining procedure.

pyridin by extraction and was therefore not due to lipid material. Tsunoda and Itikawa (1955) considered that the "oocyst wall of *E. tenella* was composed of chitin which was degenerated from glycogen". Monné and Hönig (1955) thought that the outer layer of the oocysts of *E. tenella* and *E. stiedae* might be composed of a quinone-tanned protein and that the inner layer contained lipids combined with a protein substrate. In our own studies the "plastic granules" and oocyst walls were tested for polyphenol oxidase and polyphenols, both with inconclusive results, using the methods described by Smyth (1954) who applied the techniques to egg-shell formation in helminths.

G. MUCOPOLYSACCHARIDES

Gill and Ray (1954b) adopted the methods of Lison (1935), Sylvén (1941) and Brachet (1953) for mucoid sulphate, and Hale's (1946) colloidal iron method for demonstrating by hyaluronic acid type polysaccharide. They found that mucoid sulphate occurred in the cytoplasm and hyaluronic acid type polysaccharide (HAP) was more active in the nucleus (especially the karyosome) and forms the protective covering of the oocyst. They found the highest concentration of mucopolysaccharides in the mature second generation schizogony. Young macrogametocytes contained small amounts of mucopolysaccharides, but contained more as they matured. The peripheral globules (plastic granules) were rich in the hyaluronic acid type polysaccharide.

The microgametocytes contained greater amounts of mucoid sulphate, especially in the gametes. These authors believe that the process of fertilization provides a stimulus to the peripheral globules of the macrogametocyte to discharge their acid contents, which coalesce to form the oocystic wall which is rich in hyaluronic acid type polysaccharides. Tsunoda and Itikawa also found hyaluronic acid and chondroitin sulphuric acid in the endogenous stages of *E. tenella*.

Cheissin (1957) did not succeed in demonstrating acid mucopolysaccharides of the hyaluronic acid or chondroitin sulphuric acid type. He stated that the toluidin blue metachromasia was not caused by acid mucopolysaccharides. Cheissin, like Gill and Ray, used Hale's method for demonstrating hyaluronic acid type polysaccharides. Cheissin found that the reactions were unaffected by hyaluronidase and demonstrated the presence of neutral polysaccharides, mucoprotein and some other proteins, but not acid mucopolysaccharides.

Cheissin (1957) found it difficult to explain the different results of different workers and did not think that the chemical composition of the "plastic granules" of macrogametocytes of closely related species would vary under different conditions of development. He thought the difference was more likely due to the cytochemical methods employed.

Gill and Ray concluded from the results obtained by Hale's method that acid polysaccharides are present, but did not mention whether hyaluronidase had been used to control the reaction. The Hale method detects not only acid, but neutral mucopolysaccharides as well (Braden, 1955). Toluidin blue metachromasia may be due to mucopolysaccharide, but if it persists after ribonuclease or hyaluronidase treatment, it may be explained by the presence of other highly polymerized carbodrate.

H. ENZYME ACTIVITY

Gill and Ray (1954c) and Ray and Gill (1954) have investigated both acid and alkaline phosphatase activity in experimental infection with *E. tenella*. Glick's (1949) technique for acid phosphatase was employed and Gomori's technique described by Glick for alkaline phosphatase activity. The technique of McManus cited by Bragden and McManus (1952) was used for locating 5-nucleotidase. The results showed that the *E. tenella* infection reduced the alkaline phosphatase activity of the infected tissues, particularly at the time of second generation schizogony. The nuclei of sporozoites, schizonts, gametocytes and oocysts showed strong alkaline phosphatase activity. Both acid phosphatase and 5-nucleotidase were present in the karyosomes in all the stages of *E. tenella* examined. Ray and Gill in a similar account also attempted to explain the significance of phosphatase activity. The enzymes are widely distributed in nature and play an important role in various metabolic processes such as carbohydrate metabolism, bone formation and similar reactions. Blaschko and Jacobson (1951) stated that phosphatases play a general part in phosphorylation which is of great importance in energy transfer in cellular metabolism. Alkaline phosphatases may be associated with the process of dephosphorylation and deposition of glycogen in cells (Wislocki and Dempsey, 1946). It is not possible to connect the occurrence of phosphatases in parasites with definite metabolic processes although a connection with carbohydrate utilization is probable (von Brand, 1952).

VI. IMMUNITY TO COCCIDIOSIS

A. THE PHASE OF THE LIFE CYCLE INDUCING THE IMMUNE RESPONSE

Medication experiments have shown that many anticoccidial drugs exert their maximal effect on the early second generation schizont of *E. tenella* so that merogony is inhibited. Infected chickens which had been protected from clinical coccidiosis by medication proved resistant to reinfections with the same species after the drug was withdrawn

(Horton-Smith and Taylor, 1945; Farr and Wehr, 1947; Wehr and Farr, 1947; Kendall and McCullough, 1952).

That the asexual cycles of *E. tenella* and *E. necatrix* are intimately associated with the stimulation of the immune response has also been demonstrated by injecting sporozoites or merozoites into the caeca via the rectum of susceptible chickens (Horton-Smith *et al.*, 1962a). The caeca of chickens which received sporozoites of *E. tenella* eventually became populated with second generation schizonts, gametocytes and oocysts. Challenge of these chickens 14 days after the sporozoites had been given showed that a high degree of resistance had developed. On the other hand, when second generation merozoites of *E. tenella* were injected in large numbers into the caeca, gametocytes and oocysts were formed in the absence of second generation schizogony. When these chickens were challenged they proved susceptible to infections with the same species. Similar results were obtained with *E. necatrix* in which the asexual phase is almost entirely confined to the duodenum and the sexual phase to the caeca.

As the second generation schizonts are much more numerous than the first, and are larger, it seems reasonable to assume that they provide much more antigen than the first generation schizonts. For these reasons antigen prepared from second generation schizonts was used in the serological investigations to be described. The antigenic value of the first generation schizonts has not been determined.

B. THE IMMUNIZATION OF CHICKENS AND THE IMMUNIZING POWER OF DIFFERENT SPECIES OF COCCIDIA

Chickens may become partially or wholly resistant to coccidial infection. In partially resistant chickens clinical disease does not develop but owing to reinfection and resistance the parasitism continues at a low level. This is a common state under field conditions. Fully immune chickens are resistant not only to disease but to parasitism as well. Under experimental conditions large numbers of oocysts must be given to a chicken to induce complete immunity. Because of the differing extent of multiplication between species within the host the numbers of oocysts given to a chicken to induce immunity are calculated on the basis of the numbers of each species necessary to cause gross tissue damage. Solid immunization was attained by giving the chickens two or, occasionally, three doses of sporulated oocysts in increasing numbers and at weekly intervals between dosing. The initial dose of oocysts was small except for the *E. acervulina* immunized chickens which were given greater numbers of oocysts. This was done because large doses of oocysts are usually needed to produce disease with this infection. The oocyst production following each of the immunizing doses is summarized in Table III.

TABLE III

The reproduction index for each of four species, calculated from the total oocyst output, following two successive infections

Species administered	Details	After 1st infection	After 2nd infection	Ratio of reproduction index after first infection to that after the second infection
E. acervulina	Dose	500 000	5 000 000	
	reproduction index	1026	12	86:1
E. tenella	Dose	500	5000	
	reproduction index	64 000	4600	14:1
E. necatrix	Dose	500	5000	
	reproduction index	12 000	1360	9:1
E. maxima	Dose	500	5000	
	reproduction index	30 000	5.2	5700:1

Table modified from Rose and Long (1962), "Immunology".

By comparing the total numbers of oocysts produced and the numbers administered in each of the infections (reproduction index) the various species could be graded in order of immunizing power. Rose and Long (1962) listed four species in descending order of immunizing power as follows: *E. maxima*, *E. acervulina*, *E. tenella* and *E. necatrix*. *E. acervulina* would probably not have attained this position if the immunizing doses had not been raised with this infection.

C. THE FATE OF SPOROZOITES AND SECOND GENERATION MEROZOITES OF *E. tenella* IN FULLY IMMUNE CHICKENS

Observations by Pierce *et al.* (1962) suggested that the life-cycle of *E. tenella* was halted at an early stage in an immune host.

Horton-Smith *et al.* (1962b) investigated three possibilities. (1) whether sporozoites of *E. tenella* introduced into a host which had been immunized against this species were able to invade the caecal mucosa and thereby undergo further development and (2) whether sporozoites from the intestinal lumen of an immune host were capable of infecting a susceptible chicken and (3) whether second generation merozoites could invade the caecal mucosa of an immune host and eventually form gametocytes and oocysts.

The results of this work showed that sporozoites invade the epithelium of immune chickens and migrate normally to the deep glands where they round up to form uninucleate trophozoites which fail to develop into first generation schizonts. These observations suggest that protective substances in sufficient concentration to effect sporozoites do not occur in the caecal lumen. The sporozoite itself may be protected by a resistant coat as are the sporozoites of *Plasmodium* (Garnham *et al.*, 1960). Sporozoites of *E. tenella* harvested from caecal mucosal washings of an immune or susceptible chicken were infective when introduced into another susceptible chicken. However, Morehouse (1938) found that the sporozoites of *E. nieschulzi* did not invade the epithelial cells of the intestines of immune rats.

The immune response operates on the second generation merozoites in much the same way as it does on the sporozoites. The merozoites travel to the deep glands probably by way of the lumina of the ducts but fail to develop into mature gametocytes. Figure 7 shows sporo-

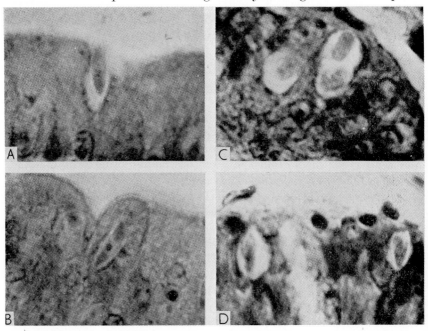

Fig. 7. Transverse sections of caecal tissue. A and B stained Picro-Mallory; C and D stained Toluidin blue. Magnification approximately × 1000.

A. Sporozoite entering caecal epithelium of an immune fowl 2½ h after challenge with oocysts *per os*; B. as A sporozoite beneath epithelium; C. and D. Merozoites in deep glands of caecal mucosa of an immune fowl 3 h after inoculation directly into the caecum of 2nd generation merozoites.

zoites in the caecal epithelium of immune fowls after challenge with oocysts and merozoites in the deep glands of the caeca after challenge with second generation merozoites.

D. THE DURATION OF IMMUNITY TO COCCIDIOSIS IN THE ABSENCE OF REINFECTION

1. *Duration of Immunity in Experimentally-immunized Chickens*

Unlike many pathogens the coccidia cannot multiply indefinitely in a susceptible host and are eventually eliminated from the host in the form of oocysts, so that the coccidial life cycle is a self-limiting one. Under ordinary husbandry conditions the duration of the immunity developing from a single immunizing infection cannot be determined owing to the continual ingestion of oocysts, with consequent repetition of life cycles, occurring until such time as the chickens become solidly immune. Absolute resistance is probably rare under these circumstances. One of the greatest difficulties encountered in this sort of investigation is to maintain fowls free of coccidial infections. The strictest precautions must be taken to avoid the accidental introduction of extraneous coccidial infections into the quarters in which the birds are kept. Although there is little published information, there is some evidence to suggest that the duration of the immunity developed in isolated experimental chickens from single or serial dosing of oocysts, may differ. The resistance developing as a result of a single small dose of oocysts of *E. tenella* showed some evidence of weakening 42 days later (Horton-Smith *et al.*, 1961) but if isolated chickens were immunized by giving them three graded infections of oocysts, each administered at weekly intervals, they were found to be completely resistant to challenge given at least 3 months later.

Long (1962) found that chickens immunized against *E. maxima* were susceptible again to reinfection 10 weeks later. He also found that chickens immunized by the combined effects of three infections with this species were susceptible to a fourth infection given 26 weeks after the third immunizing dose had been given. From the practical, as well as the parasitological point of view, a knowledge of the immunizing power and the duration of immunity developed from infections by different species coupled with knowledge of the virulence of the species contributes much to our understanding of the epidemological aspects of the different forms of coccidiosis.

2. *Duration of Immunity and Possible Age-resistance of Host*

(a) Age-resistance in fowls. There seems to be ample evidence to show that fowls maintained in a strictly isolated environment remain susceptible to coccidiosis throughout life and what appears to be an age-resistance is truly resistance developed as a consequence of earlier and current infections present in this environment. Caecal coccidiosis which is characteristically a disease of young chickens up to 6 or 7 weeks of age, can be readily produced experimentally in adult fowls which have been kept free from infections. Even under commercial conditions adult fowls may occasionally succumb to severe caecal coccidiosis.

(b) Age-resistance in turkeys. Clarkson (1958) is of the opinion that coccidiosis in turkeys is strictly a disease of young poults. He believes that an age-immunity intervenes to restrict the coccidia as disease-producing entities to turkey poults of a few weeks of age. Turkeys do not develop a complete age-resistance to the parasite as coccidial oocysts are commonly found in the faeces of both growing and adult turkeys.

E. THE TRANSFERENCE OF RESISTANCE TO *E. tenella* FROM ONE CAECUM TO THE OTHER IN INDIVIDUAL FOWLS

The paired caeca of the fowl afforded Challey and Burns (1959) and Horton-Smith *et al.* (1961) with the opportunity of determining whether the immunity developed as the result of infection of one caecum was accompanied by an immunity developing in the other non-infected caecum. One of the two caeca was isolated by litigation from the main intestinal tract. The chickens were then given a heavy infection with oocysts *per os* resulting in infection of the patent caecum only. No infection, either on direct examination or on histological examination, was detected in the ligated caecum, and as far as is known *E. tenella* parasites limit their invasion to the caeca, apart from occasional infection of the rectum. Blood invasion is unknown following infection by the oral route.

Groups of chickens infected in this way were challenged at different times after the initial infection with sporozoites. The sporozoites were injected into the distal ends of both the ligated and open caeca. Chickens challenged 7 days after initial infection developed moderate infections in the isolated caecum. When chickens which were challenged 14 or 21 days after initial infection were examined, few, if any, parasites were found in either caecum. The results showed that immune mechanisms, operative in the caecum receiving the inital infection, were also present in the ligated caecum. Colour photographs illustrating the results of one experiment are shown in Plate 1. Challey and Burns (1959) used a slightly different technique and different methods of assessing resistance but had earlier reached the same conclusions that humoral mechanisms may be of importance in establishing an immunity to *E. tenella*. These conclusions prompted the initiation of the serological studies discussed below.

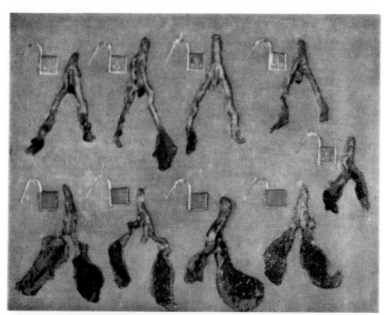

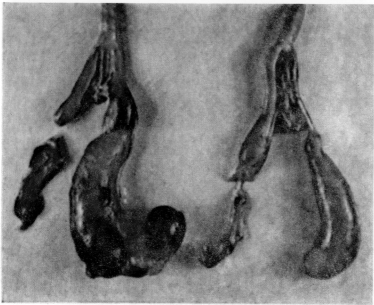

PLATE 1 (*a*). Caeca of chickens 6 days after challenge with *E. tenella* sporozoites introduced into each caecum. Group 1 (Blue wingbands) were immunized 21 days previously by an oral infection with oocysts resulting in heavy parasitism of the non-ligated areas only. Group 2. (Red wingbands) were not immunized but one caecum of each was ligated. Note the haemorrhage in both caeca of Group 2 birds compared with that of Group 1 birds. Only one bird in the Group 1 (blue, extreme right) showed any haemorrhage and this was slight compared with Group 2.

(*b*). Showing the efficiency of the ligation to the primary infection produced by the oral administration of *E. tenella* oocysts. Note the heavy infection of the areas with access to the main intestinal tract and the lack of haemorrhage in the ligated portions.

(*facing page* 96)

F. DETECTION OF PRECIPITATING ANTIBODIES AND TESTS FOR THE SPECIFICITY OF THE REACTIONS

In the experiments described by Pierce *et al.* (1962) and Rose and Long (1962) precipitins developing in fowl sera were examined using the double diffusion in agar technique of Ouchterlony (1949, 1953). Goodman *et al.* (1951) showed that in order to get maximum precipitation of fowl antibody the sodium chloride concentration should be raised to 8%. This concentration of NaCl was incorporated in the agar used in the above tests. The reactions were allowed to develop at room temperature for up to 14 days.

The antigens used in these tests were prepared from the second generation schizonts of *E. tenella* or *E. necatrix*. The soluble contents of both the tissue and the contained parasite stages were released by subjecting the vessel containing the parasites to rapid alternate freezing in an acetone-solid CO_2 and thawing in warm water. The cell debris was then removed by centrifugation. Because of the paucity of schizonts in *E. maxima* infections and because the sexual phases of the cycle might be the immunizing ones with this disease, antigens were prepared from gametocyte stages. In *E. acervulina* infection the antigen most usefully employed was that prepared from intestinal tissue containing mainly gametocyte stages, although, schizonts and merozoites were also present in varying numbers, according to the age of the infection in the host. The method of preparation was precisely as described for schizont antigens. Antigen could also be prepared from oocysts, a simple method consisted of fracturing the oocysts by exposure to ultra sound. After fracture and release of the soluble parts of the oocysts, the insoluble materials were removed by centrifugation. Pierce *et al.* (1962) also examined the specificity of the precipitates by absorbing immune sera containing the precipitins with freeze-dried caecal tissue, prepared from normal chickens, in agar-gel diffusion plates. The immune sera employed were obtained from fowls immunized *per os* by multiple infections with *E. tenella* and later injected parenterally with schizont antigen. When absorbed serum was tested against schizont antigen none of the precipitin bands was diminished by comparison with the same serum not absorbed by freeze-dried caecal extract. A caecal extract prepared from uninfected chicks prepared in the same way as schizont antigen did not react with immune serum. A cross reaction was obtained with *E. tenella* immune serum against *E. stiedae* antigen prepared from rabbit liver. Immune sera, which reacted with schizont antigen, also reacted with an antigen prepared from *E. tenella* sporulated oocysts disrupted by ultra sound. (see Plate 1). Sera from non-immunized birds did not react with schizont antigen, normal caecal tissue, *E. stiedae* antigen or *E.*

F

tenella oocyst antigen. These workers also showed that the major react-
ing components of their antigens were protein. Horton-Smith *et al.*
(1962a) were unable to immunize chickens by giving multiple inoculations of soluble extracts from *E. tenella* schizonts. The chickens produced serum precipitins which gave reactions against schizont antigen
in vitro, by the agar-gel diffusion technique. The precipitin bands
formed were often more intense and numerous than those present in
the sera of chickens immunized by the administration of serial oocyst
infections. The bands produced in the serum of immune fowls were also
present and cross-reacted with the precipitin bands produced in the
chicken which had received schizont antigen intramuscularly (See Fig.
8). Despite this, no protection of the injected birds against infection with
E. tenella oocysts was noted.

G. PRECIPITATING ANTIBODIES ASSOCIATED WITH IMMUNITY TO FOUR SPECIES OF *Eimeria* IN FOWLS

Rose and Long (1962) examined the precipitins developing in chickens
14 days after an initial injection with *E. acervulina, E. maxima, E.
necatrix* and *E. tenella*. The chickens were immunized by the administration of two or three increasing doses of oocysts at weekly intervals.
Maximum responses occurred on the 14th and 21st days of the infection
in chickens given either *E. acervulina* or *E. maxima*. Precipitins were
at their maximum on the 21st day in chickens given *E. tenella*. The
precipitins were not detected in *E. necatrix*-immunized fowls until the
21st day of the infection when slight reactions were observed; the maximum response was obtained on the 27th day. After challenge infection,
the sera of the *E. acervulina-* and *E. tenella*-immunized chickens responded and showed increased precipitations against their respective
antigens in agar-gel. No increase in serum precipitins was noted in the
E. maxima- or the *E. necatrix*-immunized chickens after the challenge
infection. When another challenge infection was given, no response in
terms of serum precipitins was noted with any of the species. A similar
finding had been noted in *E. tenella*-immune fowls receiving a second
challenge infection and it was suggested that the lack of response might
be explained by the retardation of the development of sporozoites after
invasion of the caecal tissue of immune chickens and the consequent
lack of antigenic stimulus.

It has been pointed out earlier that chickens immune to one species
of *Eimeria* were susceptible to another species. Rose and Long (1962)
showed that when chickens immune to *E. acervulina* were challenged
with either *E. necatrix* or *E. maxima* their sera reacted with the antigen
of the cross infection, but not with the *E. acervulina* antigen, which was
the immunizing species. Similar results were obtained when *E. maxima-*

immune chickens were cross-infected with *E. necatrix* or *E. acervulina.*
Chickens immunized with *E. necatrix* and challenged with *E. tenella*
responded only slightly and gave reactions with both antigens. *E. tenella*
and *E. necatrix* antigens were found to be more closely related than
any of the species studied.

125834

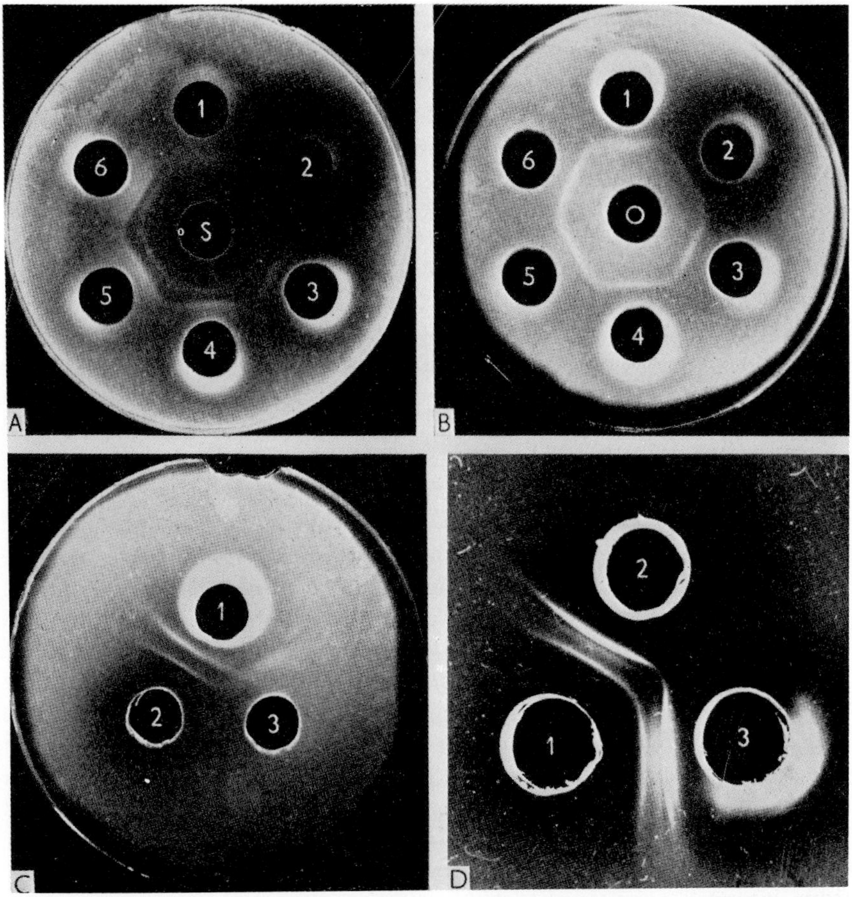

Fig. 8. Precipitation in agar comparing the schizont and oocyst antigents against sera from infected fowls. A. Schizont antigen (Centre well S); B. oocyst antigen (Centre well O). Wells 1–6 (A and B) sera from fowls inoculated *per os* with 500 oocysts and 5000 oocysts when they were 3 and 4 weeks of age. Well 1–6 days after last oocyst dose; well 2–4 days; well 3–20 days; well 4–23 days; well 5–26 days; well 6–29 days. C. The reaction of identity between the oocyst and one of the schizont lines of precipitate. D. The effect of absorbing serum with freezed-ried normal caecal extract on the precipitation in agar. Well 1–contained schizont antigen, Well 2 absorbed serum and Well 3 non-absorbed serum.

Figure after Pierce *et al.* (1962). *Immunology* Reproduced by kind permission of "Blackwell Scientific Publications", Oxford.

H. ELECTROPHORETIC STUDIES

Electrophoretic studies have been carried out in borate buffer pH 8.6 in the Perkin-Elmer version of the classical Tiselius apparatus (Pierce *et al.*, 1962). These works examined the response in two groups of fowls, one infected with *E. tenella* and the other maintained coccidia free. There was a general rise in the serum protein of both groups of chickens as they matured. It was possible to divide the globulin into four groups (i – iv); component (iv) had a mobility similar to that of gamma-globulin of mammalian origin. There was no significant difference between the amounts of the different serum proteins in young chickens during immunization with *E. tenella* and chickens of the same age not immunized. This may have been because protein synthesis in the young chickens of both groups were rising. The total protein g/100 ml of the chickens at 1 week old was 2.46 ± 0.149 compared with 3.336 ± 0.105 when 9 weeks old. The serum proteins were fractionated by electrophoresis in agar (Pierce, 1962). Serological tests on the various fractions derived from immune sera showed that the precipitins were associated with the slowest migrating proteins comprising fraction iv — the γ globulin.

I. DETECTION OF LYSINS IN THE SERA OF *E. tenella*-IMMUNE FOWLS

Horton-Smith *et al.* (1962a) have shown that merozoites and sporozoites of *E. tenella* are lysed *in vitro* after exposure to immune serum with complement. Second generation merozoites used in these studies were separated from caecal tissue by washing and centrifugation. In some experiments the sera were tested after heating to destroy complement. Fresh normal chicken serum was also employed as a source of complement to test the effect of adding complement to unheated serum samples and also the effect of the addition of complement to the heated sera. The serum-antigen mixtures were incubated for 1 h at 37°C and the degree of lysis estimated by direct microscopical examinations.

Serum from non-immunized chickens in no case lysed merozoites. even after the addition of supplementary complement. Unheated sera from immune chickens lysed merozoites. When immune sera were heated before contact with merozoites no lysis occurred, but many of the merozoites appeared to be distorted when examined microscopically. If fresh normal fowl serum (as a source of complement) was added to the heated immune serum lysis occurred at approximately the same serum dilutions that were active in the unheated sera. Merozoites exposed to immune unheated sera, or to heated immune sera + complement, were injected into susceptible fowls. Very few or no oocysts were produced as a result of these injections, whereas merozoites exposed to non-immune serum produced large numbers of oocysts. Few or no oocysts were produced in fowls following the injection of merozoites exposed to heated immune serum. No precipitates were observed on the surface of the merozoites of *E. tenella* in our studies. Precipitates were observed on *E. meleagrimitis* merozoites after exposure to *E. meleagrimitis* immune serum when examined microscopically. (Augustin and Ridges, 1962). These authors obtained these precipitates in heated *E. meleagrimitis* immune serum, but not in heated non-immune turkey serum. They also found that both *E. meleagrimitis*-immune and non-immune sera lysed *E. meleagrimitis* merozoites and so were unable to detect specific lysins to that parasite.

Sporozoites were tested in the same way as were the merozoites, except that much smaller numbers of the sporozoites were available. Unheated immune serum lysed the sporozoites after 1 hour's treatment at 37°C. Suspensions of sporozoites treated in this way produced either (a) oocysts in reduced numbers when inoculated into susceptible fowls or (b) no detectable lesions in fowls when these were examined on the 5th day of the infection. Susceptible chickens given similar numbers of sporozoites exposed to serum from non-immunized fowls produced either deaths or severe lesions, or greater numbers of oocysts at the expected time (Long *et al.*, in preparation).

Sporocysts were obtained by the mechanical fracture of sporulated oocysts. The sporocysts were exposed to immune serum, with or without the addition of fowl complement. No changes were observed upon microscopical examination and infections were produced when the treated sporocysts were inoculated into susceptible chickens. The infections produced were similar in magnitude to those produced by sporocysts exposed to normal serum.

J. ATTEMPTS TO DEMONSTRATE ANTIBODIES IN CAECAL TISSUE FROM *E. tenella*- IMMUNE FOWLS

Horton-Smith *et al.* (1962a) gave results of a limited number of experiments designed to demonstrate *in vitro* antibodies in the caecal lumen and caecal tissues of immune birds. Extracts of caecal tissue from immunized and non-immunized fowls were prepared. The extracts were tested in agar-gel against schizont antigen, but no precipitin bands were demonstrated. The extracts were also mixed with second generation merozoites with and without the presence of fowl complement. After exposure, the merozoites were introduced into susceptible chickens and the oocysts that were produced were estimated. The results of these tests are inconclusive, although a reduction in the number of oocysts produced by birds given merozoites exposed to immune caecal tissue extract was not noted. More work along these lines is proceeding.

Horton-Smith *et al.* (1962b) examined the fate of sporozoites and merozoites introduced into immune fowls. The results are given in an earlier section. One of the observations made was that sporozoites and merozoites are not destroyed by factors operating in the caecal lumen because, histologically, the parasites had invaded the caecal tissues. In addition, sporozoites were harvested from caecal tissue washings of immune chickens, a few hours after challenge with oocysts *per os*. These sporozoites produced infections comparable with infections produced by sporozoites harvested from caecal tissue washings from non-immune fowls. The results indicate that protective antibodies to *E. tenella* are not present in the lumen caeca of immune chickens.

Searches for cell-bound antibodies using fluorescent tracer techniques might detect antibodies to *E. tenella* in caecal tissue. Preliminary studies using fluoroceinisothiocyanate conjugated with *E. tenella* antibody detected antigen in second stage schizonts. At present the use of the technique has not revealed antibody with certainty in the caecal tissue of immune fowls. Such methods, if antibodies are detected, would have the additional advantage of locating the position in the tissue at which the cells are active besides providing information concerning the type or types of cells concerned.

K. ATTEMPTS TO INDUCE A PASSIVE IMMUNITY TO
E. tenella INFECTION

Attempts have been made to immunize passively fowls (Tyzzer, 1929), rabbits (Bachmann, 1930) and rats (Becker *et al.*, 1932 and Becker and Hall, 1933). All the attempts were unsuccessful and Pierce *et al.* in press using very large amounts of immune serum up to 0.88g γ globulin per kilogram body weight have also failed to protect susceptible fowls from a light challenge dose. The amount used was approximately ten times greater than that used by Vassington *et al.* (1960) to protect chickens from Newcastle disease virus.

The immune sera employed gave precipitin reactions in agar-gel with schizont antigen and judging from recent work the immune sera employed should have lysed merozite suspensions *in vitro*. Pooled serum from immune fowls was injected either intravenously or intraperitoneally into susceptible chickens. Similar amounts of serum from non-immunized chickens were given to susceptible chickens. The chickens receiving serum or γ globulin were either challenged with small numbers of oocysts *per os* or by the injection of second generation merozoites intrarectally. The serum was given before and during infection. Passive transfer of antibodies from hen to chick has been shown with certain other infections in the fowl, Newcastle disease (Brandley *et al.*

1946), infectious bronchitis (Jungherr and Terrell, 1948), and *Salmonella pullorum* (Buxton, 1952). Long and Rose (1962) attempted the transfer of protective antibodies from *E. tenella* hens to their progeny. Female chickens from the same hatch were divided between two groups when they were 5 weeks of age. One of the groups was immunized by multiple oral oocyst infections. When in lay, the immune group received a challenge infection of oocysts orally at 14 day intervals. None of the samples of yolk from embryos or from the day old progeny of immune or non-immune birds, reacted in agar-gel using schizont antigen. Progeny over ten hatches from both the immune parents and non-immune parents were challenged at either 1, 4, 7 or 14 days of age. Mortalities from caecal coccidiosis in chicks from both groups were so similar that it was concluded that no protection was afforded to the progeny of immune parents.

L. CELLULAR RESPONSES

Pierce *et al.* (1962) showed that during the primary infection with *E. tenella* heterophil-polymorphonuclear cells infiltrate into the submucosa in increasing numbers, especially on the 4th and 5th days when the second generation schizonts are developing and maturing. During the immunization there was a progressive increase of lymphoid tissue in the submucosa which contains pyroninophilic cells. In the lamina propria there was also an increase in pyroninophilic cells. Globular leucocytes-Schollenleukcozyten (Weil, 1920; Mjassojedoff, 1926) were seen in increasing numbers in the deep glands. The pyroninophilic cells were demonstrated by using the methyl-green pyronin technique (Kurnick, 1955). The globular leucocytes were best demonstrated using the Milling yellow-acid fuchsin technique (Slidders, 1961; Rootes, 1961). Preliminary studies as yet unpublished, on changes in the leucocyte numbers in circulating blood have indicated a progressive rise in total numbers of white cells in the group immunized with *E. tenella*, when compared with the non-immunized chickens. The immunized group of chickens were given increasing numbers of oocysts at 2, 3, 4 and 6 weeks old. There was a rise in the total number of white blood cells in both groups, which continued until the 7th week, when the experiment was terminated. The increase in the numbers of cells in the immune group appeared to be lymphocytes and heterophil leucocytes.

White blood cells, obtained from the peripheral blood of immune and non-immune chickens, were inoculated intravenously into two groups of susceptible chickens. The inoculations were given 4 days before and at time of infection with second generation merozoites of *E. tenella per rectum*. Oocyst production resulting from the merozoite challenge was not significantly different in the chickens which had received white blood cells from immune donors.

No experiments have yet been undertaken to discover the fate of white cells inoculated into out-bred chickens, but it was thought that cell-bound antibodies might be released if the inoculated cells were removed from circulation in the lungs or livers of the recipients. If this occurred, it is possible that released antibodies might still be alive humorally. Alternatively, cells introduced intravenously might localize sufficiently in the caecal tissue to be active immunologically. However, whatever the fate of the cells inoculated in these out-bred chickens, no effect on the course of oocyst production following a light challenge infection was observed.

Work is proceeding, using in-bred chickens known to accept skin grafts. Attempts will be made to transfer from immune birds circulating white cells as well as spleen cells and cells from the caecal tissue. The failure of immune sera to protect passively chickens and the inability to transfer passively any protection from immune hens to their progeny suggest that immunity to *E. tenella* is not mediated by circulating antibodies. However, the results *in vivo*, in the caecal ligation experiments, suggested that resistance to reinfection was not confined to tissue which had previously experienced infection. Preliminary attempts to induce a passive resistance by the transfer of white blood cells or spleen cells from immune to susceptible fowls have failed. More knowledge of the location and type of cells involved is required as well as a greater knowledge of the fate of these cells after transfer to another host. Complete resistance of fowls, in the absence of reinfection, may be relatively short-lived and resistance of fowls in the field depends upon continued exposure to infection.

REFERENCES

Al-Dabagh, M. A. (1961). *Parasitology* 51, 257–61.
Alfert, M. (1950). *J. cell comp. Physiol.* 36, 381–409.
Augustin, R. and Ridges, P. A. (1962), *in* "Immunity to Protozoa" (ed. P.C.C. Garnham). Blackwell Sci. Publ., Oxford.
Bachman, C. W. (1930). *Amer. J. Hyg.* 12, 641–49.
Becker, E. R., Zimmerman, W. J., Pattillo, W. H. and Farmer, J. M. (1956). *Iowa, St. Coll. J. Sci.* 31, 79.
Becker, E. R., Hall, P. R. and Hager, A. (1932). *Iowa St. Coll. J. Sci.* 6, 299–316.
Becker, E. R. and Hall, P. R. (1933). *Amer. J. Hyg.* 18, 220–3.
Blaschko H. and Jacobson, W. (1951) *in* "Cytology and Cell Physiology". (2nd ed., G. H. Bourne). Clarendon Press, Oxford.
Boles, J. I. and Becker, E. R. (1954). *Iowa St. Coll. J. Sci.* 29, 1–26.
Brachet, J. (1953). *Quart. J. micr. Sci.* 94, 1–10.
Brackett, S. and Bliznick, A. (1949). *Ann. N.Y. Acad. Sci.* 52, 595–610.

Brackett, S. and Bliznick, A. (1950). American Cyanamid Co. Lederle Laboratories. Division Publication.

Brackett, S. and Bliznick, A. (1952). *J. Parasit.* **38**, 133–9.

Braden, A. (1955). *Stain. Tech.* **30**, 19–26.

Bragdon, D. E. and McManus, J. R. A. (1952). *Quart. J. micr. Sci.* **93**, 391–4.

Brand, T. von. (1952). "Chemical Physiology of Endoparasitic Animals". Academic Press, New York.

Brandley, C. A., Moses, H. E. and Jungherr, E. L. (1946). *Amer. J. vet. Res.* **7**, 33–342.

Burns, W. C. and Challey, J. R. (1959) *Exp. Parasit.* **8**, 515-26.

Buxton, A. (1952). *J. gen. Microbiol.* **7**, 268–86.

Challey, J. R. and Burns, W. C. (1959). *J. Protozool.* **6**, 238–41.

Cheissin, E. M. (1935). *Ann. Parasit. hum comp.* **13**, 133–46.

Cheissin, E. M. (1940). *Uchennye Tapiski Institute Imena Gertsena* **30**, 65–92.

Cheissin, E. M. (1947). *Zool. J.* Moscow **26**, 17–30 (In Russian) English Summary.

Cheissin, E. M. (1957). *Arch. Protistenk* **102**, 265–90.

Cheissin, E. M. (1959). *XVth International Zoological Congress Lond. Sect. IX pap* **25**.

Clarkson, M. J. (1958). *Parasitology* **48**, 70–88.

Clarkson, M. J. (1959a). *Parasitology* **49**, 519–28.

Clarkson, M. J. (1959b). *Parasitology* **49**, 70–82.

Clarkson, M. J. (1960). *Ann. trop. Med. Parasit.* **54**, 253–7.

Cuckler, A. C., Malanga, C. A. and Ott, W. H. (1956). *Poult. Sci.* **35**, 98–109.

Davies, S. F. M. (1956). *Vet. Rec.* **68**, 853–7.

Davies, S. F. M. and Joyner, L. P. (1962). *Nature, Lond.* **194**, 996–7.

Dickinson, E. M. and Schofield, R. M. (1939). *Poult. Sci.* **18**, 419–31.

Dobson, E. L. (1957). "Physiopathology of the Reticulo Endothelial System". Blackwell Sci. Publ. Oxford.

Edgar, S. A. (1955). *J. Parasit.* **41**, 214–6.

Edgar, S. A. Herrick, C. A. and Frazer, L. A. (1944). *Trans. Amer. micr. Soc.* **63**, 199–202.

Farr, M. M. and Wehr, E. E. (1947). *Proc. helm. Soc. Wash.* **14**, 19–20.

Fish, F. (1931). *Amer. J. Hyg.* **14**, 560–76.

Garnham, P. C. C., Bird, R. G. and Baker, J. R. (1960). *Trans. R. Soc. trop. Med. Hyg.* **54**, 274–8.

Gill, B. S. and Ray, H. N. (1954a). *Indian J. vet. Sci.* **24**, 223–8.

Gill, B. S. and Ray, H. N. (1954b). *Indian J. vet. Sci.* **24**, 229–37.

Gill, B. S. and Ray, H. N. (1954c). *Indian J. vet. Sci.* **24**, 239–44.

Giovannola, A. (1934). *Arch. Protistenk* **83**, 270.

Glick, D. (1949). *Techniques of Histo-. Cyto-chemistry I.P. N.Y.*

Goodman, M., Woolfe, H. R. and Norton, S. (1951). *J. Immunol.* **66**, 225–36.

Grevan, V. (1953). *Arch. Protistenk* **98**, 342–414.

Hale, C. (1946). *Nature, Lond.* **157**, 802.

Hawkins, P. A. (1952). "Coccidiosis in Turkeys" Michigan State College Technical Bulletin. **200**.

Horton-Smith, C. and Long, P. L. (1959). *J. comp. Path.* **69**, 192–207.

Horton-Smith, C. and Long, P. L. (1961). *Exp. Parasit.* **11**, 93–101.

Horton-Smith, C., Beattie, J. and Long, P. L. (1961). *Immunology* **4**, 111–21.

Horton-Smith, C., Long, P. L., Pierce, A. E. and Rose, M. E. (1962a) *in* "Immunity to Protozoa" (ed. P. C. C. Garnham). Blackwell Sci. Publ., Oxford.

Horton-Smith, C. and Taylor, E. L. (1945). *Vet. Rec.* **57**, 35–6.

Horton-Smith, C., Long, P. L. and Pierce, A. E. (1962b). *(In Press).*

Johnson, W. T. (1930). *Bull. Ore. agric. Expt. Sta.* Director's Biennial Report, 1928-1930.

Johnson, W. T. (1931). *J. Parasit.* **18**, 122.

Johnson, W. T. (1938). *Bull. Ore. agric. Exp. Sta.* **358**, 3–33.

Joyner, L. P. (1958). *Parasitology* **48**, 101–12.

Jungherr, E. L. and Terrell, N. L. (1948). *Amer. J. vet. Res.* **9**, 201–5.

Kendall, S. B. and McCullough, F. S. (1952). *J. comp. Path.* **62**, 116–24.

Kurnick, N. B. (1955). *Stain. Tech.* **30**, 213–30.

Landers, E. J. (1960). *J. Parasit.* **46**, 195.

Levine, P. P. (1942). *Cornell Vet.* **32**, No. 4, 430–9.

Lillie, R. D. (1947). *J. Lab. clin. Med.* **32**, 76–88.

Lison, L. (1935). *Arch. Biol. Liege*, **46**, 599.

Long, P. L. (1959). *Ann. trop. Med. Parasit.* **53**, 325–33.

Long, P. L. (1962). *Parasitology* **52**, 89–93.

Long, P. L. and Rootes, D. G. (1959). *Trans. Roy. Soc. trop. Med. Hyg.* **53**, 308–9.

Long, P. L. and Rose, M. E. (1962). *Exp. Parasit.* **12**, 75–81.

Long, P. L., Rootes, D. G. and Horton-Smith, C. (1961). *Nature, Lond.* **192**, 1315–6.

Long, P. L., Rose, M. E. and Pierce, A. E. (in prep.).

McManus, J. R. A. (1946). *Nature, Lond.* **158**, 202.

Mjassojedoff, S. W. (1926). *Folia haemat.* **32**, 263–96.

Monné, L. and Hönig, G. (1955). *Ark. Zool.* **7**, 251–6.

Moore, E. N. (1954). *Proc. 91st ann. meeting Amer. vet. med. Ass.* 300.

Moore, E. N. and Brown, J. A. (1951). *Cornell Vet.* **41**, 125–36.

Moore, E. N., Brown, J. A. and Carter, R. D. (1954). *Poult. Sci.* **33**, 925–9.

Morehouse, N. F. (1949). *Ann. N.Y. Acad. Sci.* **52**, 589–94.

Morehouse, N. F. (1938). *J. Parasit.* **24**, 311–7.

Morehouse, N. F. and McGuire, W. C. (1958). *Poult. Sci.* **37**, 665–72.

Ouchterlony, O. (1949). *Ark. Kemi. Min. Geol.* **826**. 1–9.

Ouchterlony, O. (1953). *Acta path. microbiol. scand.* **32**, 231–41.

Pattillo, W. H. and Becker, E. R. (1955). *J. Morph.* **96**, 61–95.

Pierce, A. E. (1962). *Biochim. biophys. Acta.* **59**, 149–57.

Pierce, A. E., Long, P. L. and Horton-Smith, C. (1962). *Immunology* **5**, 129–52.

Pierce, A. E., Long, P. L. and Horton-Smith, C. (1963). *Immunology* **6**, 1.

Ray, H. N. and Gill, B. S. (1954). *Ann. trop. Med. Parasit.* **48**, 8–10.

Ray, H. N. and Gill, B. S. (1955). *Indian vet. J. Sci.* **25**, 17–23.

Rootes, D. G. (1961). *J. med. Lab. Tech.* **18**, 102.

Rose, M. Elaine and Long, P. L. (1962). *Immunology* **5**, 79–92.

Roskin, G. I. and Ginsburg, A. S. (1944). *C. R. Acad. Sci. U.R.S.S.* **43**, 122–5.

Scholtyseck, E. (1953). *Arch. Protistenk.* **98**, 415-65.

Scholtyseck, E. (1959). *Zbl. Bakt.* **175**, 305–17.

Sharma, N. N. and Reid, W. M. (1962). *J. Parasit.* **48**, No. 2, Sect. 2., 33.

Slidders, W. (1961). *J. med. Lab. Tech.* **18**, 36–7.

Smyth, J. D. (1954). *Quart J. micr.* **95**, 139-52.

Sassuchin, D. (1935). *Arch. Protistenk* **84**, 186–98.

Sylvén, B. (1941). *Acta Chir. Scand.* **86**, (Suppl) 66, 151.

Tsunoda, K. and Itikawa, O. (1955). Report No. 29 Government Experimental Station for Animal Hygiene – Japan.

Tyzzer, E. E. (1927). *J. Parasit.* **13**, 215.

Tyzzer, E. E. (1929). *Amer. J. Hyg.* **10**, 269–383.

Tyzzer, E. E., Theiler, H. and Jones, E. E. (1932). *Amer. J. Hyg.* **15**, 319–93.

Vassington, J. J., Laffer, N. G., Holst, A. P. and De Volt, H. M. (1960). *Poult. Sci.* **39**, 1418–27.

Van Doorninck, W. M. and Becker, E. R. (1957). *J. Parasit.* **43**, 40–4.

Wehr, E. E. and Farr, M. M. (1947). *Proc. helm . Soc. Wash.* **14**, 1–12.

Weil, P. (1920). *Arch. mikr. Anat.* **93**, 1–81.

Wilson, P. A. G. and Fairbairn, D. (1961). *J. Protozool.* **8**, 410–15.

Wislocki, G. B. and Dempsey, F. W. (1946). *Anat. Rec.* **90**, 249.

F*

The Infective Stage of Nematode Parasites and its Significance in Parasitism

W. P. ROGERS and R. I. SOMMERVILLE

University of Adelaide, South Australia, and McMaster Laboratory, Division of Animal Health, C.S.I.R.O., Glebe, N.S.W., Australia

I.	Introduction	109
II.	General Form of the Life Cycle	110
	A. Introduction	110
	B. Hatching of Eggs	111
	C. The Moulting of Larvae	115
III.	Modifications of the Life Cycle for Dispersal and Parasitism	118
IV.	Infective Stages	122
	A. Ensheathed Larvae as Agents of Infection	122
	B. Eggs as Agents of Infection	123
V.	The Physiology of Infective Stages	124
	A. The Food Reserves	124
	B. Oxygen Requirements	126
	C. Metabolism	128
	D. End-Products of Metabolism	129
	E. Permeability and Osmoregulation	130
VI.	The Behaviour of Infective Stages	131
	A. The Behaviour of Trichostrongyles on Pasture	132
	B. Behaviour and Infection *via* the Skin	135
	C. The Behaviour of Nematodes Infecting Plants	136
	D. Periodicity of Microfilariae	137
VII.	The Survival of Infective Stages	138
	A. Infective Larvae of Animal Parasites	138
	B. The Survival of Infective Eggs	140
	C. The Survival of Plant-Parasitic Nematodes	141
	D. General Comments on Survival Studies	144
VIII.	The Process of Infection	145
	A. The Infection of Animals *via* the gut	146
	B. Infection *via* The Surface of the Host	154
	C. The Infection of Plants	156
IX.	The Nature of Infectiousness	163
	A. Metamorphosis and Infectiousness	164
	B. Mechanisms of Moulting and Metamorphosis	165
	C. A General Hypothesis of Infectiousness as an Adaptation to Parasitism	166
	D. The Action of the Stimulus from the Host	167
	Acknowledgments	171
	References	171

I. Introduction

A basic feature of parasites which distinguishes them from other sorts of organisms is their capacity to "infect" the host. The nature of infectiousness and the mechanisms involved are therefore important in the study of parasitism. In this article we have approached these problems by first discussing infective stages independently of their relation to the host. Thus the early sections deal with the life cycles of nematodes generally and the development of specialized stages for dispersion and infection. This is followed by a brief account of the general physiology and behaviour of infective stages. The relationship of the infective stage to the host is dealt with in sections on the physiology of infection. With this more factual account completed, a discussion, largely speculative, on the nature of infectiousness and its physiological basis is given.

Though we have touched upon a variety of nematodes—free-living, parasites of vertebrates and invertebrates, parasites of plants—we have not attempted a complete review of the literature. Rather we have directed our interests largely towards that part of the subject, concerned chiefly with nematode parasites which enter the vertebrate host *via* the gut, which in our view leads most profitably to the·development of hypotheses at the present time.

II. General Form of the Life Cycle

A. INTRODUCTION

Although there is a great variation in the complexity of the life cycles of nematodes, particularly parasitic ones, an underlying pattern can be discerned which finds its simplest expression among the free-living species. This pattern is based upon a series of moults. The events which lead to moulting are associated with physiological changes during which the organism is often quiesecent and does not grow.

Juveniles or larvae may hatch from the eggs while still in the uterus or shortly after the egg leaves the female. Hatching may be delayed, and with some parasitic nematodes, may not take place until the egg is ingested by the host. While in the egg the embryo may undergo several moults. Sometimes it is difficult to detect moulting within the egg and it can be overlooked, so that a species may be described as having fewer moults than usual. However, in every instance which has been examined closely it appears that there are four moults. When moulting takes place, the old cuticle becomes detached from the epidermis and also from the buccal capsule, the excretory canal, the rectum and the vagina. Sometimes the detached cuticle may be discarded immediately, but at other times it is retained, as in infective stages of nematodes like *Haemonchus contortus* which discard it during the process of infection.

Each moult is commonly preceded by a period of inactivity called a lethargus. Worms apparently do not feed while in lethargus and may be coiled in a characteristic position. Some changes may occur in the shape of the oesophagus and buccal capsule. There are probably histological changes associated with the formation of the new cuticle and the impending detachment of the old one, but there is no information on these or on their association with lethargus.

Many worms increase in length until the onset of lethargus, when growth ceases. Growth is resumed after the worm has moulted at the termination of the lethargus. However, there is probably great variation in this pattern. Sometimes there may be several moults close together with no growth between them, as in *Meloidogyne* (Bird, 1959a). The organism appears to be in an extended lethargus during this time. On the other hand growth curves may form a series of plateaux, each of which is associated with one lethargus and ecdysis (McCoy, 1930; Sommerville, 1960; Fig. 1). In some species growth may not be interrupted by a lethargus at the time of moulting (Ackert, 1931), although the same result could be obtained if the lethargus was very short and the observations at relatively infrequent intervals.

There is great variation in the extent to which nematodes increase in length. Some, for example the sexual generation of *Heterotylenchus pawlowskyi* in fleas, undergo the third and fourth moults and attain maturity with little increase in length (Kurochkin, 1960) and some species of Paratylenchinae are almost the same size as the first-stage larvae, often less than 0.5 mm long. On the other hand the species *Ascaris lumbricoides*, with second-stage larvae 2 mm to 3 mm long, may be one hundred times longer in the adult stage. Sometimes the larva itself may be shorter after moulting than before. The significance of this is obscure, but in some instances, e.g. *Heterodera schachtii*, the total mass may not change because shorter larvae are thicker (Raski, 1950).

B. HATCHING OF EGGS

1. *The Nature of the Egg Membranes*

Eggs of nematodes, especially those of nematodes parasitic in animals, show great variation between species (Chitwood and Chitwood, 1938). Although the eggs of *Ascaris lumbricoides* and *Parascaris equorum* are not typical they are probably better known than any others and for this reason much of what follows must concern them. This subject has been reviewed by Fairbairn (1957). The eggs of both species, referred to as Ascaris, have a primary envelope of three or four layers and a tertiary, sometimes called secondary, layer contributed by the uterus. The innermost layer of the primary envelope, usually, but wrongly, called the vitelline membrane, is primarily composed of lipid but amino acids have been isolated from it (Jaskoski, 1960). This membrane is considerably thicker and has greater structural complexity in Ascaris than in other species so far examined (Monné and Hönig, 1954). Although it is soluble in lipoid solvents and may be penetrated or at least damaged by a number of gases, it is inert to a wide range of substances. The remaining two or three layers are apparently composed of chitin and of protein which may be quinone tanned. The tertiary envelope is proteinaceous and is apparently secreted by the uterus. The number of eggs produced by species like *A. lumbricoides* is very large and although it might be

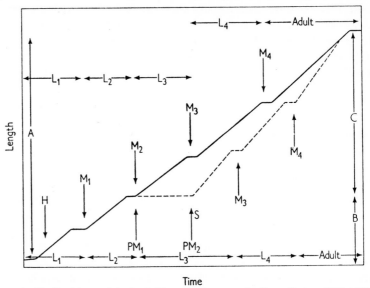

Fig. 1. An idealized form of the basic life cycle of nematodes (from Rogers, 1961a). The life cycle of a free living nematode is represented by a solid line. Hatching (H) is "spontaneous" and there are four moults (M_1–M_4). The broken line represents a life cycle in which a change in environment is necessary to stimulate (S) the completion of the second moult (PM_2). A, B and C are different environments.

expected that cells secreting the tertiary layer would therefore be prominent, they have not been described.

Monné and Hönig (1954) have studied the eggs of more than sixteen nematode species parasitic in vertebrates. The tertiary envelope is commonly absent. The primary envelope tends to be well developed in those species which remain within the egg during the free-living stage; it may be absent in parthenogenetic forms. In species which hatch shortly after leaving the host, the primary envelope is reduced to a lipoid membrane enclosed in a layer of quinone tanned protein. Some chitin may be present.

Some species of plant parasitic nematodes, which, like *Heterodera*, remain within the egg for considerable periods, have an additional protective layer in the form of the body of the female, the wall of which is tanned (Ellenby, 1946a). On the other hand the eggs of *Hemicycliophora arenaria* are enclosed within a sticky substance, the nature and function of which is not known (van Gundy, 1959). There is no evidence to suggest that this species remains within the egg for long periods; in laboratory tests eggs hatched in 3 to 5 days. In general it seems that the eggs of most nematodes parasitic in plants are like those of *Heterodera*, with thin transparent walls. Egg membranes of *H. rostochiensis* contain chitin (Tracey, 1958), but there is no detailed information on their structure. Eggs of phyto-parasitic nematodes are apparently similar to those of free-living and marine species, but although it has been suggested that the lipoid membrane may be lacking in the latter, it seems unlikely that this would be true of fresh water and plant nematodes. A lipoid membrane is present in eggs of *Radopholos similis* (Weerdt, 1960).

2. The Breakdown of the Egg Membranes

Eggs may be classified as (1) those which hatch "spontaneously" when a particular stage of development has been reached, and (2) those which do not hatch until provided with an external stimulus. It should be emphasized, however, that cricital data is available for very few species and the process of hatching has been elucidated only in one or two of these.

Eggs which hatch spontaneously seem to be thin shelled, because these species do not as a rule require the protection of egg envelopes for more than a short time. Wilson (1958) has shown that an increase in permeability to water is an essential step in the hatching of *Trichostrongylus retortaeformis* eggs. This is associated with a breakdown in the lipoid envelope, apparently by a process of emulsification achieved by movement of the larva in the presence of an emulsifying agent. An increase in hydrostatic pressure within the larva follows and pressure is thereby exerted on the protein layer of the shell. Wilson believed a second process was also involved in which the outer layer of protein was chemically weakened, but little evidence of this process is available. If a "hatching fluid" were present, it might be expected that there would be differences between the rate at which eggs hatched in large samples compared with small, but no differences were detected. However, this could mean that the hatching fluid had no effect from the outside of the eggs.

Eggs of *Nematodirus filicollis* and *N. bathus* require exposure to low temperatures for some months before they will hatch; subsequently hatching takes place "spontaneously" at temperatures as low as 10°C (Thomas and Stevens, 1960). Moisture is also important for hatching (Kates, 1950) but quantitative data are lacking. Evidently the filariform larvae of these species, although infective if artificially hatched, are unable to initiate the hatching process unless first "sensitized" by low temperatures. The similarity to diapause in insects is clear; it seems unlikely that low temperatures have a direct action on the membranes of the egg.

Possibly the eggs of *Heterodera major* are similar to those of *Nematodirus filicollis* and *N. bathus*. Certainly a rise in temperature seems to be important (Hesling, 1956), but if the mechanisms were closely similar it might be expected that there would be a mass hatching of short duration when temperatures rose. However, there is no evidence for this (Hesling, 1958).

It is not known whether species which possess a stylet can use this alone to leave the egg, or whether it is used in conjunction with enzymes which weaken the membranes, or whether it has no significance. In *Meloidogyne arenaria*, *Paratylenchus projectus*, *Aphelenchus projectus* and *Neotylenchus linfordi* (Dropkin *et al.*, 1958; Rhoades and Linford, 1961; Taylor, 1962; Hechler, 1962) hatching is preceded by great activity of the enclosed embryo and the egg membranes are changed so that the egg is no longer a rigid structure, but stretches and becomes distorted by movement of the nematode. Taylor noted that the egg membrane became flexible only after pulsations were observed in the metacorpal valve, which suggests that the larva discharged something into the fluid about it. The stylet was observed to puncture the egg membranes repeatedly and ultimately the egg ruptured. On the other hand *N. linfordi* apparently bursts the egg membranes by straightening itself out.

In species in which the egg forms the infective stage, hatching occurs within the host and as the result of some stimulus, simple or complex, provided by the host. Hatching of infective eggs then, may be regarded as part of the process of infection (Section VIII). Some nematode parasites of plants are also dependent upon a stimulus from the host to start the hatching of eggs but here of course the stimulus acts externally to the host. This is especially notable in certain species of *Heterodera*; *H. rostochiensis* for example, requires a specific stimulus in the form of substances secreted by the host, usually a species of *Solanum*. Work on this problem is difficult. The response to the hatching stimulus is slow, and is influenced by previous treatment (Ellenby and Gilbert, 1958). Tests take a long time and large numbers of larvae are involved (Fenwick, 1952). The eggs and other material of unknown nature are packed within the cyst and this structure, together with the slow response to stimuli, has made it difficult to study the actual process of hatching. The concept of the cyst as an ecological unit, in which each egg affects the behaviour of others about it (Ellenby, 1946b) has drawn attention to this gap and has led the way to a study of the individual egg and its environment within the cyst (Ellenby, 1955a, 1956, 1957; Onions, 1955; Wallace, 1956a; Fenwick and Widdowson, 1959).

The stimulus for the hatching of *H. rostochiensis* comes from the root system of the host plant. Many attempts have been made to isolate the active principle which has been called eclepic acid (Calam *et al.*, 1949; Janzen and van Tuin, 1956). It seems that the essential part of the stimulus is an unsaturated lactone ring, although the evidence for this is not decisive. However, it is suggestive that concentrated preparations of the hatching factor possess cardiotonic activity (Ellenby and Gilbert, 1957, 1960) and could therefore influence the same fundamental mechanisms as other lactones, for example, ion transport.

Little appears to be known about the sequence of events following stimulation with the hatching factor. However, "free" eggs isolated from cysts of *H. rostochiensis* not only hatch in the presence of the hatching factor, but do so more rapidly than a mass of eggs or eggs in a cyst (Ellenby, 1956; Fenwick and Widdowson, 1959). These observations suggest that whatever inhibitory role the cyst may play in terms of the hatching of the individual egg, there is nothing within the cyst which is an integral part of the actual mechanism itself. The hatching factor evidently affects the egg membranes, the contents or both, but the immediate nature of the response is unknown.

The work on hatching is not sufficiently extensive to permit many generalizations about the process. However, it seems that in these instances where the infective stage is enclosed within an egg, the host commonly supplies a stimulus which induces hatching (Section VIII). In species which have been examined in greatest detail, the stimulus from the host has not been found to break down the egg membranes directly, but induces the larva to release enzymes which do this.

When eggs hatch "spontaneously" the stimulus must come from the larva itself. Probably, once a particular stage of development is attained, hatching fluid is released, although it must be emphasized that the presence of hatching fluid has yet to be demonstrated in this type of egg. Rowan (1956) has developed a technique which might be useful for this purpose.

Eggs of some species of *Nematodirus* (and perhaps *Heterodera*) are in a sense intermediate between those which hatch "spontaneously" and those which require specific stimuli from the host. Climatic conditions and hatching are closely associated so that the infective stages are released at a time when the host is especially numerous.

C. THE MOULTING OF LARVAE

1. *The Structure of the Cuticle*

Although the gross morphological features of the cuticle such as annulations, punctations and spines have been catalogued extensively

(Chitwood and Chitwood, 1938; Hyman, 1951), the histology is known in detail in only a few species. A recent review is given by Fairbairn (1960a) and earlier papers have been reviewed by Chitwood and Chitwood (1938). Much of the information about the nature of substances in the cuticle has been obtained by histochemical studies and many results await confirmation by more direct chemical examination.

In general it seems that the larger the nematode, the more complicated is the cuticular structure (Monné, 1959) although it might be advisable to know more about some of the free-living nematodes before extending this generalization beyond the species parasitic in vertebrates. The cuticle cannot, even for one species, be said to be composed of one substance. The best known is probably *Ascaris lumbricoides* (Bird, 1956, 1957, 1958b; Bird and Deutsch, 1957; Kreuzer, 1953; Monné, 1955, 1959). Briefly the cuticle can be described as a basement membrane on the epidermis (or hypodermis), above which are three fibre layers. On this is superimposed a structureless layer (the so-called "homogeneous" layer) and finally a cortex of considerable complexity.

Both fibre layers and basement membrane are collagenous. The nature of the homogeneous layer is not well understood but it probably contains several water-soluble albumins as well as fibrous proteins rich in sulphur. When sections of *Ascaris* are incubated in the presence of collagenases from *Clostridium welchii* the fibrous and homogeneous layers disappear; only the external cortical layer remains (Dawson, 1960). This layer is believed to be tanned. Bird (1957) believes that the cuticle of *Ascaris* is a secreted collagen, underlying a tanned protein layer over which is superimposed a thin layer of lipid.

The cuticles of other parasitic nematodes have been examined less extensively, but in a general way they seem to be similar to *Ascaris*. The cyst wall of *Heterodera rostochiensis* evidently contains a tanned protein (Ellenby, 1946a). Two layers can be distinguished by both light and electron microscopy (Wieser, 1953; Ferris and Siegel, 1957), but as yet there is little reconciliation between the structures depicted by these two methods. In *Heterodera glycines* (males) and *Hoplolaimus tylenchiformis* three layers (cortex, homogeneous layer and fibre layers?) have been noted (Hirschmann, 1959), but it would not be surprising if the structure of the cyst wall was changed from that of the living worm. In *Meloidogyne* spp. there is no evidence of the two layers seen in *Heterodera* cysts (Bird, 1958b). Little or nothing is known of the cuticles of marine or other free-living forms.

Unfortunately detailed knowledge of the cuticle is largely confined to the adult stages, and this can have little relevance to the problem of moulting. Information on the structure and chemical composition of larval cuticles is not easy to obtain, chiefly because of the small size and difficulty of collecting enough specimens for chemical analysis. Further, cuticles collected either naturally or artificially during any moult will not necessarily be the same as before the commencement of moulting. Cuticles of fourth-stage *Nippostrongylus brasiliensis* resemble collagen (Simmonds, 1958) and second-stage cuticles of the same species, as well as of *Haemonchus contortus* and *Trichostrongylus* sp. are probably secreted collagens. There was no evidence that these cuticles were tanned (Bird and Rogers, 1956). In general, it seems that cuticles of larvae are less complex than those of adults. Certainly the cuticle is unlikely to be inert, not only in terms of probable changes at moulting but even in the adult, in which it evidently has some activity (Bird, 1957; Lee, 1961). If this concept is correct it might be expected that wound healing would be well defined. However, this phenomenon does not appear to have been examined extensively in nematodes. One early reference (Cleland and Johnston, 1911) to wound healing in *A. lumbricoides* suggests that the various layers of the cuticle are not replaced, but that the wound is healed by the epidermis.

2. *The Physiology of Moulting*

Although detailed studies have not been carried out it seems that moulting in nematodes probably occurs in several steps: (a) the formation of the new cuticle under the old, (b) the freeing of the old cuticle as an inert structure still enclosing the organism and (c) the casting, ecdysis or exsheathment of the old cuticle or sheath as it is sometimes called. These steps may be discrete or merged closely one into the other. In third-stage strongyle larvae, where the uncast cuticle may be retained as the protective sheath until infection occurs, casting of the sheath has been described in some detail (Lapage, 1935; Looss, 1911). In many species of trichostrongyles the third-stage larva escapes from the sheath after the anterior end has been broken off as a small cap. In other stages, both parasitic and free-living, in which the uncast cuticle is not retained as a protective layer, the moulting is completed in the same way, or else the organism breaks through a longitudinal slit in the old cuticle.

Though some studies on the formation of the new cuticle have been described it is clear that much more information on the histology and physiology of the formation and loosening of the cuticle as a part of the process of moulting is needed. Indeed, the possible similarity between insects and nematodes suggested by Looss (1911) has been little explored. Some knowledge of the physiology of exsheathment of infective larvae which takes place during infection has been obtained (see Section VIII). In these larvae an external stimulus from the host leads to secretion of an "exsheathing fluid" which attacks the sheath, enabling the larva to escape. It is not known whether exsheathing fluid is released at the first and fourth ecdysis, but indirect evidence suggests that it may be released at the third ecdysis (Soulsby, Sommerville and Stewart, 1959).

Not very much is known about the physiology of ecdysis in other nematodes, but recent work suggests that infective stages of the lung-worms *Muellerius capillaris* and *Protostrongylus rufescens* exsheath by a mechanism very similar to that described above. Similar mechanisms may operate in the fourth moult of *Paratylenchus projectus* and *P. dianthus*. These are described in more detail in Section VIII.

III. Modifications of the Life Cycle for Dispersal and Parasitism

Probably most free-living nematodes and many parasites of plant roots are able to persist for an indefinite number of generations in the same environment. In the life cycle of *Hemicycliophora arenaria* and *Crico-nemoides xenoplax* (van Gundy, 1959; Thomas, 1959), there is no special-ized infective stage. It seems that such species are often less sedentary than those parasites of plants which have specialized infective stages. All stages from the gravid female to the newly-hatched juvenile are motile and all stages can infect the host. However, the host-parasite relationship of many of these species is not clear. They tend to feed on superficial rather than deeper tissue. In these respects, they resemble nematodes which are free living and indeed, the distinction is often hard to make. Usually they do not survive for long in the absence of the host.

But certain more specialized environments such as rotting vegetation, dung and slime fluxes undergo changes in their suitability as a habitat. The life cycles of nematodes which live in these places have been modi-fied and show adaptations which help dispersal to new environments when the old one has become unsuitable. This has been demonstrated experimentally with *Panagrellus silusiae* for example. Gravid females tend to migrate to higher points and to the periphery of cultures. Here they readily became attached to legs of *Drosophila funebris*, which pro-vides a means of transportation. As with other stages, the gravid female is not especially resistant to the desiccation inherent in this mode of travel but larvae are able to survive in, and eventually escape from, the dead mother (Lees, 1953).

More usually the life cycle is modified to produce a specific stage which can survive the rigours of transport, and which is likely to have patterns of behaviour which increase the chances of obtaining trans-port. Examples are common in such forms as *Rhabditis, Cheilobus* and *Diplogaster*.

Rhabditis dubia spends its entire life cycle in cow dung (Bovien, 1937), but at times, presumably stimulated by an unsuitable environment, special third-stage juveniles called dauer larvae, are produced. These become attached to psychodid flies. When the flies reach fresh dung the juveniles leave the psychodid to continue the life cycle. The life cycle of *Cheilobus quadrilabiatus* which lives on decaying vegetation is similar, because many generations may be produced without the occurrence of dauer larvae. Later, as decay advances, dauer larvae appear.

Another example which has been studied more extensively is that of *R. coarctata* (Triffitt and Oldham, 1927; Oldham, 1937). This species lives in dung, but third-stage juveniles are always dauer larvae and cannot complete the moult and develop further unless moved to fresh dung. Transport is provided by dung beetles on which the dauer larvae encyst.

Dauer larvae seem to have patterns of behaviour which enhance the chance of association with a transport host. The best known example of this is probably seen in some species of *Diplogaster*: the dauer larvae aggregate in clusters on the surface of cow dung, usually on small projections, where they stand erect and wave the anterior end to and fro (Bovien, 1937).

The typical dauer larva is enclosed within two cuticles. The outer one, an uncast sheath, may assume bizarre shapes, as for example in *Rhabditis coarctata*. The presence of the outer cuticle or sheath shows that moulting is incomplete, and is completed only when the nematode is stimulated by an environment suited for subsequent development. Probably the dauer larva does not feed, because the outer cuticle blocks the mouthparts. Further, the buccal cavity is usually very small and lips and papillae seem to be absent. Some species, e.g. *Cheilobus quadrilabiatus* and *Diplogaster stercoralis*, apparently have large quantities of reserve nutrients stored in the intestinal cells (Bovien, 1937). There is also some evidence that dauer larvae can withstand dryer conditions than other stages in the life cycle. Species of *Diplogaster* on cow dung are "resistant to desiccation". The precise significance of the outer sheath in this phenomenon is not known, but in several species it apparently produces an oily secretion (Bovien, 1937), which permits movement in the absence of water.

The stimuli which lead to the production of facultative dauer larvae and which, in the new environment, restart the processes of moulting and ensuing development, are largely unknown. Encystment of *R. coarctata* seems to be accomplished by mechanical stimuli arising from motion of the beetle which serves as a carrier host. Some species, which, like *R. maupesi*, live within the body of the earthworm, restart development when stimulated by the decomposition of the tissue of the host

(Johnson, 1913). If the formation of dauer larvae is stimulated by over-crowding or shortage of food, the problem might well be studied with some of the methods which are used for cultivating nematodes. The stimulus to start development on arrival in fresh faeces could not be nutritional, because these larvae cannot feed until the outer cuticle is detached. But species like *Haemonchus contortus* detach their cuticle under the influence of carbonic acid; mechanisms similar in principle to this could operate in dauer larvae.

These adaptations and modifications of the life cycle which help in dispersion are similar to those which are associated with parasitism (Table I). Although, in infective stages, the modifications tend to be more varied and sophisticated (Hyman, 1951, page 260) they are similar to those for dispersal. In both, a change in the normal sequence of events occurs at a moult. The moult is incomplete and the old cuticle is retained, with the juvenile lying free within it. Neither dauer larvae nor infective stages feed, but use reserves stored in the intestine. Both differ from preceding and succeeding stages because they survive under environmental conditions which would probably kill earlier or later stages and their behaviour increases the chance of contact with the transporting insect or the host.

Infective larvae of, for example, *Haemonchus contortus* and *Trichostrongylus axei*, show many similarities to dauer larvae. The infective larvae survive under conditions which would kill earlier stages and their behaviour is such that they tend to leave the faecal mass and migrate onto the herbage which the host eats. Infective larvae of those species which infect by penetrating the host's skin, like *Necator americanus*, move onto projecting objects and wave the anterior end to and fro in the same way as dauer larvae of *Diplogaster* sp. on cattle dung. (Sasa *et al.*, 1960). Ensheathed infective larvae do not feed but use food reserves, chiefly lipid (Section V) stored in the intestinal cells. Like dauer larvae the moult is incomplete and the sheath is usually retained; stimuli from the host are required to induce exsheathment (Section VIII).

Pre-adult or fourth-stage larvae of some nematodes parasitic in plants are in some ways similar to ensheathed infective larvae. They provide a means whereby the nematode can survive in the absence of food. They are unable to complete the final moult and grow until they encounter suitable stimuli which may sometimes be specific. Pre-adult *Paratylenchus* spp., for example, require stimuli from the root diffusates of the host plant in order to moult and continue development (Rhoades and Linford, 1959). The stimuli for development of pre-adult *Ditylenchus dipsaci*, on the other hand, are probably moisture and temperature.

The infective eggs of species like *Ascaris lumbricoides* represent a more complicated modification of the life cycle which superficially is

TABLE I

Specializations in Life Cycles of Nematodes

Species	Habit	Specialized stage in the life cycle	External stimulus for (a) formation of special stage	(b) resumption of development	References
Rhabditis terrestris	Free-living in soil	None	Unnecessary	Unnecessary	Stephenson (1942a, 1944)
Turbatrix aceti	Free-living in vinegar	None	Unnecessary	Unnecessary	Peters (1928)
Diplogaster labiata	Parasitic and saprophytic in insect tissue	None*	Unnecessary	Unnecessary	Merrill and Ford (1916)
Rhabditis dubia	Free-living in dung	3rd-stage larva; dispersal, (?) facultative	(?)Unnecessary	Probably necessary (?) mechanical	Bovien (1937)
Rhabditis coarctata	Free-living in dung	3rd-stage larva; dispersal, obligate	Unnecessary	Necessary; mechanical	Oldham (1935, 1937)
Neoaplectana bibionis	Saprophytic in insect tissues	3rd-stage larva; ensheathed, facultative, "infective"	Necessary; unfavourable conditions	Necessary; (?) autolysis of tissue	Bovien (1937)
Neoaplectana glaseri	Parasitic; saprophytic	3rd-stage larva; ensheathed, facultative, infective	Necessary; unfavourable conditions	Necessary; (?) conditions in the gut of the host	Glaser et al. (1940)
Haemonchus contortus	Parasitic; part free-living	3rd-stage larva; ensheathed, infective, obligate	Unnecessary	Necessary; conditions in the gut of the host	Rogers and Sommerville (1960)
Ascaris lumbricoides	Parasitic; part free-living	2nd stage, in the egg, infective, obligate	Unnecessary	Necessary; conditions in the gut of the host	Rogers (1958, 1960)

* It seems that it was the illustration (Fig. 1E, Merrill and Ford, 1916) of a moulting female which lead Chitwood (1938, p. 248) to suggest, mistakenly, that a "dauer larva" might be formed during the life cycle.

without any counterpart in modifications for dispersal. But fundamentally infective eggs do not differ from dauer larvae or infective larvae.
The nematode in the egg is often enclosed within a partially shed sheath.
Development is halted at this stage and the organism is comparatively
resistant to adverse climatic conditions. In the absence of the host the
enclosed juvenile cannot live for long after it has left the egg. For
example, hatched larvae of *Heterodera* spp. do not survive for long in
the soil (Den Ouden, 1960; Shepherd, 1960). The infective egg of animal
parasites does not hatch until it is eaten by the host. In all instances it
is probable that external stimuli are required to initiate the hatching of
infective eggs, just as they are required for the further growth of dauer
larvae, infective larvae or dormant pre-adults. The nature of this stimulus is known for a few species only (Section VIII).

It is not surprising that dauer larvae and infective larvae or eggs are
fundamentally similar, because they have the same function. They
bridge the gap between favourable environments. This is accomplished
by a modification of the life cycle in which hatching or moulting is
delayed until stimulated by some component of the environment which
is suited for subsequent growth (Section VIII). The absence of specialized infective stages from some plant nematodes may be expected, for
their hosts are readily available.

We have stressed these similarities between dauer larvae and infective stages because it seems to illustrate rather well the special characteristics of and the function of the infective stage.

IV. Infective Stages

This section deals with the ensheathed larva and the egg as infective
stages. More is known about these than about most other infective
stages and consequently much of this review is concerned with them.

A. ENSHEATHED LARVAE AS AGENTS OF INFECTION

Ensheathed larvae are the infective stages of many species in the order
Strongyloidea. In *Haemonchus contortus*, the juveniles which hatch
"spontaneously" from the egg are in the first stage (Veglia, 1915). They
immediately commence to feed and grow until they enter the first
lethargus. The old cuticle is replaced by a new one, becomes detached
and is discarded as the worm again becomes active. The second-stage
juvenile commences to feed and to grow. As before, growth ceases with
the onset of the second lethargus, and the worm is quiescent for a few
hours. A new cuticle is formed and the old one separates from the epidermis. The cuticular lining of the anus, excretory pore and buccal capsule are detached and become flattened against the inside of the cuticle.
But, unlike the comparable stage in the first moult, the cuticle or sheath

does not break at a line circumscribing the anterior end and remains complete. The juvenile again becomes active, and now in the third stage, is enclosed in two cuticles. It cannot feed and undergoes no further development while in this stage; in these respects it has much in common with the lethargic stage. However, its behaviour is quite different and there are probably physiological differences also. The stimulus for completing the moulting process in *Haemonchus contortus* is provided by the sheep's rumen (Sommerville, 1954, 1957; Rogers and Sommerville, 1957, 1960; Rogers, 1960). After a few minutes in the rumen, a line appears about the anterior end of the sheath some 20μ from the end of the worm. This is associated with changes in the inside of the outer cuticle which, as in the first ecdysis, ultimately lead to fracture of the sheath and to the escape of the larva. Sometimes the sheath splits longitudinally about the level of the base of the oesophagus just as it does in the third ecdysis in the host (Stoll, 1940).

There are many variations of this process, although the essentials are the same. Some species, for example in *Dictyocaulus*, may retain the first- and second-stage sheaths. Others, particularly some of those which infect the host by penetrating the skin, lose the sheath before, or at the time of making contact with the host. Little information on the mechanisms involved in these processes is available.

B. EGGS AS AGENTS OF INFECTION

Many species infect the host as an egg which contains a juvenile at a particular stage of development. The best known example is *Ascaris lumbricoides* in which the larva is in the second stage, but the cuticle of the first stage is retained (Alicata, 1935). This suggests that development ceased during the first moult in much the same way as it ceases during the second moult of ensheathed infective larvae. Apparently eggs of *Heterodera rostochiensis* and *Heterakis spumosa* contain juveniles which are also in the second stage (Hagemeyer, 1951; Smith, 1953). Adaptations of this sort must ensure that the egg hatches in the alimentary tract of a suitable animal host or in the vicinity of the roots of a plant host. The stimuli which induce hatching and allow infection to take place are therefore provided by components of the environment in the intestine or near the roots (Triffitt, 1930; Rogers, 1960). This is the same sort of adaptation to parasitism which we have already discussed in relation to ensheathed infective larvae. Another feature in which these infective stages resemble one another is in their resistance to hazardous environmental conditions.

V. The Physiology of Infective Stages

Infective stages have a highly specialized role in the life cycle. Thus they form a "bridge" by which the nematode parasite moves from one environment in which it is free-living to another in which it is parasitic, or from an environment in one sort of host to an environment in a very different sort of host (see Section II). During this period the infective stage does not feed or grow, its behaviour is different and the harmful factors in its environment may include climatic conditions as well as the offensive and defensive mechanisms of the hosts. The sensory physiology of the infective larva must also differ from that of other stages because it must be able, within certain limits, to "recognize" its host, i.e. it must respond to the physical and chemical stimuli provided by the proper host for the initiation of development. These and other features of the infective stage indicate that it must have unusual characters. In general, however, the information we have does not yet tell us about the unusual mechanisms which are involved. We have decided therefore to present this Section as a brief summary.

Those aspects of infective stages which bear more directly on the process of infection are discussed separately in Section VIII. This is because we are not yet able to correlate our scanty knowledge of infective processes with the basic physiology of infective stages.

A. THE FOOD RESERVES

The infective stages of most species of nematodes can remain alive for long periods. It seems that in free-living infective stages this is achieved without feeding; as far as we are aware no free-living infective stage has been observed to feed and indeed the presence of the sheath on many prevents the intake of solid food. This applies to at least some parasitic infective stages (Fairbairn, 1958b) but in other species it seems that materials may be taken up from the host possibly through the cuticle. For example, it has been shown that C^{14} appears in the infective larvae of *Trichinella spiralis* after they have been exposed to labelled amino acids *in vivo* or *in vitro* (Stoner and Hankes, 1955, 1958; Hankes and Stoner, 1956, 1958) even when the cyst wall was well developed. Also the survival of parasitic infective stages *in vitro* is prolonged when nutrients are available in the medium, e.g. *Eustrongylides ignotus* and *Dirofilaria immitis* (von Brand and Simpson, 1942; Taylor, 1960). As larvae of *Trichinella spiralis* survive for many years even within calcified cysts, the uptake of materials in solution which will pass through the cyst wall may be important in the economy of the species.

The food reserves of infective stages may be carbohydrate or fat. Carbohydrate predominates in many parasitic infective stages though the amounts vary greatly (Table II). Glycogen is the most abundant

TABLE II

Reserve materials in infective stages

| Species | Reserve materials as per cent dry wt. | | References |
	Glycogen	Total lipid	
Porrocaecum decipiens (larvae)	55	3.7	Fairbairn (1958b)
Eustrongylides ignotus (larvae)	28	4.4	von Brand (1938)
Trichinella spiralis (larvae)	12	5.5	von Brand *et al.* (1952)
*Ascaris lumbricoides** (eggs)	6	2.2	Passey and Fairbairn (1957)

* Results are given as per cent of solids of decoated eggs.

component though appreciable amounts of trehalose are often found (Fairbairn, 1958a). Indeed the infective eggs of *Ascaris lumbricoides* contain more trehalose than glycogen (Passey and Fairbairn, 1957). Lipid, it seems, is less important than carbohydrate as a reserve substance in parasitic infective stages. On the other hand, lipid predominates in free-living infective stages, eggs and larvae. Only a few species have been examined by chemical analysis but histochemical studies, though less precise, support this view in a variey of species (Payne, 1922, 1923a, 1923b; Giovannola, 1936; Rogers, 1940a; Elliott, 1954). A number of investigations have shown that histologically-demonstratable fat and the infectivity of free-living stages decreases with the physiological age of the organism (Payne, 1923b; Rogers, 1940a; Jaskoski, 1960). These results also suggest that fat is the chief reserve substance in these organisms. The reason for this is obscure. Perhaps the increased production of water resulting from the oxidation of fat is important for infective stages which can survive for long periods as cleidoic eggs, or for larvae with a pattern of behaviour, which, though helping infection, may also lead to shortages of water. In other respects, however, the conservation of water is not strongly developed; for example ammonia is the major end-product of nitrogen metabolism.

B. OXYGEN REQUIREMENTS

All infective stages so far examined consume oxygen when it is available at atmospheric pressure and some species at least can respire at low oxygen tensions (Stannard *et al.*, 1938; von Brand, 1947; Passey and Fairbairn, 1955). The rate of use of oxygen and dependence on it for survival vary greatly. Thus the $Q\,o_2$ at 30°C varies from 28.5 for larvae of *Strongyloides papillosus* to about 0.1 for eggs of *Ascaris lumbricoides*. As pointed out by Costello and Grollman (1958) the infective stages with high respiratory rates survive for shorter periods (Table III).

The need for oxygen varies considerably. Infective stages of *Strongyloides papillosus* which enter the host by routes where oxygen is freely available are so susceptible to lack of oxygen that they have been called strict aerobes. On the other hand, many species which enter the host *via* the gut where the pO_2 is low, e.g. *Ascaris lumbricoides* can survive in the absence of oxygen for some weeks (Brown, 1928). There is no general relationship between resistance to the lack of oxygen and the route of infection; the larvae of *Ancylostoma caninum*, which enter the host through the skin, will live for days without oxygen (McCoy, 1930).

The effect of pO_2 on the $Q\,o_2$ of infective stages has been examined in a few species only. The parasitic infective stage of *Trichinella spiralis* retains a relatively high oxygen uptake down to 7.6 mm of mercury (Stannard *et al.*, 1938); infective free-living stages of strongyle parasites

TABLE III

The relationship between longevity and Q o$_2$ in infective stages of nematodes

Species	Type of larva	Longevity	Q o$_2$	Author
Strongyloides papillosus	Infective, filariform (free-living)	7 days	28.5	Costello and Grollman (1958)
Nippostrongylus brasiliensis	Infective, filariform (free-living)	30 days	18.4	Rogers (1948)
Haemonchus contortus	Infective, filariform (free-living)	90 days	12.6	Rogers (1948)
Trichinella spiralis	Infective, encysted (parasitic)	5 years	2.35	Stannard *et al.* (1938)
Eustrongylides ignotus	Infective, encysted (parasitic)	4 years	0.56	von Brand (1952)
Ascaris lumbricoides	Infective egg (free-living)	5 years	0.1	Passey and Fairbairn (1955)

of horses are not greatly affected by the pO_2 down to about 30 mm (Bair, 1955). But the infective stages of both *Ascaris lumbricoides* and *Eustrongylides ignotus* have a steeply rising oxygen uptake as the pressure is raised to 50 mm of mercury (Passey and Fairbairn, 1955; von Brand, 1947). The adaptive advantages of these different oxygen relationships cannot be assessed until a more representative group of infective stages has been examined.

If the limited reserve materials in non-parasitic infective stages are to be used effectively, oxidative metabolism would be important; on the other hand, capacity to withstand anaerobic conditions would be necessary for species which develop in faeces and which infect the host *via* the gut. For these reasons the capacity to retain partly oxidized substrates formed during anaerobiosis or to develop an "oxygen debt", might be expected as a feature of infective stages, as in the larvae of *Eustrongylides ignotus* for example (von Brand, 1942).

C. METABOLISM

The infective stages of a few species only have been examined. The results obtained by Passey and Fairbairn (1957) who examined eggs of *Ascaris lumbricoides* are most interesting, not only in relation to parasitism, but in relation to comparative biochemistry generally. Preceding the development of the infective stage, the total lipid fell and the total carbohydrate rose considerably, although lipid still remained the quantitatively important reserve material. Though unequivocal proof of the conversion of fat to carbohydrate was not possible the evidence pointed strongly in this direction. Giovannola (1936), who used relatively crude histochemical methods, studied several species of strongylids. He found that early stages in the life cycle stained heavily for "glycogen" and lightly for "fat". In the infective stages this was reversed.

Carbon dioxide is produced as a result of respiration in infective stages. The respiratory quotient varies from about $1.0 - 0.8$ in eggs of *Ascaris lumbricoides* and *Parascaris equorum* (Fauré-Fremiet, 1913; Huff, 1936; Jaskoski, 1952) to $0.7 - 0.6$ for infective stages of strongyles (Rogers, 1948; Schwabe, 1957). Studies with labelled carbon dioxide showed that it is taken up by eggs of *Ascaris lumbricoides* and appears at the three and four positions in the glycogen and trehalose of the embryo (Passey and Fairbairn, 1957). Evidently fixation by the classical Wood-Werkman reaction, or something similar, takes place in this organism.

Intermediary metabolism of fat and carbohydrate has been examined in some species of free-living infective larvae. Glycolysis and also some features of the Krebs tricarboxylic acid cycle have been demonstrated

(Schwabe, 1957; Costello and Grollman, 1958, 1959). Phosphate esters associated with glycolysis have been identified as have adenosine triphosphate and a labile compound which is probably a phosphagen (Jones, et al., 1955a, 1955b). The detailed work of Costello and Grollman (1958, 1959) indicated that the classical tricarboxylic acid cycle and cytochrome system or something like it was present in the larvae of *Strongyloides papillosus*. The eggs of *Ascaris lumbricoides* do not respond to sensitive tests for cytochrome c and cytochrome oxidase. Nevertheless their respiration is inhibited by low concentrations of hydrogen cyanide and hydrazoic acid, and carbon monoxide inhibits strongly in the dark but not in the light. These results lead Passey and Fairbairn (1957) to suggest that cytochrome oxidase, or a similar enzyme, was the major component of the terminal respiratory enzyme system.

The intermediary metabolism of the parasitic infective larvae of *Trichinella spiralis* follows the classical pattern of glycolysis, tricarboxylic acid cycle and cytochrome system (Goldberg, 1957). Lipids are used actively under aerobic conditions and their oxidation seems to be the major source of energy for mobility in this parasite (von Brand et al., 1952).

D. END-PRODUCTS OF METABOLISM

It seems probable that carbon dioxide and water form a large proportion of the end-products of carbohydrate and fat metabolism in free-living infective larvae under aerobic conditions. Some unusual substances are excreted as end-products, e.g. 1:2-dicarboxylic acids are produced by the filariform larvae of *Nippostrongylus brasiliensis* (Weinstein and Haskins, 1955). Significant results on the products of intermediary metabolism of free-living infective stages under anaerobic conditions are not available. Some work has been done with parasitic infective stages however. Thus under aerobic conditions the end-products formed by *Eustrongylides ignotus* are carbon dioxide and water but in the absence of oxygen organic acids are produced (von Brand, 1938). Larvae of *Trichinella spiralis* produce large amounts of n-valeric acid; as a result of oxidative metabolism it forms 48% of the total acid produced. This figure rises to 85% under anaerobic conditions. In addition to valeric acid, von Brand et al. (1952) found that C_6 and C_2 acids were certainly formed and C_4 and C_3 acids were probably formed. Lactic acid was present in traces only.

Due largely to the work of Weinstein and Haskins (1955) and Haskins and Weinstein (1957a, 1957b, 1957c) the end-products of the nitrogen metabolism of several species of infective stages are known. They show a similarity, whether the infective stage is an egg (*Ascaris lumbricoides*), a free-living third-stage larva (*Nippostrongylus brasiliensis*) or a parasitic larva (*Trichinella spiralis*). It is probable that ammonia is the chief end-product, but a variety of primary aliphatic amines are also produced. *Trichinella spiralis* also excretes some amino acids and peptides which resemble those excreted by some adult parasites (Rogers, 1955).

E. PERMEABILITY AND OSMOREGULATION

The egg shells of infective stages probably all have a low permeability to most substances. The embryos of many species are unaffected even when the eggs are placed in strong salt solution; clearly the passage of water is severely limited. Some gases, but not their related ions, readily penetrate the egg shells of *Ascaris lumbricoides* (Passey and Fairbairn, 1955) and this possibly applies to eggs of other species as well.

The mechanisms of osmoregulation in the embryo are unknown. There are considerable changes in the volume of the embryo during development and the concentration of the vitelline fluid may also change. In free-living third-stage infective larvae one mechanism of osmoregulation, the pulsating excretory ampulla, has been recognized. In larvae of *Ancylostoma caninum* and *Nippostrongylus brasiliensis* the rate of pulsation is generally inversely proportional to the concentration of sucrose or sodium chloride between 0 to 1.5% in the medium (Eisma, 1932; Raven and Schuurmans Stekhoven, 1934; Weinstein, 1952; Fig. 2). The

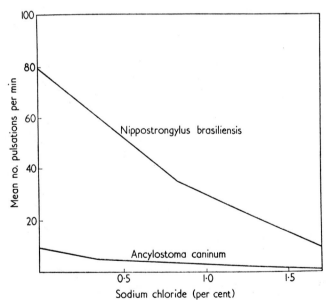

Fig. 2. The activity of the excretory ampullae of infective larvae of *Nippostrongylus brasiliensis* and *Ancylostoma caninum* in solutions of sodium chloride of different concentrations (adapted from Rogers, 1961, after Weinstein, 1952).

amount of fluid transferred from the organism to the medium is considerable. In distilled water larvae of *Nippostrongylus brasiliensis* excrete a volume of fluid equal to their own volume in 10.8 h; for larvae of *Ancylostoma caninum* the same task takes 74.9 h (Weinstein, 1952).

The loss of water from some infective larvae is very rapid. Thus the filariform larvae of *Strongyloides papillosus* placed in a drop of water were dead within 5 min after the evaporation of the water at 22°C. Strongyle larvae, however, are generally more resistant, especially *Nematodirus* spp. and *Ostertagia* spp. (Kates, 1950). Infective larvae of *Haemonchus contortus*, which under field conditions are less resistant to drought than many other species, will survive in balanced saline solution ranging in concentration from 40 to 120 mM (Stoll, 1940). Some parasitic infective larvae are equally robust; larvae of *Eustrongylides ignotus* survive in solutions containing sodium chloride from 85 to 170 mM. They lived up to 16 days in solutions containing 510 mM sodium chloride (von Brand and Simpson, 1942). It is not known if resistance to this range of osmotic pressures is due to impermeability of the cuticle or to an unusual capacity to carry out metabolic processes independent of the concentration of tissue fluids.

VI. THE BEHAVIOUR OF INFECTIVE STAGES

The probability that infection will occur may be strongly affected by the behaviour of infective larvae. This is not always obvious however, especially in species which, like *Ascaris lumbricoides*, enter the host confined within the egg membranes. Nevertheless, the behaviour of the larva immediately after hatching probably plays a significant role in its location and establishment within the host. Immediately after infection of the sheep, the third-stage larvae of certain nematodes become established in a regular order along the small intestine (Tetley, 1937) but the behaviour which leads to this is unknown.

In this section we discuss some examples in which the behaviour of the infective stages is clearly important in gaining access to the host. We do not propose to review exhaustively all aspects of behaviour in nematodes, because many aspects of this have been covered in a careful and critical review by Wallace (1961a).

The published work on the behaviour of nematodes, in so far as it is related to infection, is not sufficiently extensive to lead to any general concepts. For this reason we have considered behaviour of plant and animal nematodes separately, although we agree with Wallace (1961a) that this approach hinders the study of nematodes as a group and perpetuates an artificial and undesirable dichotomy in the study of parasitism.

G

A. THE BEHAVIOUR OF TRICHOSTRONGYLES ON PASTURE

A number of nematodes of the order Strongyloidea are parasitic in the intestinal tract of herbivores. Eggs pass to the exterior in the faeces, hatch, and the juveniles attain the third or infective stage enclosed within the partially moulted sheath of the second-stage larva. In order to infect the host it must migrate from the faecal mass onto the surrounding herbage on which the host grazes, and it is this migratory behaviour which is of special interest here.

Very little work has been done on the actual migration out of the faecal mass deposited by animals like sheep and rabbits, and it is often assumed, or stated explicitly that the first- and second-stage larvae do not take part in this migration. However, if faecal pellets from sheep are enclosed within glass tubes, some first-stage larvae and many in the second stage do migrate (Silverman and Campbell, 1958). Probably this can happen whenever there is sufficient water in the pellet to allow the larvae to move readily. Silverman and Campbell suggested that migration of first-stage larvae could be explained on the basis of random movement, but considered that the migration of comparatively large numbers of second-stage larvae may represent a real taxis. However, it is also possible that the migration of the second stage is dependent upon random movement. First-stage larvae of *Haemonchus contortus* move quite differently from second-stage larvae; they are less active and do not swim readily (Veglia, 1915). Consequently, other things being equal, they would be unlikely to move as far or as fast as second-stage larva. The situation may be similar to that in *Aphelenchoides ritzema-bosi*. The juveniles of this species with a mean length of 230μ, have smaller wave frequencies, produce smaller propulsive forces and consequently have lower speeds than juveniles 550μ long or adults nearly 900μ long (Wallace, 1960a).

However, although all stages may migrate from faeces, it seems that the ensheathed infective larva does this more readily than preceding stages. The reason for this is unknown, although it may be connected with the inability of the infective stage to feed.

For infection to take place larvae must not only migrate from the faecal mass but also climb onto those parts of the herbage which are eaten by the host.

The presence of larvae on herbage has been attributed to an innate tendency to migrate upwards, often called "negative geotropism" or "negative geotaxis". Many workers have shown (see Croften, 1949a) that the movement of larvae is modified by such factors as temperature, humidity, light intensity and type of herbage, but reactions to these factors were supposed to be superimposed upon a fundamental behaviour called "negative geotaxis". In a series of elegant experiments Crofton,

(1949a, 1954) showed that larvae tend to move at random, and that vertical migration on herbage could be described in terms of normal larval movements without reference to inherent patterns of behaviour such as geotaxis. The places on herbage where larvae tended to accumulate were those where climatic changes were least.

Probably there is also extensive lateral movement of larvae but little information is available. Lateral migration of infective larvae from pats of cattle dung has been described (Tarshis, 1958; Durie, 1961). For this moisture is essential (Roberts *et al.*, 1952; Durie, 1961), a condition which probably applies to other types of faeces. The "moisture characteristic" has been found to supply most of the information on physical properties of soil needed for the study of movement of nematodes (Wallace, 1961a) and application of these principles to movement within and from faeces, especially faeces with pronounced crumb structure, may be profitable.

Many factors on pasture might be expected to influence the random movement of larvae and thus may be important in determining their location. Temperature, moisture and light have received most attention, but of these it is probable that moisture is the most important. Although some specialized stages, like the dauer larvae of *Diplogaster* spp. can move on a dry surface (Bovien, 1937) most nematodes can move in films of water only. In spite of the early recognition of the importance of soil structure and the capillary film in affecting the movement of infective larvae (Payne, 1923a), little attention has been given to the mobility of larvae in soil or on leaves. This is surprising because an understanding of mobility seems to be fundamental to a study of the effects of other components. The subject has been extensively studied with plant nematodes (Wallace, 1961a) and it is clear that the mobility of eelworms in soil is influenced by their size, by the moisture content and by the particle size of the soil.

Probably the most extensive investigations of movements of infective larvae on pasture have been made by Rogers (1940b), Crofton (1949a) and Rees (1950). Their results have shown that a rise in temperature above about 13°C leads to increased activity and consequently more larvae tend to appear on herbage. If the temperature is too high, migration is reduced, presumably because evaporation increases. At low temperatures there is little or no migration. However, activity of larvae is not necessarily related in a direct way to temperature. At high (45°C) and low (5°C) temperatures *Haemonchus contortus* may be more active than at intermediate temperatures (Rogers, 1940b) and the direction of vertical migration may vary with temperature (Buckley, 1940). These results are open to some criticism however, and need verification (Crofton, 1954).

Migration is favoured by moisture but it seems that the amount of water which is best for migration is not the same for all species. *H. contortus* moves more readily under drier conditions (i.e. thin moisture films) than *Ostertagia* spp. Migration of all species seems to be retarded by very high humidities. There are also differences between species in their ability to migrate from wet soil onto grass.

Larvae tend to migrate upwards when the light intensity is low. *Strongyloides papillosus* is an exception to this (Rogers, 1940b), although in these experiments failure to migrate may be an indication of poor mobility on soil and grass, rather than a failure to respond to low light intensities. Rees (1950) has suggested that the primary stimulus for vertical migration of *H. contortus* is light at a particular range of intensity. This conclusion is supported by the observation that the greatest numbers of larvae are recovered in the early morning and evening (Rogers, 1940b; Rees, 1950; Nekipelova, 1956). But these diurnal migrations might also result from the effect of temperature on moisture films (Nekipelova, 1956) although such an explanation could not be generally applicable because Rees recorded maximum numbers of larvae on pasture morning and evening, even on days of continuous rain.

The greatest number of infective larvae on herbage were found near the bottom of the blades of grass. It is this part of the pasture which exhibits least change of temperature and humidity (Crofton, 1949a). Crofton's study of the climate of pastures in England has been especially valuable, and similar studies are badly needed under other climatic conditions, especially in dryer regions when there is no "mat" between foliage and soil.

Because of the importance placed on the role of light intensity in migration, it is important to examine more closely studies which have been made on the reactions of infective larvae to light. A number of experiments show that such species as *Ostertagia circumcincta*, *Bunostomum phlebotomum* and *Trichostrongylus* spp. are apparently attracted to light (Monnig, 1930; Furman, 1944; Sprent, 1946b). This behaviour has been called positive phototropism, or more correctly, positive phototaxis. On the other hand, using a different technique, Furman failed to find any evidence that *O. circumcincta* reacted to light. Other species which are also apparently not influenced by light are *Trichostrongylus axei* and *Dictyocaulus viviparous* (Stewart and Douglas, 1938; Soliman, 1953).

Many of the experiments are difficult to interpret and moreover, measurements of light intensity are rarely given. Furthermore, it seems that too little attention has been paid to the effect of heat from the light source. Thus it has been shown that some larvae which infect the host by penetrating the skin do not respond to light (Parker and Haley,

1960; Sasa *et al.*, 1960). When heat filters are interposed between the light source and the larvae, the migration becomes random. The activation of *Strongyloides agoutii* which has been attributed to light (Reesal, 1951) may be a reaction to heat. Although these studies were not made with ensheathed infective larvae of strongyles, it does suggest that a new investigation of the role of light intensity in larval migration is warranted.

B. BEHAVIOUR AND INFECTION VIA THE SKIN

The behaviour of larvae which penetrate the skin seems to be different from those which must be eaten by the host. In many the capacity to migrate onto pasture or herbage seems to be limited. Infective larvae of *Bunostomum phlebotomum* are found on the surface of the faecal mass and probably penetrate the skin of the host when dung adheres to the animal's feet and sides (Sprent 1946a, 1946b). Even if larvae of *Strongyloides papillosus* migrate away from faeces their ability to migrate onto herbage is not great (Rogers, 1940b).

Infective larvae tend to climb to the edges of decaying vegetation or to the top of prominent particles of soil. Their behaviour has been closely studied by the earlier workers (Augustine, 1922b) and more recently by Sasa and his co-workers (1960). Larvae of *Ancylostoma caninum*, *Nippostrongylus brasiliensis*, *Trichostrongylus orientalis* and *Necator americanus* all tend to stand on their tails in an erect posture. But infective larvae of *Ancylostoma duodenale* and *Strongyloides stercoralis* rarely do this. The ability to assume the erect posture is determined by the depth of the moisture film.

When in the erect posture larvae may be still, or else they may wave the anterior end from side to side. When there are clusters of individuals, as is common, the clusters move in a rhythmic fashion "like the flame of a candle". This movement is a reaction to the concentration of carbon dioxide about the worms. The concentration of carbon dioxide in air (about 0.03%) is normally too low to elicit this response but a few larvae respond at 0.16% and all respond at 2.88% carbon dioxide in air, or to expired breath. Those species which do not normally assume an erect posture are also activated by carbon dioxide apparently in a similar way. The effects of light, vibration and heat were also examined; only heat caused activity and this was not of the type associated with carbon dioxide. Infective larvae of *Bunostomum phlebotomum* move vigorously and stretch out into space when breathed upon (Sprent, 1946a); probably this is a reaction to carbon dioxide also.

Sasa *et al.* (1960) have pointed out that many parasitic mites and insects are activated by carbon dioxide in the same way as these nematodes. They believe that the reaction is a response to the presence of a host and increases the chance of contact between the host and parasite.

Thus species which infect the host by the penetration of skin behave differently from those which infect the host by the mouth. They do not climb onto herbage readily but tend to stay in close association with faeces, or when the faecal mass disintegrates, with the soil. In this situation the host is not likely to ingest them, a factor of considerable importance because many of these infective stages die in the alimentary tract. Larvae tend to climb onto projections, and as a response to the approach of a suitable host, they become active and extended. The sheath, which might be expected to be a barrier to rapid skin penetration, may be lost before a suitable host appears, or as soon as contact is made.

C. THE BEHAVIOUR OF NEMATODES INFECTING PLANTS

So far as the aerial systems of plants are concerned, there is little information on the mechanisms of behaviour which are associated with infection. Two principal factors are concerned in the infection of chrysanthemum leaves by *Aphelenchoides ritzema-bosi* (Wallace, 1959a). These are, first a tendency on part of the nematode to migrate upwards in what has been described as a negatively geotropic response. Second, the nematodes cannot enter the stomata until the water film is very thin. As a film becomes thinner movement becomes slower and invasion occurs when the speed of the nematode is very low.

Considerably more attention has been given to the behaviour of nematodes in the vicinity of roots, and this has been discussed in Section VIII. Larvae of many species aggregate about roots, especially near wounds. Over distances of the order of a few centimetres these aggregations are probably determined by concentration gradients of substances released from the root itself.

Fourth-stage larvae of *Ditylenchus dipsaci* appear to respond directly to gradients of both temperature and moisture. Response to moisture was observed in gradients of 1% over 10 cms (Wallace, 1961b). In sand particles of different sizes arranged in a gradient, the larvae aggregated in the region of the smaller particles. This is probably a simple orthokinesis.

Several species are affected by electric currents. For example *Ditylenchus dipsaci* will move to the cathode in potential gradients of 30 to 200 mV per mm, an effect which is independent of products of electrolysis (Jones, 1960). Apparently this response is not orthokinetic. Jones noted that, when orientation was taking place, the heads of larvae moved through a wide arc. Movement became rhythmic and spread to the hinder part of the body which straightened out as the nematode began to swim freely toward the cathode. Presumably movements like this would be modified in the soil by the physical structure. The electrical potentials developed by living roots are similar to those which characterize the threshold of response in *Heterodera schachtii* and *D. dipsaci*. This observation is important because it has been suggested (Bird, 1959b) that potential gradients about roots attract larvae (Section VIII).

Substances which attract larvae, such as gibberellic acid, reducing agents and carbon dioxide (Bird, 1959b, 1960; Klinger, 1959, 1961) do not appear to have been studied in gradients and indeed their measurement in gradients may be difficult. Glutamic acid attracts larvae of *Meloidogyne* spp., although the effect is transitory (Bird, 1959b). However, neither in gradients of this substance nor in gradients of aspartic acid, could a well defined effect on *D. dipsaci* be established (Jones, 1960).

It is not sufficient to demonstrate attraction along a gradient without considering the effect which soil conditions may have on the gradient itself, as well as on the capacity of the nematode to respond. Information is needed on these subjects as both Jones (1960) and Wallace (1961a) have indicated. Further, as Wallace has also shown, there is little information on sensory reception in nematodes, although the histology of possible receptors has been examined and functions have been suggested.

D. PERIODICITY OF MICROFILARIAE

Nematodes of the order Filaroidea release embryos or microfilariae into the tissue or blood stream, from which they are ingested by blood-sucking arthropods. Development to the next infective stage then takes place. Infection of a new host is accomplished when the vector feeds. The microfilariae escape and enter the host through the wound made by the mouth parts of the vector, so that infection of new hosts is thus dependent upon the presence of vectors carrying infective stages. But the behaviour of microfilariae in the reservoir host is important in determining which species of arthropod will become a vector because the numbers of microfilariae in the peripheral blood undergo regular fluctuations. For example, the simian strain of *Loa loa* has a nocturnal periodicity and the vectors, *Chrysops langi* and *C. centurionis*, bite in the evening and early part of the night. They dwell in the forest canopy and under natural conditions do not bite man. However, the human parasite has a diurnal rhythm and the vectors are *C. silacea* and *C. dimidiata*, which have a close association with man. Thus, the differences between the behaviour of microfilariae of *L. loa* in human and simian hosts has led to an effective ecological isolation between the two strains. The reservoir infection in the monkey is without significance for infection in man (Duke 1957, 1958, 1959). Many hypotheses have been advanced to explain periodicity of microfilariae but for none of these is experimental proof available.

VII. The Survival of Infective Stages
A. INFECTIVE LARVAE OF ANIMAL PARASITES

1. *Ensheathed Infective Larvae*

Survival of the infective larvae of strongyles on pasture is of great importance to the husbandman. This aspect has been investigated extensively and the earlier literature has been summarized by Kates (1950). More recent papers on this subject are those of Goldberg and Rubin (1956), Drudge *et al.* (1958), Goldberg and Lucker (1959) and Wertejuk (1959).

These investigations commonly use pasture which has been contaminated either directly by heavily infected animals or by the even distribution of dung collected from infected animals. Survival of infective larvae is then assessed either by grazing for a short period with parasite-free animals, or by the isolation of larvae from samples of pastures. As a result, infective stages of some of the more common parasitic nematodes of domestic stock can be judged according to their relative abilities to survive under various types of climate (Kates, 1950). For example, infective larvae of *Haemonchus contortus* are unlikely to survive more than 6 months on pasture over a wide range of climatic conditions. *Ostertagia* spp. survive better at lower mean temperatures than *H. contortus*. *Trichostrongylus* spp. are similar to *H. contortus* so far as summer conditions are concerned, but are more resistant to adverse conditions in the cooler months. Sometimes this information can be valuable for planning the management of stock particularly under circumstances where there is a very cold winter and animals are housed. More usually, the sort of information gained from these experiments has at best a local application and probably makes little contribution to our understanding of the ecology of the organism in the wider sense.

On the other hand a combination of observations on survival and experimentation may provide fundamental information. An example of this is provided by recent work with *Nematodirus* spp. Members of this genus become infective while enclosed within the eggshell. The developing egg and the infective larva, whether within the egg or free, are unharmed by conditions which would kill infective stages of many other species (Turner, 1953; Poole, 1956; Marquardt *et al.*, 1959). Eggs of two species, *N. filicollis* and *N. bathus*, are deposited on pasture in spring, but larvae are not found until autumn and then in relatively small numbers, mainly of *N. filicollis*. Eggs containing either infective larvae or earlier stages can survive over winter and larvae are recovered in large numbers in the spring. Eggs of both species apparently require a period of exposure to cold in order to hatch when the temperature rises (Thomas and Stevens, 1960). The appearance of large numbers of infective larvae coincides with the presence of susceptible lambs.

2. Survival of Larvae which Penetrate the Skin

Infective larvae of some of those species which infect the host by penetration of the skin are not especially resistant to adverse conditions. *Strongyloides* spp. are susceptible to dessication (Cordi and Otto, 1934; Reesal, 1951; Turner, 1961) and so are infective larvae of *Stephanurus dentatus* (Alicata, 1935). Even when conditions are favourable infective larvae of *Necator americanus* probably survive for a few weeks only (Beaver, 1953). This is unlikely to be disadvantageous however, because these species are usually found in warm moist climates. *Bunostomum* is less limited because larvae can be revived after drying on a slide for 5 days and after drying in faeces for 14 days. Its chances of survival might be better than in the other species, but infection can only take place if the dung, in which they are found, is sufficiently moist to stick to the host's skin (Sprent, 1946b).

3. Significance of the Second-stage Sheath in the Survival of Ensheathed Larvae

It is often implied that the second-stage sheath has a "protective" effect on ensheathed larvae, although this has not been demonstrated in experiments on desiccation, for example. The sheath itself is permeable to water (Rogers and Sommerville, 1960) and seems unlikely to prevent the larva from becoming desiccated.

Probably it was thought that the sheath had a protective effect because infective larvae of *Strongyloides* which lack a sheath die quickly if dried, whereas other infective larvae can survive under comparable conditions. But ensheathed larvae of *Nector americanus* live as long as exsheathed larvae in the warm wet tropical and semi-tropical regions in which they are usually found (Augustine, 1922a). However the sheath gives some protection against formalin. Sometimes larvae which have been subjected to extreme conditions which reduce their vitality will discard the sheath (Mönnig, 1930; Prasad, 1959), so that interpretation of the death of exsheathed larvae should be treated with caution unless their previous history is known.

4. Survival of Infective and Pre-infective Stages

Survival of the non-feeding ensheathed infective larva is commonly said to be better than the second stage and most certainly better than

G*

the first. This has been noted in *Dictyocaulus* spp. (Soliman, 1953; Rose, 1955; Schanzel, 1958) in relation to temperature and desiccation and in *Trichostrongylus* spp. (Mönnig, 1930). The advanced second-stage of *Haemonchus contortus* is a critical one in the life cycle. Once it is attained larvae can survive at temperatures which kill earlier stages (Berberian and Mizelle, 1957). Species which have a resistant infective stage may also be resistant in the other free-living stages. *Trichostrongylus retortae-formis* eggs are apparently resistant to desiccation (Crofton, 1949b). Furthermore, the hatching of eggs is inhibited by high concentrations of solutes (Wilson, 1958), which may also enhance survival in drought. Pre-infective stages of this species can be frozen without apparent harm and the first-stage larvae will develop to the infective stage at 5°C. Once eggs hatch, subsequent development is said to be "fairly normal" even under adverse conditions (Prasad, 1959; Gupta, 1961).

When the infective stage is itself a first-stage larva, it becomes a re-sistant stage. First-stage larvae of *Muellerius capillaris* are infective for molluscs, and Rose (1957) has shown that about half of a population exposed to freezing temperatures can survive for 1 week. At room temperature, about half of a population exposed to 50% relative humid-ity can survive for 6 weeks. Similar conditions are rapidly fatal for the first-stage larvae of *Dictyocaulus* spp., which are non-infective (Rose, 1955).

5. *Effect of Intermediate Hosts on Survival*

Intermediate hosts protect infective larvae from desiccation and sun-light. Infective larvae of *Metastrongylus apri*, a lungworm of pigs, can survive as long as the intermediate hosts, which are earthworms. In nature the longevity of these earthworms is not known exactly but is probably of the order of years rather than months (Rose, 1959). When isolated from earthworms larvae live well in the cold, but cannot resist desiccation.

B. THE SURVIVAL OF INFECTIVE EGGS

There is an extensive literature on survival of infective eggs, much of which relates to *Ascaris lumbricoides*, but detailed quantitative data on survival of eggs of this species in relation to temperature and moisture seem to be lacking. The developing egg is immediately affected by lack of moisture (Seamster, 1950) but the infective egg is probably more tolerant and is adversely affected only by very dry conditions (Germans, 1954; Gudzhabidze, 1961). The infective egg can survive in soil at −8°C, but is readily killed after a few hours at 45°C. Soil type has a profound influence on survival (Brown, 1927; Beaver, 1952), probably because it affects soil moisture. Eggs in clay or loam soils can survive for long periods even in the absence of shade, but in sand they are rapidly killed. The literature contains many instances in which eggs have survived for years in garden soils (Müller, 1953). Similar remarks can be made about eggs of the genus *Trichuris*, which seem particularly able to survive under conditions of extreme cold (Nakladova, 1956; Hill, 1957). Infective eggs of *Neoascaris vitulorum* are said to be "resistant to desiccation", although their time of survival on pasture seems to be only of the order of 70 days (Refuerzo and Albis Jimenez, 1954).

Protection from the harmful effects of ultra-violet radiation may be achieved by substances in the shell in both *Ascaris* and *Trichuris* (Nolf, 1932; Miretski, 1952), although under direct sunlight it might be expected that the effects of dryness and heat would become important.

Eggs of *Enterobius vermicularis* are often found in household dust which might be expected to be dry. Survival of eggs at low humidities is greatest only when temperatures are also low. At any particular temperature, survival is greatest when conditions are most humid. The best temperatures for survival under conditions of maximum moisture were 3° to 5°C (Jones and Jacobs, 1941).

Although the data cited are not extensive, it seems clear that infective eggs are capable of surviving under conditions which many organisms could not tolerate. In this respect they are probably superior to ensheathed larvae, but the latter have the advantage of being mobile. Moisture seems to be a very critical factor, but there is little or no information on the way in which "desiccation" affects the egg (Fairbairn, 1957) or how the egg is protected from water loss.

C. THE SURVIVAL OF PLANT-PARASITIC NEMATODES

1. *Species in which Infection is not Confined to One Stage*

Many nematodes parasitic on plants do not have specialized infective stages. Nevertheless, there is great variation between species in their ability to survive in the absence of the host plant. *Hemicycliophora arenaria* cannot survive for more than 4 or 5 weeks in the absence of food (van Gundy, 1959) and although a few adult *Rotylenchus buxophilus* may survive in the absence of the host for as long as 8 months, 98% may die within 16 weeks (Golden, 1956). *Radopholus similis* did not survive for more than 6 months buried with citrus roots (Birchfield, 1957), apparently because the feeder roots died. These were the sole source of food and were not replaced until the nematodes had perished.

Other species which do not have a specialized infective stage may have a "resistant" stage. Second-stage female larvae of *Tylenchulus semipenetrans* are by far the most persistent stage of the life cycle and will persist in fallow land for more than 3 years (Baines, 1950). Females can produce viable eggs in the absence of males, so that failure of the males to survive as long as the females is no disadvantage (van Gundy, 1958). Adults and fourth-stage larvae of *Aphelenchoides ritzema-bosi* survive in dried leaves, sometimes for many years (Wallace, 1960a; Bovien, 1937). All stages can infect the chrysanthemum leaf, although it is the adult which is chiefly responsible for infection. Both in this species and in *T. semipenetrans*, the "resistant stage" is a juvenile or young adult which can live for long periods without food and in which development is suspended. Obviously these larvae are the only ones which can retain infectivity in the absence of the host. Under ordinary conditions the resistant stage is not the only one capable of initiating infection.

2. *Cryptobiosis*

Some species have extraordinary powers of resistance to desiccation and to cold. For example 20% of a population of the bulb and stem nematode *Ditylenchus dipsaci* revived 5 years after lyophilization at −80°C and subsequent storage at room temperature (Bosker, 1960). A majority of second-stage larvae of *Anguina tritici* were alive after 21 years in dry glass tubes which had been sealed (Limber, 1962). Under more variable conditions, such as encountered in the soil, *D. dipsaci* may persist more than 2 years (Lewis and Mai, 1960). The ability to survive at extremes of desiccation and low temperature has been called anabiosis, although it now seems that the term cryptobiosis (Keilin, 1959) is preferable. This condition is found amongst plant and soil nematodes, especially those parasitic on aerial parts of plants (Steiner, 1939). Although cryptobiosis has been recognized in nematodes since Needham's work with *Anguina tritici* in 1743 (see Keilin, 1959), little is known about the phenomenon. Pre-adults of ·*D. dipsaci* can be recovered, in a state of cryptobiosis, as nematode "wool" from the basal region of infected narcissus bulbs (Hastings and Newton, 1934), so that sources of material in large quantities are more readily available than for many nematodes, but it appears that little work on the physiology of this state has been done.

It has been suggested that all stages of an undescribed sp. of *Ditylenchus* can participate in cryptobiosis (Cairns, 1952). Apparently eggs and second-stage larvae are resistant to adverse conditions, but do not survive as well as later stages and it seems unlikely that they represent cryptobiosis as Keilin defines it.

In spite of the impressive records for longevity of cryptobiotic larvae, mortality may be high when the ground is frozen (Lewis and Mai, 1960), probably because moisture impairs longevity at low temperatures (Hastings and Newton, 1934; Limber, 1962). There can be no doubt however, that cryptobiosis has considerable significance in the survival of *D. dipsaci* and of other species in which it occurs.

3. *Survival in the genus Heterodera*

In the genus *Heterodera*, infective larvae are not only enclosed within the egg membranes, but also most eggs are enclosed within a cyst formed by the body wall of the female. It is not surprising therefore, that under some circumstances cysts which have remained in the soil for many years are still viable. For example, cysts of *Heterodera schachtii* may contain viable eggs for at least 6 years under field conditions (Thorne, 1923). Once larvae have left the cyst their survival in the soil is relatively brief. About 50% of *Heterodera rostochiensis* larvae died within 7 weeks after leaving the cyst (Den Ouden, 1960) and the rate of decay of *H. schachtii* larvae is about 34% per week in soil with a moisture content corresponding to field capacity (Shepherd, 1960). But under some conditions a few may remain alive and infective for as long as 12 months (Golden and Shafer, 1960).

Cysts of *H. major* are apparently susceptible to desiccation (Winslow, 1955; Hesling, 1956), although there is some disagreement about the actual amount of dessication which is lethal (Duggan, 1960).

H. rostochiensis is apparently very resistant to drying, *H. schachtii* less resistant, while *H. punctata* and *H. glycines*, like *H. major*, are comparatively susceptible (Christie, 1959). However, we have not found any data in which these species are compared under the same conditions of temperature and humidity. As an example of what is meant by *H. rostochiensis* being "very resistant" to drying, it has been shown that "air dry" cysts were not affected by storage for 6 months at a variety of temperatures, except for the highest, 37°C. On the other hand, survival in "moist soil" decreased as the temperatures increased (Mai, 1952). Very low relative humidity (1.5%) may reduce viability at moderate temperatures (24°C and "room temperatures") but not at lower temperatures (4°C) (Mai and Mechow, 1952). Böhm (1956) has shown that cysts were little affected by exposure for 2 years in soil at 50–80% relative humidity, with temperatures ranging between 5°C and 30°C. "Standing water" greatly reduced viability. In contrast to this cysts have been shown to survive in water for 15 months (Oostenbrink, 1950). It is difficult to compare these results, because the conditions under which they were obtained were not always closely defined.

Some species of *Heterodera*, in particular *H. rostochiensis*, do not hatch as readily in the winter as at other times of the year. This is referred to as "dormancy" and it is presumably an adaptation which aids survival by allowing eggs to hatch at the most favourable periods of the year.

Nothing is known of the physiology of this process and its existence has been disputed. Some of the more recent workers who found evidence for winter dormancy are Feldmesser and Fassuliotis (1950), Lownsbery (1951), and Winslow (1956). No evidence of this phenomenon is found in *H. schachtii*, but it is marked in *H. cruciferae* and *H. carotae* and partial dormancy has been noted in three other species. It is not certain whether the phenomenon should be regarded as inherent in the physiology of the worm or induced by earlier environmental conditions. Apparently it is not entirely dependent upon immediate environmental conditions, but some workers have failed to find any evidence whatsoever for the existence of dormancy (Fenwick and Reid, 1953; Ellenby, 1955b). Their results have been questioned by Cunningham (1960) who found evidence for a dormancy period over 'the northern winter from mid-August to late February. He suggested that failure to demonstrate dormancy could be explained by collection of cysts outside the period when dormancy set in (Fenwick and Reid, 1953) or by prolonged storage (Ellenby, 1955b). He concluded that dormancy is not inherent in the seasonal hatch cycle of *H. rostochiensis*, but is induced by soil conditions in late summer and autumn. The nature of these changes has yet to be defined, but it is possible that a mechanism similar to diapause in insects may be involved.

4. *Survival in the genus Meloidogyne*

Delayed hatching does not seem to occur in the genus *Meloidogyne* except for limited periods occasioned by dryness and cold (Christie, 1959, page 63). Usually there are several generations per year, more in the tropics and fewer in temperate regions. Thorne (1961, page 327) quotes unpublished work by Allen who showed that *M. hapla* overwinters as third-stage larvae on strawberry roots. Eggs and infective larvae of this species seem to be more "cold hardy" than those of *M. incognita acrita* or *M. javanica* (Bergeson, 1959) but they are less tolerant of higher temperatures than are those of *M. j. javanica* (Doulton, 1960). However, there were big differences in thermal tolerance between three separate populations of *M. j. javanica*. Both desiccation and excessive moisture reduce survival and desiccation has been used as an effective basis for controlling populations (Peacock, 1957). Eggs of all these species seem to be somewhat more resistant to adverse conditions than larvae.

D. GENERAL COMMENTS ON SURVIVAL STUDIES

Most papers on the survival of nematodes have been very difficult to interpret. In many instances their significance is probably limited to the time and place in which the observations were made, and for this reason collation of the results other than in a very general way has proved difficult.

There are several reasons why this is so. Measurements of such components of the environment as light intensity, temperature, availability of oxygen, relative humidity and saturation deficit are sometimes not made, even when the experiment is directly concerned with them. Occasionally one component will be measured and another left to vary in an unknown way. The significance of measurements of temperature and other factors is increased if they are made as close as possible to the organism, but there are some instances in which their effects are detailed when the actual measurements probably have little relationship to the micro-climate of the animal. There are good arguments for studying the effect of environmental components on infective stages in their natural habitats, for example soil or faeces, but this should not be made without some appreciation of the ways in which these sorts of environments can probably modify and complicate the effects of such factors as moisture content or temperature.

Unfortunately, many of the results on survival are quoted as "such and such survive as long as x days". But the time required to kill all animals depends upon the size of the sample and indeed, could not be measured precisely unless the samples were infinitely large. Results expressed in these terms would seem to be of limited significance, but recourse is rarely made to probit analysis, which gives an estimate of the mean duration of life under the particular treatment.

Although studies on survival and development of infective stages have been made for many years, much of this work has been done without reference to ecological thought and experimentation on similar work with other organisms. Parasitology would have been richer had this barrier been broken down.

VIII. The Process of Infection

Infectiveness is one of the features which distinguish parasites from other sorts of animals. But as yet the physiology of the process of infection has been studied in few parasites only and no broad generalizations can be made. Indeed, it is doubtful if generalizations concerning the mechanisms of infection embracing parasitism in the Nematoda generally will ever be possible. There seems little doubt that adaptations to parasitism have occurred independently in many groups of nematodes so that the process of infection may vary considerably.

It is possible that similarities in the process of infection among different parasites might be related to the site at which infection occurs rather than the phylogenetic relationships of the parasites. Thus infection *via* the gut may in principle be similar for some protozoan and metazoan parasites. This is because factors operating in the process of infection must also provide the signal by which the infective stage "recognizes" an appropriate site at which infection may take place. It is possible then that the characteristic features of the invertebrate or vertebrate alimentary canal may play a similar role in infection with a variety of parasites (Rogers, 1961a).

With these thoughts in mind we have divided the discussion on the process of infection into three sections: infection of animals *via* the gut, infection of animals *via* the body surface, and infection of plants.

A. THE INFECTION OF ANIMALS VIA THE GUT

Most of the work on this subject has been carried out with eggs of ascarids or larvae of trichostrongylids which are the infective stages of parasites of vertebrates (Sommerville, 1954, 1957; Rogers and Sommerville, 1957, 1960; Rogers, 1958, 1960; Fairbairn, 1960b; Taylor and Whitlock, 1960). The results obtained with these organisms indicate that the process of infection with these parasites takes place in two stages. In the first of these stages the host provides a stimulus which acts on the infective embryo or larva. This causes the secretion of a substance which attacks the egg shell or the sheath.

1. *The Stimulus for Infection via the Gut*

The chief factor in the stimulus provided by the host seems to be carbon dioxide or a related compound. But various other factors such as the Eh, pH (independent of its effect on the Eh or on the concentration of carbon dioxide and its derivatives) and the presence of salts may become important under certain conditions.

a. The effect of carbon dioxide. It seems that dissolved gaseous carbon dioxide or undissociated carbonic acid or both these substances are the active agents in the stimulus. Bicarbonate alone in the medium is not sufficient; if carbon dioxide is present in the gas phase in appropriate concentrations, whether added bicarbonate is present or not, the stimulus will, in some degree, be effective. This suggests that it is dissolved gaseous carbon dioxide or the unionized acid which is important. This seems reasonable because egg shells of *Ascaris lumbricoides* are permeable to gases but not to related ions. It may be dissolved gaseous carbon dioxide or undissociated carbonic acid or both of these substances which are active, but it is not possible for us to distinguish between them. Here we will simply refer to undissociated carbonic acid or $[H_2CO_3]$ as including both these components.

Taylor and Whitlock (1960) found that 0.2M buffered solutions of propionic, butyric, *iso*butyric, valeric, *iso*valeric and α-methylbutyric acids above pH 3 were effective in causing exsheathment in the absence of added carbon dioxide. Though Taylor and Whitlock referred to a similarity between carbonic acid and these acids they also considered the possibility that their actions were different.

In bicarbonate-carbon dioxide buffers containing a reducing agent Rogers (1958, 1960) found that for the hatching of eggs of *Ascaris lumbricoides* the optimum $[H_2CO_3]$ was about $1 \times 10^{-3}M$ to $2 \times 10^{-3}M$ at pH 6 and 37°C. As the pH was raised the effective $[H_2CO_3]$ fell and the range of concentrations which caused hatching was greatly reduced. Thus at pH 7.3 the optimum $[H_2CO_3]$ was about $0.2 \times 10^{-3}M$ to $0.3 \times 10^{-3}M$ and at pH 8 the $[H_2CO_3]$ necessary for hatching the eggs fell to very low levels. Somewhat similar results were obtained with infective eggs of *Toxocara mystax* and *Ascaridia galli*, but the results, especially with *A. galli*, varied greatly with different batches of eggs (Rogers, 1961b). It is notable that with infective eggs there was an upper as well as a lower limit to the effective concentrations of undissociated carbonic acid. In this respect the eggs differed from most species of larvae which have been examined.

Bicarbonate-carbon dioxide buffers containing a reducing agent stimulated the exsheathment of at least 50% of infective larvae of *Trichostrongylus axei* in 3 h at 37°C and pH 7.3 when the $[H_2CO_3]$ was above $0.5 \times 10^{-3}M$. For larvae of *Haemonchus contortus* more than three times this concentration of carbonic acid was needed to obtain a similar effect (Rogers, 1960). As with infective eggs the $[H_2CO_3]$ necessary for exsheathment increased greatly as the pH was decreased. With the larvae of *Trichostrongylus colubriformis* which normally exsheath in the acidic environment of the stomach the optimum $[H_2CO_3]$ was about $5 \times 10^{-3}M$ in a medium of which the principal component was 0.025 M hydrochloric acid.

Taylor and Whitlock (1960) found that a high proportion of the larvae of *Haemonchus contortus* exsheathed in solutions of a variety of salts when carbon dioxide was present. The hydrogen ion concentrations reached in these solutions have not been stated so it has not been possible to calculate the effective concentrations of undissociated carbonic acid. However, it seems that in most of the experiments the pH must have been about 4 or 5.

b. The effect of reducing agents. The hatching of eggs and the exsheathment of larvae may be enhanced in the presence of reducing agents. Sodium dithionite, cysteine and ascorbic acid have been used in experiments with larvae. In addition to these reducing agents, sodium bisulphite, sulphur dioxide and glutathione have been used in experiments with eggs (Rogers, 1958, 1960; Fairbairn, 1960b). Generally sodium dithionite was most effective but this was sometimes influenced by the pH (Rogers, 1960). It seems reasonable to suppose that these reducing agents acted by lowering the redox potential of the medium. In order to protect the reducing agent Rogers (1958, 1960) carried out experiments under anaerobic conditions. There is no evidence that the absence of oxygen was required apart from the chemical necessity of preventing the breakdown of the reducing agent, i.e. sodium dithionite. Indeed, under conditions which gave effective exsheathment without a reducing agent, Taylor and Whitlock (1960) found anaerobic conditions unnecessary.

Rogers (1960) found that the effect of reducing agents on the hatching of eggs of *Ascaris lumbricoides* and the exsheathment of larvae of *Trichostrongylus axei* and *Haemonchus contortus* was generally appreciable at the higher end of the pH range, pH 6.0 to pH 8.0, and when the $[H_2CO_3]$ was relatively low. With the larvae of *Trichostrongylus colubriformis* which required an acid medium (about pH 3) and a relatively high $[H_2CO_3]$ (about $5 \times 10^{-3}M$), reducing agents had no effect. This may explain at least some of the results obtained by Taylor and Whitlock (1960) who showed that reducing agents had no effect on the exsheathment of *Haemonchus contortus* in solutions of 0.5% sodium chloride which had been gassed with mixtures containing carbon dioxide. In these experiments the pH was probably about 4.5 and the $[H_2CO]$ may have been relatively high.

c. *The effect of salts.* The importance of salts in inducing exsheathment of larvae of *Haemonchus contortus* has been studied by Taylor and Whitlock (1960). In these experiments carbon dioxide was present in the gas phase but no reducing agent was added. At concentrations of sodium chloride about 0.1% to 0.8% exsheathment occurred freely; below 0.1% activity fell. The action of salts was not simply an osmotic effect; osmotically equivalent solutions of glucose and lactose were ineffective. Moreover the efficiency of different salts in inducing exsheathment varied. Oxy-acid salts were more effective than neutral salts and it was suggested that this may have been due to their capacity to catalyse the reaction $CO_2 + H_2O \rightleftharpoons H_2CO_3$ (Roughton and Booth, 1938).

Detailed experiments with infective agents of other species have not been carried out. Rogers (1960) found that the addition of 0.1 M sodium chloride to bicarbonate-carbon dioxide buffers (0.013 M sodium bicarbonate) containing reducing agents increased the hatching of eggs of *Ascaris lumbricoides* and exsheathment of *Trichostrongylus axei* and *Haemonchus contortus*. But greatest effects were obtained with larvae of *Trichostrongylus colubriformis*; in 0.025 N hydrochloric acid under a gas containing carbon dioxide 0.05 M sodium chloride increased exsheathment up to 30%.

d. *The hydrogen ion concentration.* In addition to its effect *via* $[H_2CO_3]$

and redox potential, pH may have an independent effect on the hatching of infective eggs and the exsheathment of infective larvae. Thus Rogers (1958, 1960) found that exsheathment of *Trichostrongylus axei* and *Haemonchus contortus* and the hatching of eggs of *Ascaris lumbricoides* at a given $[H_2CO_3]$ was increased as the pH was raised from 6.0 to 8.0.

e. *Other factors.* The addition of sodium taurocholate, horse serum and "Tween 80" lead to increased exsheathment of larvae or hatching of eggs. The effects due to these substances were small however and they had little effect except in the presence of $[H_2CO_3]$ and reducing agents (Rogers, 1960).

Temperature has, of course, an effect on the efficiency of the stimulus and there is some evidence that low temperatures have a more marked effect on the stimulus than on the subsequent processes involved in exsheathment (Rogers and Sommerville, 1960).

2. *The Physiological Action of the Stimulus*

The early work of Sommerville (1957) demonstrated the indirect action of the stimulus on larvae of several species of trichostrongyles. More recently this work has been extended to include the eggs of ascarids and to provide more understanding of the physiology of the process.

Under favourable conditions the stimulus has its full effect on larvae within 30 min. Thus larvae of *Trichostrongylus axei* in bicarbonate-carbon dioxide buffer containing a reducing agent and at 37°C were stimulated within 15 min to give a high rate of exsheathment over a period of 3 h. Though less than 20% of the larvae had exsheathed in 15 min in the stimulating medium, subsequent incubation in a simple saline solution for 2.75 h raised exsheathment to over 70%. Experiments of this sort indicate the "triggering" nature of the stimulus, but this has been even more clearly demonstrated by collecting the "exsheathing fluid" which has an effect on sheaths independent of the stimulus. It is evident that the stimulus, acting for quite short periods, leads to the secretion of an amount of exsheathing fluid which is sufficient, acting over a period of 2 to 3 h, to attack and disrupt the sheath of each larva.

With the eggs of *Ascaris lumbricoides* hatching does not continue to such an extent as the exsheathment of larvae when the stimulus is withdrawn, and the process is much slower. Thus after placing eggs in bicarbonate-carbon dioxide buffer containing a reducing agent for 1 h, when about 12% of the eggs hatched, subsequent incubation in a saline for 12 h only increased the hatching to about 30%. Longer periods in the stimulating medium were no more effective. Nevertheless it was possible to collect, after stimulating the eggs, a hatching fluid which, in the absence of a stimulating medium, attacked the egg shells so causing the release of the embryos (Rogers, 1958, 1960). It seems therefore that though the process of infection here involves a "trigger" mechanism, the sustained action of the stimulus is necessary to provide sufficient hatching fluid for the rapid breakdown of the egg shells. This is not surprising because exsheathing fluid acts on a relatively thin part of the cuticle in a strictly circumscribed area (Sommerville, 1957; Rogers and Sommerville, 1960), whereas the hatching fluid, though it usually has a localized effect on the hard layer of the egg shell also attacks other regions as well. Moreover, the chief layer of the shell, chitin, is a substrate which is hydrolysed relatively slowly by the action of enzymes.

It is not known how the stimulus works. Because carbon dioxide affects the activity of a variety of third-stage larvae (Sasa *et al.*, 1960) it may act on some external sense receptor, possibly on amphids and then *via* nervous connections to internal tissues. It could, of course, act directly on the cells which produce the exsheathing or hatching fluid, though there is some evidence that it is probably concerned with the release of exsheathing fluid rather than its production (Rogers and Sommerville, 1960).

3. *The Stimulus* in vivo

The conditions necessary for stimulating exsheathment *in vivo* are probably similar to those which have been demonstrated by experiments *in vitro*. *Trichostrongylus axei* and *Haemonchus contortus* normally exsheath in the rumen and the $[H_2CO_3]$, pH, redox potential, temperature and salt concentration (Turner and Hodgetts, 1955; Dewey *et al.*, 1958) are such that this would be expected (Rogers, 1960). It is notable that the high $[H_2CO_3]$ needed as a stimulus for exsheathment of *Haemonchus contortus* would not commonly be found outside the rumen and this may to some degree account for the narrow host range of this parasite relative to *Trichostrongylus axei* for which the $[H_2CO_3]$ required in the stimulus is less critical. However, *Haemonchus contortus* will exsheath to some degree in a dialysis sac placed in an abomasal fistula though not as well as in a rumenal fistula (Sommerville, 1954, 1957), and conditions for this might occur in a wide range of animals. Nevertheless it seems clear that it is the rumen, with its high $[H_2CO_3]$ and low Eh at pH values near neutrality, which provides the best stimulus.

Infective larvae of *Trichostrongylus colubriformis* exsheath in the abomasum and the adults live in the small intestine. Thus for this species also the stimulus demonstrated *in vitro* would seem to give an explanation for events *in vivo* and is in accordance with the difference in its behaviour within the host as compared to infective larvae of *Haemonchus contortus* and *Trichostrongylus axei*.

The eggs of *Ascaris lumbricoides, Toxocara mystax* and *Ascaridia galli* hatch in the small intestine. The range of conditons, $[H_2CO_3]$, pH, Eh and temperature which is suitable for the hatching of eggs *in vitro* seems appropriate for hatching *in vivo*. Unfortunately analytical figures for the factors in the intestinal fluids of the hosts of these parasites are not known but it is clear that the requirements found from tests *in vitro* explain the observation that eggs hatch in the small intestine and not in the foregut.

4. *Formation of the Parasitic Stage*

After the appropriate stimulus from the host has acted the parasitic stage is formed. The changes which may be observed are the emergence of the embryo from the egg shell or the emergence of the larva from the sheath. In some species of course the infective stage is not protected in these ways and immediate anatomical changes do not occur when the host is entered; apparently these take place very largely at the time when the infective stage is formed. At the onset of development as a parasite however, marked physiological changes must occur. Unfortunately these have not been studied yet and our knowledge of the physiology of this part of the process of infection is restricted to the hatching of the eggs of some ascarids and the exsheathment of some trichostrongyle larvae.

5. *The Secretion and Action of Exsheathing Fluid*

Exsheathing fluid of the infective stage of trichostrongyles is present in tissue near the base of the oesophagus of the larva. A material which has the same property of exsheathing fluid in attacking the sheath can be obtained from infective larvae which have not been exposed to the stimulus (Sommerville, 1957; Rogers and Sommerville, 1960). The stimulus evidently leads to the secretion of the fluid rather than its formation. It seems probable that secretion takes place *via* the excretory pore and the glandular cells which synthesize the major components of the exsheathing fluid are probably associated with the excretory systems of larvae.

The mechanism by which the exsheathing fluid attacks the sheath is unknown. Judged by changes which can be observed with a microscope only a small region of the sheath is attacked and that from the inside only. Some of the conditions under which changes in the sheath took place were examined by Rogers and Sommerville (1960). Dialysis reduced activity but it could be restored by adding Mn^{++} or Mg^{++}. Activity was abolished by heating to 60°C for 10 min and was inhibited by Hg^{++} and by iodoacetic acid.

Presumably, after the loss of the sheath the larvae follow the pattern of behaviour appropriate to the species at this stage of development. Feeding, growth and development is restarted and the organism becomes truly parasitic. No information on the physiology of these processes is available.

6. *The Action of Hatching Fluid*

When they have reached the infective stage, after the second moult has started, the eggs of *Ascaris lumbricoides* respond to the stimulus and produce a hatching fluid. It is not known where this fluid is produced, but evidently it is secreted into the fluid surrounding the embryo. The chief components in the hatching fluid found by Rogers (1958) were an esterase and a chitinase which hydrolysed parts of the hard shell. The embryos usually emerged by rupturing the thin inner membrane at a point where the hard outer shell was weakened or completely broken down (Fairbairn, 1960b; Rogers, 1958).

In vivo these processes occur in the small intestine. In the appropriate host the larvae commence development as parasitic stages and infection is completed.

7. *Infection via the Gut in other Species*

The process of infection described above is based on observations with a few species only. But indirect evidence indicates a similar mechanism in closely related species. Thus the infective stages for the vertebrate hosts of the lungworms *Muellerius capillaris* and *Protostrongylus rufescens* release an "exuvial fluid" from the excretory canal. This may be due to stimulation from components in the alimentary tract of the sheep which the larvae encounter as the molluscs in which they are contained become digested. *In vitro* observations show that the sheath at the head and tail swells and ultimately bursts at a defined region, so enabling the larva to escape (Švarc and Zmoray, 1960; Zmoray and Švarc, 1960). This mechanism is evidently similar to that found in infective larvae of trichostrongylids. It appears to involve an external stimulus provided by the host, together with a response which leads to release of a secretion. This secretion weakens the cuticle and enables the larva to escape. It is questionable however whether such a secretion should be called exuvial fluid.

Many other examples may be cited in which mechanisms similar to those which have been described probably operate to restart development of an infective egg or larva, but the nature of the stimulus is not known. *Neoaplectana glaseri* may live for two generations in dead beetles, *Popillia japonica*. When food is exhausted, it becomes infective after completing the second stage and, as a dauer larva, can survive for considerable periods. Moulting is incomplete and the larva is enclosed in the cuticle of the second stage. This cuticle is often lost and seems to be of little significance. Resumption of development is apparently associated with presence of food in the shape of a new insect host. Similar observations have been made with cultures (Glaser, McCoy and Girth, 1940; Stoll, 1959). Other nematodes have complex life cycles involving several hosts. Eggs of *Tetrameres americana* do not hatch until they are ingested by grasshoppers. Although the grasshopper provides stimuli which induce hatching, as well as an environment suited for subsequent growth, the nematode cannot attain maturity, but becomes encysted, apparently as a third-stage larva. When the grasshopper is eaten by a bird the parasitic infective stage in the insect's muscles is released, presumably by digestion, and is able to continue development (Cram, 1931). Life cycles of this type have two infective stages, that is, two stages during which feeding does not take place and growth is suspended. In both instances a stimulus from the next host is required so that development can continue.

Arthropods are hosts for many species of microfilariae and descriptive accounts of events occurring during infection have been compiled (see Lavoipierre, 1958b; Hawking and Worms, 1961) so that the information on which physiological experiments might be based is available. However, little of this work has been carried out.

Though a wide range of arthropods will often serve as hosts, races which are highly resistant to infection may develop within a species (e.g. see Kartman, 1954). On the one hand this may be due to a lack of critical requirements for the development of the infective stage into a parasitic stage, and on the other, because the larvae may be highly susceptible to damaging reactions of the host, either by the formation of antibodies or by other adverse physiological conditions. Generally, within an hour of ingestion by the host the microfilariae have exsheathed and penetrated the gut wall, usually at a particular site which depends on the species (e.g. see Bertram, Unsworth and Gordon, 1946; Freer, 1953; Wharton, 1957). Though it has been suggested that the hook-like structure at the anterior end of most microfilariae may be concerned with penetration of the tissues of the host, the actual processes by which the development of microfilariae is restarted in the intermediate host have not been determined. Reduction in temperature from that of the definitive host may be concerned. Thus Yoeli *et al.* (1958) found that whereas microfilariae of *Dirofilaria immitis* developed partially when injected into the haemolymph of the larvae of *Galleria mellonella* at 27–30°C, development did not take place at 37°C. It is also evident that factors necessary for restarting development are not confined to the gut, but occur in the haemolymph of this species.

It is possible that a system of internal secretions triggered by the host might be concerned with the process of infection with microfilariae. Indeed it has been suggested that glandular cells around the anal pore might be the site of production of the secretion (see Hawking and Worms, 1961).

The wide range of hosts which often serve for a single species of microfilariae shows that the stimulus for renewed development is unspecific; it may even be similar to that required for the infection of vertebrate hosts *via* the alimentary canal. But superimposed on this may be factors which are largely independent of the taxonomic relationship of the hosts such as the presence or absence of anticoagulants (Kartman, 1953).

B. INFECTION VIA THE SURFACE OF THE HOST

A large number of parasites infect the host, usually as third-stage larvae, by penetrating the skin of the host by their own efforts. For many species which are transferred from definitive host to definitive host *via* the arthropod intermediate host, unaided skin penetration is not possible. The infective stage enters the tissues of the vertebrate host either directly after the mouth parts have passed through the stratum corneum or more by their own efforts through abrasions on the surface of the skin. There now seems little doubt that for most filarids the infective stage for the vertebrate host cannot penetrate unbroken skin (Hawking and Worms, 1961).

Whether infection is achieved by skin penetration or *via* punctures in the skin, little is known of the processes by which the infective stage is stimulated to resume development. The brief summary which follows is largely concerned with what may be seen during the process of infection.

1. *The Penetration of the Host's Skin*

Much of the early work on infection through the body surface (Cort, *et al.*, 1922; Augustine, 1923; Goodey, 1925) was concerned with the effect of the second-stage sheath on penetration of skin. Many species always discard the sheath before making contact with the body surface, e.g. *Strongyloides* spp.; *Nippostrongylus brasiliensis* discards the second-stage sheath in the normal charcoal faeces culture, but not if it is permitted to migrate away from intact faecal pellets onto the sides or lid. Sometimes *Necator americanus* will discard the sheath while in the soil (Cort *et al.*, 1922). But if the sheath is retained until the larvae reaches the skin of the host it is apparently discarded as penetration is about to commence. The structure of the sheath is such that it would be surprising if larvae could even commence penetration with the sheath still covering the anterior end. On the other hand the prompt exsheathing which takes place on the host's skin seems unlikely to be evoked by mechanical means, such as rubbing against the skin, though simple physical factors may act as a stimulus.

The penetration of skin is influenced by the thickness of the water film. Some species (*Strongyloides* spp.) can penetrate while in a thick film but others require a thin film (see Goodey, 1925). Skin penetration may also be influenced, at least in *Nippostrongylus brasiliensis*, by the positive thermotactic behaviour of the larvae (Parker and Haley, 1960) but this is evidently not important in others which can penetrate cold skin (see Goodey, 1925; Mönnig, 1930). The nature of events which leads to skin penetration probably involves, first, some form of orientation to the skin which may be influenced by the depth of the water film and by temperature of the skin. Second, it probably involves secretion of substances which aid in penetration of the skin and deeper tissues. These substances include proteases (true collagenases are rare) and hyaluronidase-like spreading factors. Perhaps in those forms which reach the skin while still in the sheath, these enzymes, which subsequently aid in skin penetration, may first help to break down the sheath. Third, the actual movements of the larvae may lead to the penetration of tissue by purely mechanical effects. The nature of the stimuli which bring about these events is unknown. Whatever the stimuli are, they do not reside in the skin alone because infection with many species can be obtained without passage through the skin. Indeed direct intravenous injection of infective stages may cause infection.

2. *Arthropods as Agents of Infection*

The filarids form a specialized but large group of nematodes in which the infective stage is introduced into the vertebrate host by the action of the intermediate host. The sequence of events for many species is as follows.

1. Under certain conditions, such as raised temperature, increased intra-coelomic pressure and movements of mouthparts, either separately or together (e.g. Kartman, 1957; Lavoipierre, 1958b; Gordon and Crewe, 1953) infective larvae move to the head of the intermediate host and emerge, either from some region of the mouthparts or from the thin membranes at their base (Lavoipierre, 1958a).

2. For most and perhaps all species infection will not occur unless punctures in the superficial layers of the skin of the vertebrate host provide a route of entry into the underlying tissues (Hawking and Worms, 1961). The features which these infective larvae lack and which distinguish them from species which can penetrate the host's skin have not been examined critically. There are characteristic morphological

differences, of course, but behaviour and the production of tissue-disrupting enzymes should be compared in the two types of larvae under similar conditions.

Presumably the infective larvae start development as parasitic stages as soon as they have entered the tissues of the vertebrate host. The features of the new environment which are concerned in inducing this change are not known. They may be similar to those which stimulate the development of skin penetrating nematodes of species with direct life cycles. It is likely that the stimulus lacks specificity and it may be due to simple mechanical or physico-chemical factors.

C. THE INFECTION OF PLANTS

Many nematodes which feed exclusively on plant tissue behave like free-living nematodes, in that they do nòt have specialized infective stages. Any stage of the life cycle may initiate infection, which is often "ectoparasitic", with only the stylet entering plant tissue. Some aspects of this sort of relationship will be discussed later when we consider attachment to the host and the initiation of feeding. For the present we are concerned with species which have specialized infective stages. Some of these species require host secretions to initiate hatching or moulting, while others respond to non-specific stimuli such as moisture and temperature.

1. *The Role of Host Secretions in Infection*

A good example of the role of plant secretions in infection is given by *Heterodera rostochiensis*. "A chemical substance is given off from the roots of growing potato plants which stimulates the larvae of *H. schachtii* (syn. *H. rostochiensis*) to hatch from the eggs and emerge from the cysts" (Triffitt, 1930). The exact chemical nature and mode of action (Section II) of the active principle in root diffusate, "eclepic acid", is still unknown, but there is an extensive literature about its action.

In the absence of root diffusate very few larvae emerge from cysts. Under laboratory conditions, there is a steady increase in the number of larvae which emerge when diffusate is added, until a maximum is attained. Emergence then decreases to zero, even when fresh diffusate is added. Not all larvae leave the cyst but after an interval addition of more diffusate will lead to further emergence.

The response of *H. rostochiensis* is limited largely to diffusates from two host plants, potato and tomato (Winslow, 1955) but there is a slight response to diffusate from the weed *Solanum nigrum* which, however, is not a good host (Doncaster, 1953). Some other species in this genus are also quite specific in this response to root diffusate. For example *H.*

carotae will hatch only in presence of diffusate from the cultivated carrot. However beet eelworm, *H. schachtii*, responds not only to diffusate from the host, but gives a high response to *Chenopodium album*, on which cysts do not readily form and to *Matthiola incana*, on which cysts do not form at all. Some other species respond more readily to nonhosts than they do to their own host and others, *H. major* and *H. gottingiana*, do not respond to diffusate of either host or non-host plants. It is evident that this genus shows great variation in the dependence of the hatching mechanism on the host, but taking the genus as a whole, it seems that good responses are generally obtained to diffusate from host plants, while poor responses are more usual from non-host plants.

Host secretions also play a part in the moulting of pre-adult *Paratylenchus projectus* and *P. dianthus* (Rhoades and Linford, 1959). In moist soil these larvae, which do not feed, survive for long periods in the absence of the host plant. In the laboratory, a few can be induced to moult in water, but moulting is greatly stimulated by root diffusate from actively growing plants. The agreement between suitability of plants as hosts and their production of active root diffusate is not complete. For example red clover, *Trifolium pratense*, although a suitable host for both species, yielded root diffusate which induced moulting in *P. projectus* but not in *P. dianthus*. The parallel with the stimulation of hatching in *Heterodera* by root diffusate is obvious.

We are not aware of any other plant nematodes which use host secretions as a part of their adaptation to parasitism, although this phenomenon may be more extensive than the literature at present suggests. Eggs of *Ditylenchus dipsaci* may hatch in response to diffusates from alfalfa roots (Thorne, 1961, page 118) but detailed information is not available.

2. *Non-specific Factors and Infection*

Sometimes an encysted infective stage may accumulate until hatching or emergence is induced by non-specific factors like moisture or temperature, which at the same time induce germination and growth of the host plant.

The expulsion of the larval mass of *Anguina agrostis* from galls is purely a physical process resulting from the imbibition of water by a matrix in which the larvae are embedded. The environmental conditions suitable for maximum expulsion and movement of larvae occur only when the soil is draining to and about field capacity. These same conditions appear to be optimum for germination of host seedlings (Collis-George and Blake, 1959). The authors comment that "expulsion of larvae from the gall . . . appears to be an adaptation comparable in its survival significance to the chemical hatching factor in *Heterodera* spp."

Possibly the hatching of *Heterodera major* which seems to be associated with a rise in temperature in the spring, is a similar sort of mechanism (Hesling, 1957).

3. *The Influence of Soil Conditions on Infection*

The success of the infective process in the situations which we have discussed will be determined in part by the influence of soil conditions on the production of root diffusate by the plant, on the movement of diffusate through the soil and also on the movement of the hatched or moulted larvae through the soil. Unfortunately there is little or no information about the diffusion and concentration of root diffusates in soil. On the other hand, our understanding of the way in which soil conditions can influence the emergence of larvae and their migration has greatly increased in recent years. We propose to draw attention to some major features of recent work. For further details, a review by Wallace (1961a) may be consulted.

a. Factors associated with soil structure. Soil structure may influence the ability of nematodes to locate the host plant in many ways, but chiefly through soil moisture, aeration and particle size.

The movement of a nematode, such as the infective stage of *Heterodera* spp. is limited to and dependent on films of moisture in the soil. These films are of very irregular shape and thickness and are bounded either by solid particles or by air, according to the shape and size characteristics of the pore spaces. In saturated soil, all the pores are filled with water. When suction is applied the pores begin to loose water, slowly at first, then more quickly and then slowly again. The moisture content of a soil can be related to the suction, the curve being called the "moisture characteristic".

There is a clear relationship between the distribution of water in the pores and the rate of larval emergence. In a series of experiments, Wallace (1954, 1955a, 1955b) showed that optimum emergence of larvae of *Heterodera schachtii* takes place when the pores begin to empty. This corresponds to the point of inflexion of the moisture characteristic, when there is a large change in moisture content over a small change in suction. With further increase in suction the rate of emergence is reduced. The rise in emergence of larvae as suction increases from zero is believed to be associated with increased aeration of cysts as air replaces water. The point of optimum emergence is not related to suction so much as to the distribution of water in the pores, which is a function of particle size. Inhibition of emergence may occur at the cyst openings, where very thin films could act as barriers at high suctions, or by actual removal of water from the cyst.

The mobility of larvae is evidently controlled in a similar way

(Wallace, 1956b). Mobility is low both at low suctions when little air is available and at high suctions, when the moisture films may be thin and discontinuous. Mobility increases as suction increases from a low level and is at a maximum when the pores begin to empty. It declines as suction rises further.

b. *Influence of soil temperature.* Temperature, particularly fluctuating temperatures, influence the pattern of emergence. Possibly the reduced response to root diffusate of cysts of *H. rostochiensis* in the winter is a temperature effect, but the evidence on this is conflicting (see Section VII). However, diurnal fluctuations in the soil probably stimulate the emergence of larvae in the same way as they do in the laboratory when cysts in root diffusate or anhydrotetronic acid are exposed to temperatures which alternate between 25° and 15°C (Bishop, 1955).

Temperature presumably affects the mobility of infective larvae as well, but there does not seem to be any detailed information on this.

4. *Location of the Plant*

a. *Leaf and seed nematodes.* Little information appears to be available on leaf and seed nematodes and the way in which they find their host. Species like *Anguina agrostis* and *Aphelenchoides ritzema-bosi* (Collis-George and Blake, 1959; Hesling and Wallace, 1961; Wallace, 1960a) become most active when the moisture exceeds critical levels. But at least for *A. ritzema-bosi*, host finding is not a matter of random movement, because the larvae tend to climb upwards (Wallace, 1959a).

b. *Root nematodes.* The problem of location has been examined more extensively for roots than for the aerial parts of plants. The subject has been reviewed recently by Jones (1960).

Some species tend to be attracted to specific parts of roots in preference to others. In roots of young actively growing tomato seedlings, three regions can be distinguished. The top 2 mm (calyptra and apical meristem) is repellent to larvae of *Melodogyne hapla*, the succeeding 6 mm or so (zone of elongation) is attractive but behind this the piliferous zone is neutral or perhaps slightly repellent (Wieser, 1955). However, work with another species, *M. incognita*, on the same host did not give evidence of repellent areas (Peacock, 1959). When linear growth of the tomato roots ceased, larvae were no longer attracted. Larvae of *Heterodera schachtii* show a clear preference for the points of origin of lateral roots (Kämpfe, 1960) but those of *H. rostochiensis* concentrate behind the root tips as well as at points of origin of lateral roots (Widdowson *et al.*, 1958). Larvae sometimes ignore one root nearby in favour of an apparently identical root at a distance. They also congregate at sites along the main roots where lateral rootlets subsequently appear. Second-stage larvae of *Hemicycliophora arenaria* migrate, shortly after hatching, along roots of tomato seedlings until a root tip is reached where they begin to feed (van Gundy, 1959).

Some species do not invade special parts of the roots. Second-stage larvae of *Criconemoides xenoplax* for example, show no partiality towards any region of roots of peach seedlings (Thomas, 1959).

c. *The mechanism of location.* One way in which larvae might locate the host is by random movement. On the other hand, they might be attracted to roots by orientation to a gradient. Such gradients might arise from substances released by the roots themselves, or from the rhizospere as a result of activity of microflora and fauna. All these views have been advocated.

Kühn (1959) argued that larvae of *Heterodera rostochiensis* meet roots by chance and that root diffusates do not directly attract nematodes but influence the rate of movement of larvae, a conclusion supported by Weischer (1959). However there is evidence to suggest that larvae of *Heterodera* spp. do not move at random, at least up to a distance of 2 cm from the host root, but are orientated to a concentration gradient about roots due to some substance (Wallace, 1958, 1960b). It is not known whether this is identical with the hatching in root diffusate. Peacock (1959) and Lownsbery and Viglierchio (1958, 1960) have shown that roots of tomato seedlings release a substance which can diffuse through a cellophane membrane and attract larvae of *Meloidogyne*. The nature of this substance is unknown.

Larvae of *Meloidogyne javanica*, *M. hapla* and *Ditylenchus dipsaci*, as well as some other species, are attracted to a source of carbon dioxide (Klinger, 1959, 1961; Bird, 1960) but will desert this in favour of a piece of living root in the vicinity. Rohde (1960) thought that carbon dioxide may be the orthokinetic substance which Kühn (1959) had suggested decreased the activity of nematodes in the vicinity of roots and thus prevented them from leaving the area. However, greater activity might be required to actually penetrate the root than to leave it. Furthermore, at least with *Meloidogyne incognita* on tomato seedlings, carbon dioxide can at best play a minor role as an attractant, for localization is not changed in the presence of basic resins which remove CO_2 (Peacock, 1961). Bird (1959b) has proposed that *Meloidogyne* larvae are primarily attracted to roots along a potential gradient and that contact with roots is maintained by lower surface potentials of specific parts of the root, for example, the zone of elongation. However, Bird (1960) subsequently suggested that oxidation-reduction potentials may not be as important as at first thought, while Klinger's (1961) experiments suggest they may be of little or no consequence in attraction to the roots.

In contrast to the foregoing, Bergman and van Duuren (1959a) failed to find evidence that larvae of *Heterodera schachtii* were attracted by roots of host plants or by their secretion products, but they were able to show (1959b) that suspensions of some bacteria isolated from the rhizospere of host plants were attractants, whereas others were repellents. Whether oxidation-reduction potentials of these suspensions influenced the results is not known.

The results of these experiments leave much room for debate. Wallace (1958) has shown how difficult it can be to interpret experiments in which plants are used. The moisture content of the medium may have a profound influence in several ways upon experiments involving attraction of larvae, in particular by its influence upon mobility of larvae, and also by its effect upon concentration and diffusion of the attractant. In view of the results of Bergman and van Duuren (1959a, 1959b) it seems possible that bacteria may influence attraction if allowed to accumulate in sufficient numbers. This seems unlikely in the experiments detailed here in which it was demonstrated that a diffusable attractant was released from roots of tomato seedlings (Peacock, 1959; Lownsbery and Viglierchio 1958, 1960) and in Wallace's (1958) experiment which gave good evidence of release of a substance from roots which influenced the movements of *Heterodera schachtii* larvae.

d. Summary. Substances which attract larvae seem to be present in root diffusates and in some instances, e.g. damaged roots, these must have come directly from the root itself. The attraction of plant parasites to roots may result from responses to "different combinations of factors which vary according to the species" (Bird, 1960). Some idea of the complexity which these combinations of factors may produce is shown diagramatically by Jones (1960) and Wallace (1960b). It is probable that experiments with living roots will have to be considerably simplified if a clear picture of host finding is to be obtained. This applies even to "simple" systems like living roots in agar, which can lead to equivocal results (Bergman and van Duuren, 1959a; Sandstedt and Schuster, 1962).

5. *Attachment to the Plant*

a. Penetration of leaves. Nematodes which live on leaves, such as *Aphelenchoides ritzema-bosi* penetrate into the interior of the leaf by the stomata and are only enabled to do this when their movements are slowed up by thin films of water (Wallace, 1959a). The guard cells offer no resistance. Thorne (1961, page 119) quotes Quanjer (1927) as saying with reference to *Ditylenchus dipsaci*, that the "cells beneath the stomatal aperture begin to enlarge before the larvae entered", and suggested that "salivary secretions had been injected". This interesting observation does not appear to have been repeated.

b. Penetration of roots. Nematodes may gain entrance *via* damaged root tissue, which is attractive to *Meloidogyne* spp. (Linford, 1941; Peacock, 1959). However, many nematodes rarely reach the interior, but remain as ectoparasites. The behaviour of *Criconemoides xenoplax* appears to show a definite sequence or behaviour pattern in approaching and penetrating a root (Thomas, 1959). Three stages can be distinguished. (1) When in the immediate vicinity of a root, the nematode made characteristic "probing movements" with the head. No movement of the stylet was observed. (2) Once the lip region had made contact with the root, the stylet began to probe, being thrust short distances while the head moved regularly with lips very close to the root surface. (3) The stylet was inserted slowly over a period of several minutes while all other movement ceased. It seems that the probing movements of the head are responses to the environment close to the root surface, which must stimulate the larva in some way. It also seems that the lip region plays an important tactile role.

The importance of the lips has been emphasized by Dickinson (1959) as providing anchorage (although this is not to be taken as their only role). The essential anchorage for the stylet to penetrate the root tissue is believed to be provided by suction built up by adherence of fused lips to the surface. The stimulation for adhesion is thus a physical one and any surface would be satisfactory provided it is hydrophobic. A hydrophilic surface could not maintain a suction.

Unlike *C. xenoplax*, many nematodes live inside the root tissues and must therefore possess means of penetrating into or between the tissue cells. Second-stage larvae of *Heterodera schachtii* migrate a short distance in the cortex to the pericycle surrounding the central vescular tissue and usually lie parallel to the longitudinal axis of the root with the tail toward the tip and the head close to the vascular system (Raski, 1950). Penetration of *H. rostochiensis* is usually associated with a localized swelling, due to hypertrophy of the root tissue. From the classical description given by Linford (1942) it seems that *Meloidogyne* larvae brace themselves so that the lips make firm contact with the surface of the root. The stylet makes many fast thrusts and once penetration has been achieved, there follows a period of quiescence. This is succeeded in turn by rhythmic pulsations of the oesophagus. These phenomena are believed to be associated respectively with injection of "saliva" and withdrawal of cell contents (Linford, 1937). But if a cell breaks open under this onslaught, the contents spill out and the larva inserts its head. Further penetration of plant tissue follows, generally between cells. The larva is believed to feed as it moves, and periods of activity alternate with periods of quiescence. A large number of larvae may invade simultaneously through a small puncture probably made by the first larva to gain entry (Godfrey and Oliveira, 1932; Peacock, 1959). Larvae of *Meloidogyne incognita* entering the root were reported to be disposed "like the petals of a daisy" and the size of the hole enlarged, accompanied sometimes by necrosis of cells about it.

c. *Secretions as an aid to penetration.* Probably these migrations are made with the aid of secretions. Almost certainly such secretions are concerned in gall formation and it seems that they are also released during penetration of tissue with the aid of the hollow stylet. Secretion of "saliva" has been noted in penetration of cellulose membranes by *H. schachtii* (Dickinson, 1959), in penetration of root hair cell of corn by *Helicotylenchus nannus* (Sledge, 1959) and penetration of roots by *Meloidogyne* spp. (Linford, 1937). Recently studies have been made on the presence of enzymes which might be concerned in the initial stages of infection (Zinovjev, 1957; Tracey, 1958; Krusberg, 1960). Indications of the presence of protease, amylase and invertase have been found in distilled water in which *Meloidogyne* spp. and *Ditylenchus* spp. were incubated and are perhaps enzymes which are released from the stylet (Linford, 1937). From homogenates of these same species cellulolytic enzymes have been found. Amylase and protease activity could also be distinguished although activity of the protease could not be demonstrated consistently (Krusberg, 1960). Krusberg also demonstrated the presence of pectin-methylesterase activity in *Ditylenchus* spp. On the other hand although both Tracey (1958) and Krusberg (1960) showed slight polygalacturonase activity, Krusberg has suggested that this enzyme is not present in the nematodes. Possibly nematodes interfere with plant metabolism in such a manner as to cause release of polygalacturonase which leads to breakdown of cohesiveness between cells.

The species of *Ditylenchus* have gullets too small to admit bacteria (Tracey, 1958), and it seems that the washing processes were adequate to remove bacteria adherent to the cuticle. Therefore the results obtained can without doubt be referred to the nematodes themselves. Some of these enzymes would presumably be secreted into the intestine, but others probably pass along the stylet and aid in penetration of tissues. Histochemical techniques could probably be used with advantage to determine something of the location of those enzymes within the nematode, and their function in the infection of the plant.

IX. THE NATURE OF INFECTIOUSNESS

By infectiousness we mean the capacity of an organism to infect its host and to live on or in the host as a parasite. With micro-organisms infectiousness also implies a capacity to cause disease (see for example Salle, 1961, page 674). This is not so with metazoan parasites; these organisms do not normally multiply within the host and infection of even the most susceptible host will rarely lead to disease if the number of infective agents is small. However we are not concerned here with the parasite or

H

host after infection has occurred; rather we are concerned with the host-parasite relationship when the infective stage makes contact with the host and begins to develop as a truly parasitic stage.

It is the infective stage which enables the organism to live in several different environments during the course of its life cycle. The infective stage is a "bridge" by which the organism moves from one environment to another. It is characteristic of parasites that one of these environments must be on or in another living organism. The other environment may be that of free-living animals or in a very different sort of host. This change in environments which almost all metazoan parasites undergo during their development must be hazardous. The infective stage may have to withstand large physical changes, e. g. temperature, or physico-chemical changes, e.g. osmotic pressure, as well as changes in diet. It goes from one environment where the harmful factors may be climatic or a shortage of food, to another where the harmful factors are quite different—the antibodies, antienzymes and unspecific tissue reactions of the host. It is this capacity to live in two environments of which one is necessarily on or in another species of organism, which is characteristic of metazoan parasites. Thus the biology and chemistry of the processes which are involved constitute some of the major problems in the study of parasitism and any hypothesis about the nature of parasitism must be framed with this in mind.

A. METAMORPHOSIS AND INFECTIOUSNESS

The capacity to live in two different environments during the course of a life cycle is often found in free-living animals. The changes which these animals undergo may constitute a metamorphosis. This is the outcome of rapid changes in anatomy and physiology "which herald an ecological transition, for they are followed by radical changes in habitat" (Wald, 1960). The classical examples of metamorphosis are found among the Cyclostomata and Amphibia. Generally, marked and sudden changes take place in the transition from larva to adult and these are correlated with adaptations which allow the animals to move from freshwater to a marine environment, or from fresh water to land. In many vertebrates there is a second metamorphosis in the life cycle which allows the adult to return to the natal environment for spawning.

Metamorphosis occurs in the life cycles of many invertebrates. The best known are in the Arthropoda, especially the Crustacea and Insecta where the general principles of the underlying mechanisms are now apparent (Passano, 1960). In these groups, where the life cycle is interrupted by moults, metamorphosis is associated with the processes of moulting. As in the vertebrates the adaptive value of metamorphosis lies in the specialization of the larval form for one mode of life and the adult for another. In some species metamorphosis or moulting may involve a period of quiescence or of diapause.

In parasites of many sorts metamorphoses take place and are associated with the change from a life as a free-living organism to parasitism, or the change from a parasite in an intermediate host to a parasite in a definitive host. For example, metamorphosis occurs in the transition from the free-living aquatic miracidium to the parasitic sporocyst, and in the change from the larval cestode in an invertebrate host to the adult in a vertebrate. The anatomical features of metamorphosis may be more marked in parasitic forms than in their near free-living relatives (e.g. in the Crustacea, Waterman and Chase, 1960, page 20). The physiological and biochemical changes involved in metamorphosis, though less well known than anatomical changes, are far reaching (Wald, 1960), perhaps especially so in parasites.

Metamorphosis may be regarded as a "definitely delimited period in post-embryonic development during which marked developmental changes in non-reproductive structures occur" (Etkin, 1955, page 631). It is clear that anatomical changes of this sort do not occur in nematodes and that the larvae are, properly speaking, juveniles. This is not surprising. The structure of nematodes is remarkedly uniform because the mechanical features which determine form are probably the same throughout the group and are even independent of size (Harris and Crofton, 1957). In some species the shape of the adult does change (e.g. in *Spaerularia bombi* and *Tetrameres fissipina*) but this is due to the enlargement of the reproductive systems and the accumulation of eggs.

Though anatomical changes amounting to metamorphosis do not occur in nematodes the biochemical changes which allow the transition from the free-living to parasitic form of life must approach a metamorphosis. And as in the Arthropoda these changes are associated with moulting.

B. MECHANISMS OF MOULTING AND METAMORPHOSIS

The underlying processes of metamorphosis, even in such widely separated groups as the Arthropoda and Amphibia, are closely analogous (Etkin, 1955). Among the invertebrates, insects with complex life cycles have been most studied (Wigglesworth, 1954). In these animals the neurosecretory cells produce a material which moves along axons and is stored in the corpora cardiaca. Under appropriate conditions the activity of the central nervous system is changed and the stored neurosecretory hormone is released. This activates the prothoracic glands and the moulting hormone is released. The hormone acts on the tissues, each of which responds in a characteristic way during the moult. This process is influenced by the secretion of the juvenile hormone from the corpora allata. When, in later stages of development, the proportion of juvenile hormone is reduced the character of the moult is changed. In hemimetabolous insects, nymphs metamorphose to give the imago; in the holometabolous insects the larvae give rise to pupae and the pupae moult to give imagos. In the ametabolous insects, however, the juvenile which emerges from the egg shell looks like a small adult and each moult to the adult stage is accompanied by a simple increase in size without profound changes in anatomy or physiology. Though it is probable that the mechanisms which control moulting in the ametabolous insects are similar to those in insects with complex life cycles, little definite information is available at present.

Superficially at least the moulting and life cycle of free-living nematodes is similar to that of ametabolous insects and it is a reasonable assumption that the mechanisms controlling moulting are as closely analogous with the Insecta as between the Insecta and the Amphibia. It can be expected therefore that moulting in unspecialized free-living nematodes might be governed by some intrinsic mechanism, influenced to some extent by the external conditions, and involving neurosecretory cells. The secretion of these cells would activate the glands which secrete substances more directly concerned with the process of moulting. Some system, perhaps involving a "juvenile hormone" may control the development of the sexually mature stage.

There is evidence that adaptations which would allow nematodes to exploit the environment more effectively might be superimposed on this basic system. Thus the physiological metamorphosis which must take place in nematodes which live in at least two different environments during their life cycles seems to be closely associated with the process of moulting. Indeed there are indications that the infective stage of nematodes, whether it is enclosed in an egg shell, or whether it is a free-living or parasitic larva, is a stage between the beginning and end of a moult during which period the processes of development are suspended. That is, the developmental change from one juvenile stage to the next is started, so giving the infective stage, but remains incomplete until infection occurs. Thereupon development is restarted and the organism becomes a true parasite (Rogers, 1961a; see Sections III, IV). This argument leads to the hypothesis that one of the major adaptations to parasitism in the Nematoda, the development of infectiousness, is the outcome of, or is accompanied by, changes in a neurosecretory and associated system concerned in moulting and other developmental processes.

C. A GENERAL HYPOTHESIS OF INFECTIOUSNESS AS AN ADAPTATION TO PARASITISM

It appears (see Section III) that the infective stage, whether it is within the egg shell, or is a free-living or parasitic larva, is formed immediately after a moult or partial moult has occurred. Moreover, at the time when the infective stage is formed development ceases; there is no growth or further differentiation until infection occurs. These changes must be reflected in the physiology of the infective stage but, so far as our knowledge goes at present, the physiology of infective stages is not characteristically different from adults or uninfectious larvae or eggs (see Section V). It is clear, however, that the infective stage is, as it were, poised between two environments and development does not start again until the appropriate new environment is reached. When the infective stage is formed the mechanism controlling moulting no longer operates as in other stages of the life cycle. The new environment provides a stimulus which leads to renewed development, this time as a true parasitic stage. This process constitutes one of the basic adaptations to parasitism. It involves an infective agent which has the capacity to act as a "bridge" between two different environments and which does not resume development until the appropriate environment, in or on the host, is reached.

Earlier discussion suggested that the life cycles of nematodes may be controlled by a system analogous to that in insects. Moreover this system might in a modified form be associated with the adaptation which allows these animals to live in two different sorts of environments during the life cycle. The mechanism by which this is achieved is probably similar to that which governs metamorphosis in other animals, and it operates in the infective or dispersal stages in the life cycles of nematodes. Further, the examples of life cycles discussed in Section III indicate that to a varying degree in different species, the system controlling development may become dependent upon a stimulus from the environment either for stopping or restarting its action. With these points in mind we have made a model of the system which might control part of the development of nematodes. The form of this model which is applicable to a parasite with an infective, ensheathed third-stage larva, is shown in Fig. 3. The model is highly speculative, but it does embody hypotheses which are open to disproof and which we believe may be of some importance.

D. THE ACTION OF THE STIMULUS FROM THE HOST

The system in nematodes which controls the hatching of eggs, the moulting of larvae, and the co-ordination of post-embryonic development generally, is unlikely to be a purely nervous process and probably consists of (1) a mechanism which regulates the time of production of "internal secretions", (2) the "internal secretions" themselves, and (3) the structures and tissues on which these secretions act. In parasites part of this system may be changed or lost when the infective stage is formed so that the host would be required to rectify these losses or changes. Thus the stimulus from the host which initiates infection and the development of

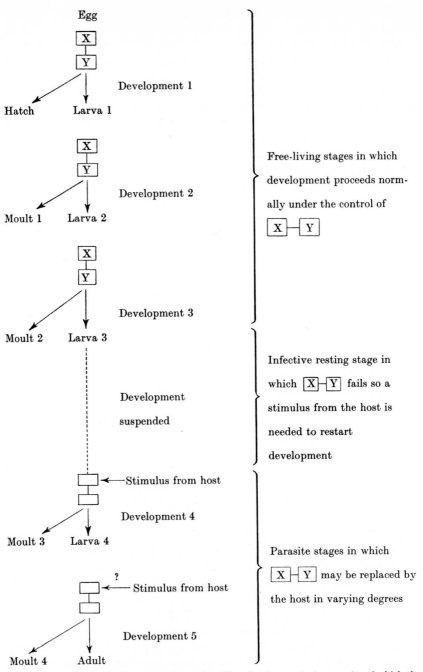

FIG. 3. A model of possible mechanisms controlling development of a parasite of which the infective stage is an ensheathed third-stage larva.   (*Continued on facing page*)

the parasitic stage may act in one of at least three ways (Fig. 4). (i) It may replace the mechanism which regulates the time of production of the "internal secretions"; (ii) it may replace missing "internal secretions", or (iii) it may have a direct action on structures and tissues by providing

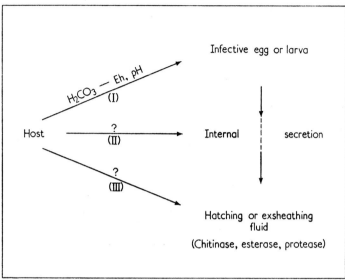

FIG. 4. Host-parasite relationships in the process of infection. The host may start infection by providing an environment (I) which stimulates the infective agent to produce, directly or indirectly, hatching or exsheathing fluids which contain certain enzymes. There is no evidence, as yet, to show that the host may function as in (II) or (III).

substrates necessary for metabolic processes or it may make these substrates accessible.

There is some evidence which supports (i). Thus the stimulus needed for the hatching of infective eggs of ascarids or for the moulting of infective larvae of several species of trichostrongylids primarily contains concentrations of undissociated carbonic acid plus dissolved carbon dioxide

---

Key to Figure 3

Hatch	Production of fluid containing the appropriate enzymes (and change in the activity of the embryo) for the rupture of the membranes of the egg shell.
Moult 1, 2, 3, 4	Production of fluid (and change in the behaviour of the larva) which causes the rupture of the outer cuticle and escape of the larva.
Development 1	Embryonic development culminating in the hatching of the egg.
Development 2, 3, 4	Developmental changes, under a "juvenile influence" in tissues and organs including the formation of a new cuticle underneath the old one.
Development 5	Developmental changes in the absence of a "juvenile influence" and without the formation of a new cuticle.
X-Y	Internal system governing the timing of moulting, the production of moulting fluid and the substances causing differentiation etc. Analagous to the neurosecretory cell-prothoracic gland-corpora allata system. Stimuli from the host may either replace X or Y or change one or both from an inactive to an active state.

(see Section VIII) which has no direct effect on egg shells or sheaths (Rogers, 1958; Rogers and Sommerville, 1960). Its action is indirect and is mediated *via* glands which secrete the fluids which actually attack the loosened cuticle and egg shells so causing the release of the next developmental stage.

There is no evidence which directly supports (ii). It has been suggested (Rogers, 1961a) that the hatching factor of the plant parasite *Heterodera rostochiensis* may act in this way. It seems that the active principle of "root diffusate", eclepic acid (see Section II) has marked pharmacological properties similar to those of other unsaturated lactones. It is not unreasonable to suppose that this substance may play some basic role in the physiology of nematodes. Root diffusates affect moulting of some larval stages of nematodes such as *Paratylenchus projectus* (Rhoades and Linford, 1959) as well as affecting the hatching of eggs of *Heterodera rostochiensis* and may contain substances related in some way to the postulated "internal secretions".

Though this hypothesis may be reasonable when *Heterodera rostochiensis* alone is considered, it seems less acceptable when other species of this genus are considered. Thus several other species, *H. cruciferae*, *H. carotae* and *H. humuli* showed a marked dependence upon hatching factors in root diffusates (Jones, 1950; Winslow, 1954, 1955). The hosts and non-hosts which produce active hatching factors for each species are related, but they do not overlap for the different species (Winslow, 1960) so that the hatching factor may be quite different for each species. It seems unlikely that the different hatching factors could all play the same fundamental physiological role in nematodes generally. However, the possibility that eclepic acid or related compounds are of physiological importance in the group needs examining.

It is possible that the host may cause the infective stage to resume development by its direct action on the shells of infective eggs and on the uncast cuticles of infective larvae (iii, Fig. 3). If the halt in the development of infective stages was due to a lack of certain requirements, e.g. a lack of nutrients which, owing to the impermeability of the egg shell or sheath, were not accessible to the embryos or larvae, the host might, by removing these barriers, restart development. This is unlikely to be important in parasites of vertebrates for which the egg is the infective stage. The egg shells of many nematodes, and especially of infective eggs, contain chitin (Fairbairn, 1960a). Chitinases, though they occur in some vertebrates (Jeumaux, 1961) are largely restricted to animals which normally have a diet containing chitin.

The sheaths of infective larvae so far examined are not readily attacked by the digestive enzymes of vertebrates. Indeed the bulk of material in the sheaths of some infective larvae, obtained by the action of sodium hypochlorite, lacks the amino acids required for the action of most mammalian digestive proteases (Bird and Rogers, 1956). Nevertheless the possibility that the provision of substrates which can be metabolized directly by the larvae may be the chief factor for renewed development after infection through the body surface has occurred, or when the infective stage is parasitic in the intermediate or definitive host, should be considered.

ACKNOWLEDGMENTS

We wish to thank Miss H. Biggs, Miss J. Franklin, Miss M. Goodman and Miss C. Monkley of the staff of the McMaster Laboratory who checked the references for us.

One of us (W.P.R.) wishes to acknowledge assistance given by grants from the U.S. Public Health Service (E-4093) and by Parke, Davis and Company.

REFERENCES

Ackert, J. E. (1931). *Parasitology* **23**, 360.
Alicata, J. E. (1934). *Proc. helm. Soc. Wash.* **1**, 12.
Alicata, J. E. (1935). *Tech. Bull. U.S. Dep. Agric.* **489**.
Augustine, D. L. (1922a). *Amer. J. Hyg.* **2**, 177.
Augustine, D. L. (1922b). *Amer. J. Hyg.* **2**, 172.
Augustine, D. L. (1923). *Amer. J. Hyg.* **3**, 280.
Baines, R. C. (1950). *Calif. Agric.* **4**(8), 7.
Bair, T. D. (1955). *J. Parasit.* **41**, 613.
Beaver, P. C. (1952). *J. Parasit.* **38**, 445.
Beaver, P. C. (1953). *Amer. J. trop. Med. Hyg.* **2**, 102.
Behrenz, W. (1956). *Z. wiss. Zool.* **159**, 129.
Berberian, J. F. and Mizelle, J. D. (1957). *Amer. Midl. Nat.* **57**, 421.
Bergeson, G. B. (1959). *Nematologica* **4**, 344.
Bergman, B. H. H. and Duuren, A. J. van. (1959a). *Meded. Inst. nat. Suikerprod. Bergen-op-Zoom.* **29**, 1. (Original not seen. Abs. in *Helminth. Abs.* **29** (1960), No. 2153).
Bergman, B. H. H. and Duuren, A. J. van (1959b). *Ibid*, **25** (Original not seen. Abs. in *Helminth. Abs.* **29** (1960), No. 2154).
Bertram, D. S., Unsworth, K. and Gordon, R. M. (1946). *Ann. trop. Med. Parasit.* **40**, 228.
Birchfield, W. (1957). *Phytopathology* **47**, 161.
Bird, A. F. (1956). *Exp. Parasit.* **5**, 350.
Bird, A. F. (1957). *Exp. Parasit.* **6**, 383.
Bird, A. F. (1958a). *Parasitology* **48**, 32.
Bird, A. F. (1958b). *Nematologica* **3**, 205.
Bird, A. F. (1959a). *Nematologica* **4**, 31.
Bird, A. F. (1959b). *Nematologica* **4**, 322.
Bird, A. F. (1960). *Nematologica* **5**, 217.
Bird, A. F. and Rogers, W. P. (1956). *Exp. Parasit.* **5**, 449.
Bird, A. F. and Deutsch, K. (1957). *Parasitology* **47**, 319.
Bishop, D. (1955). *Ann. appl. Biol.* **43**, 525.
Böhm, O. (1956). *Pflanzenarzt. Vienna* **9**, 76. (Original not seen. Abs. in *Helminth. Abs.* **25**, (1956) No. 271a).

Bosker, J. E. (1960). *Proc. helm. Soc. Wash.* **27**, 127.
Bovien, P. (1937). *Vidensk. Medd. dansk naturh. Foren. Kbh.* **101**, 1.
von Brand, T. (1938). *J. Parasit.* **24**, 445.
von Brand, T. (1942). *Biol. Bull. Wood's Hole* **82**, 1.
von Brand, T. (1947). *Biol. Bull. Wood's Hole* **92**, 162.
von Brand, T. (1952). "Chemical Physiology of Endoparasitic Animals". Academic Press, New York.
von Brand, T. and Simpson, W. F. (1942). *Proc. Soc. exp. Biol. Med.* **49**, 245.
von Brand, T., Weinstein, P. P., Meklman, B. and Weinbach, E. C. (1952). *Exp. Parasit.* **1**, 245.
Brown, H. W. (1927). *J. Parasit.* **14**, 1.
Brown, H. W. (1928). *J. Parasit.* **14**, 141.
Buckley, J. J. C. (1940). *J. Helminth.* **18**, 173.
Cairns, E. J. (1952). *Phytopathology* **42**, 464.
Calam, C. T., Todd, A. R. and Waring, W. S. (1949). *Biochem. J.* **45**, 520.
Chitwood, B. G. and Chitwood, M. B. (1938). "An Introduction to Nematology". Monumental Printing Co., Baltimore, Md.
Christie, J. R. (1959). "Plant Nematodes". Agric. Expt. Sta. University of Florida.
Cleland, J. B. and Johnston, T. H. (1911). *Rep. Aust. Ass. Adv. Sci.*, 13th Meeting, Sydney 1911, p. 299.
Collis-George, N. and Blake, C. D. (1959). *Aust. J. biol. Sci.* **12**, 247.
Cordi, J. M. and Otto, G. F. (1934). *Amer. J. Hyg.* **19**, 103.
Cort, W. W., Augustine, D. L., Ackert, J. E., Payne, F. K. and Payne, G. C. (1922). *Amer. J. Hyg.* **2**, 17.
Costello, L. C. and Grollman, S. (1958). *Exp. Parasit.* **7**, 319.
Costello, L. C. and Grollman, S. (1959). *Exp. Parasit.* **8**, 83.
Cram, E. B. (1931). *Tech. Bull. U.S. Dep. Agric.* **227**.
Crofton, H. D. (1949a). *Parasitology* **39**, 17.
Crofton, H. D. (1949b). *Parasitology* **39**, 26.
Crofton, H. D. (1954). *J. Helminth.* **28**, 35.
Cunningham, P. C. (1960). *Sci. Proc. R. Dublin Soc.* (B) **1**, 1.
Daulton, R. A. C. (1960). *Diss. Abst.* **20**, 4237.
Dawson, B. (1960). *Nature, Lond.* **187**, 799.
Dewey, D. W., Lee, H. J. and Marston, H. R. (1958). *Nature, Lond.* **181**, 1367.
Dickinson, S. (1959). *Nematologica* **4**, 60.
Doncaster, C. C. (1953). *J. Helminth.* **27**, 1.
Dropkin, V. H., Martin, G. C. and Johnson, R. W. (1958). *Nematologica* **3**, 115.
Drudge, J. H., Leland, Jr., S. E., Wyant, Z. N. and Rust, J. W. (1958). *J. Parasit.* **44**, 434.
Duggan, J. J. (1960). *Nature, Lond.* **185**, 554.
Duke, B. O. L. (1957). *Nature, Lond.* **179**, 1357.
Duke, B. O. L. (1958). *Ann .trop. Med. Parasit.* **52**, 24.
Duke, B. O. L. (1959). *Ann. trop. Med. Parasit.* **53**, 203.
Durie, P. H. (1961). *Aust. J. agric. Res.* **12**, 1200.
Eisma, M. (1932). *Acta leidensia* **7**, 1.
Ellenby, C. (1946a). *Nature, Lond.* **157**, 302.
Ellenby, C. (1946b). *Nature, Lond.* **157**, 451.
Ellenby, C. (1955a). *Ann. appl. Biol.* **43**, 12.
Ellenby, C. (1955b). *Ann. appl. Biol.* **43**, 1.
Ellenby, C. (1956). *Ann. appl. Biol.* **44**, 1.
Ellenby, C. (1957). *Proc. Symposium "Insect and Foodplant", Brill, Leiden,* **99**.

Ellenby, C. and Gilbert, A. B. (1957). *Nature, Lond.* **180**, 1105.
Ellenby, C. and Gilbert, A. B. (1958). *Nature, Lond.* **182**, 925.
Ellenby, C. and Gilbert, A. B. (1960). *Nematologica Suppl. II*, **106**.
Elliot, A. (1954). *Exp. Parasit.* **3**, 307.
Etkin, W. (1955). *In* "Analysis of Development" (Villier, B. H., Weiss, P. and
    Hamburger, V. eds.) Saunders, London.
Fairbairn, D. (1957). *Exp. Parasit.* **6**, 491.
Fairbairn, D. (1958a). *Canad. J. Zool.* **36**, 787.
Fairbairn, D. (1958b). *Nature, Lond.* **181**, 1593.
Fairbairn, D. (1960a). *In* "Nematology" (Sasser, J. N. and Jenkins, W. R., eds.)
    University of North Carolina Press, Chapel Hill.
Fairbairn, D. (1960b). *In* "Host Influence on Parasite Physiology" (L. A. Stauber
    ed.) Rutgers University Press, New Brunswick.
Fairbairn, D. (1961). *Canad. J. Zool.* **39**, 153.
Fauré-Fremiet, E. (1913). *C. R. Soc. Biol., Paris.* **75**, 90.
Feldmesser, J. and Fassuliotis, G. (1950). *J. Wash. Acad. Sci.* **40**, 355.
Fenwick, D. W. (1952). *Ann. appl. Biol.* **39**, 457.
Fenwick, D. W. and Reid, E. (1953). *Nature, Lond.* **171**, 47.
Fenwick, D. W. and Widdowson, E. (1959). *Ann. appl. Biol.* **47**, 140.
Ferris, V. R. and Siegel, B. M. (1957). *Nematologica* **2**, 16.
Freer, P. M. (1953). *Ann. trop. Med. Parasit.* **47**, 13.
Furman, D. P. (1944). *Amer. J. vet. Res.* **5**, 79.
Germans, W. (1954). *Z. Parasitenk.* **16**, 93.
Giovannola, A. (1936). *J. Parasit.* **22**, 207.
Glaser, R. W., McCoy, E. E. and Girth, H. B. (1940). *J. Parasit.* **26**, 479.
Godfrey, G. H. and Oliveira, J. (1932). *Phytopathology* **22**, 325.
Goldberg, E. (1957). *Exp. Parasit.* **6**, 367.
Goldberg, A. and Rubin, R. (1956). *Proc. helm. Soc. Wash.* **23**, 65.
Goldberg, A. and Lucker, J. T. (1959). *Proc. helm. Soc. Wash.* **26**, 37.
Golden, A. M. (1956). *Bull. Md. agric. Exp. Sta..* **A 85**, 28.
Golden, A. M. and Shafer, T. (1960). *Nematologica* **5**, 32.
Goodey, T. (1925). *J. Helminth.* **3**, 51.
Gordon, R. M. and Crewe, W. (1953). *Ann. trop. Med. Parasit.* **47**, 74.
Gudzhabidze, S. I. (1961). *Med. Parasit., Moscow*, **28**, 578. (Original not seen. Abst. in
    Helminth. Abs. **30** (1961), No. 356).
Gundy, S. D. van. (1958). *Nematologica* **3**, 283.
Gundy, S. D. van. (1959). *Proc. helm. Soc. Wash.* **26**, 67.
Gupta, S. P. (1961). *Canad. J. Zool.* **39**, 47.
Hagemeyer, J. W. (1951). *Proc. helm. Soc. Wash.* **18**, 112.
Hankes, L. V. and Stoner, R. D. (1956). *Proc. Soc. exp. Biol. Med.* **91**, 443.
Hankes, L. V. and Stoner, R. D. (1958). *Exp. Parasit.* **7**, 92.
Harris, J. E. and Crofton, H. D. (1957). *J. exp. Biol.* **34**, 116.
Haskins, W. T. and Weinstein, P. P. (1957a). *J. Parasit.* **43**, 25.
Haskins, W. T. and Weinstein, P. P. (1957b). *J. Parasit.* **43**, 19.
Haskins, W. T. and Weinstein, P. P. (1957c). *J. Parasit.* **43**, 28.
Hastings, R. J. and Newton, W. (1934). *Canad. J. Res.* **10**, 793.
Hawking, F. and Worms, M. (1961). *Ann. Rev. Entomology* **6**, 413.
Hechler, H. C. (1962). *Proc. helm. Soc. Wash.* **29**, 19.
Hesling, J. J. (1956). *Nematologica* **1**, 56.
Hesling, J. J. (1957). *Nematologica* **2**, 123.
Hesling, J. J. (1958). *Nematologica* **3**, 274.

Hesling, J. J. and Wallace, H. R. (1961). *Ann. appl. Biol.* **49**, 195.

Hill, C. H. (1957). *J. Parasit.* **43**, 104.

Hirschmann, H. (1959). *Proc. helm. Soc. Wash.* **26**, 73.

Hollis, J. P. (1962). *Nature, Lond.* **193**, 798.

Huff, G. C. (1936). *J. Parasit.* **22**, 455.

Hyman, L. H. (1951). "The Invertebrates" III. McGraw-Hill, New York.

Janzen, G. J. and Tuin, F. van der. (1956). *Nematologica* **1**, 126.

Jaskoski, B. J. (1952). *Exp. Parasit.* **1**, 291.

Jaskoski, B. J. (1960). *Exp. Parasit.* **10**, 333.

Jaskoski, B. J. (1960). *J. Parasit.* **46**, Suppl., p. 27.

Jeumaux, C. (1961). *Nature, Lond.* **192**, 135.

Johnson, G. E. (1913). *Quart. J. micr. Sci.* **58**, 605.

Jones, C. A., Swartzwelder, J. C. and Abadie, S. H. (1955a). *J. Parasit.* **41**, Suppl. 48.

Jones, C. A., Swartzwelder, J. C. and Abadie, S. H. (1955b). *J. Parasit.* **41**, Suppl. 48.

Jones, F. G. W. (1950). *Ann. appl. Biol.* **37**, 407.

Jones, F. G. W. (1960). *Overdruk Meded. Landb.Hoogesch. Gent.* **25**, 1009.

Jones, M. F. and Jacobs, L. (1941). *Amer. J. Hyg.* **33**, 88.

Kämpfe, L. (1960). *Nematologica* **5**, 18.

Kates, K. C. (1950). *Proc. helm. Soc. Wash.* **17**, 39.

Kartman, L. (1953). *Exp. Parasit.* **39**, 571.

Kartman, L. (1954). *Amer. J. trop. Med. Hyg.* **3**, 329.

Kartman, L. (1957). *Rev. Brasil malariol e doencas trop. Publ. avulsas.* No. 5.

Keilin, D. (1959). *Proc. roy. Soc. B.* **150**, 149.

Klinger, J. (1959). *Mitt. schweiz. ent. Ges.* **32**, 311.

Klingler, J. (1961). *Nematologica* **6**, 69.

Kreuzer, L. (1953). *Z. vergl. Physiol.* **35**, 13.

Krusberg, L. R. (1960). *Phytopathology* **50**, 9.

Kühn, H. (1959). *Nematologica* **4**, 165.

Kurochkin, Y. V. (1960). *Akad. Nauk . SSSR. Doklady* **135**, 1281.

Lapage, G. (1935). *Parasitology* **27**, 186.

Lavoipierre, M. M. J. (1958a). *Ann. trop. Med. Parasit.* **52**, 326.

Lavoipierre, M. M. J. (1958b). *Ann. trop. Med. Parasit.* **52**, 103.

Lee, D. L. (1961). *Nature, Lond.* **192**, 282.

Lees, E. (1953). *J. Helminth.* **27**, 95.

Lewert, R. M. and Lee, C. L. (1956). *J. infect. Dis.* **99**, 1.

Lewis, G. D. and Mai, W. F. (1960). *Phytopathology* **50**, 341. (Original not seen. Abs. in *Helminth. Abst.* **30**, (1961.)No. 1158).

Limber, D. P. (1962). *Proc. helm. Soc. Wash.* **29**, 91.

Linford, M. B. (1937). *Phytopathology* **27**, 824.

Linford, M. B. (1941). *Phytopathology* **31**, 634.

Linford, M. B. (1942). *Phytopathology* **32**, 580.

Looss, A. (1911). *Rec. Sch. Med. Cairo* **4**, 159.

Lownsbery, B. F. (1951). *Phytopathology* **41**, 889.

Lownsbery, B. F. and Viglierchio, D. R. (1958). *Phytopathology* **48**, 395.

Lownsbery, B. F. and Viglierchio, D. R. (1960). *Phytopathology* **50**, 178.

Mai, W. F. (1952). *Phytopathology* **42**, 113.

Mai, W. F. and Mechow, J. von. (1952). *Phytopathology* **42**, 469.

Marquardt, W. C., Fritts, D. H., Senger, C. M. and Seghetti, L. (1959). *J. Parasit.* **45**, 431.

McCoy, O. R. (1930). *Amer. J. Hyg.* **11**, 413.

Merrill, J. H. and Ford, A. C. (1916). *U.S. J. agric. Res.* **6**, 115.

Miretski, O. Y. (1952). *Dokladi Akad. Nauk SSSR.* **82**, 1021.
Monné, L. (1955). *Arch. Zool.* **9**, 93.
Monné, L. (1959). *Arch. Zool.* **12**, 343.
Monné, L. and Hönig, G. (1954). *Arch. Zool.* **7**, 261.
Mönnig, H. O. (1930). *Rep. vet. Res. S. Afr.* 16th. 175.
Müller, G. (1953). *Zbl. Bakt.* **159**, 377.
Nakladova, V. B. (1956). *Problemi Parazitologii. Transactions of the Scientific Con-
ference of Parasitologists of the Ukrainian SSR.* 2nd (1956), 89. (Original not seen.
Abs. **25** (1956), No.931u).
Neilin, D. (1959). *Proc. roy. Soc. Lond. B.* **150**, 149.
Nekipelova, R. A. (1956). *Problemi Parazitologii. Transactions of the Scientific Confer-
ence of Parasitologists of the Ukrainian SSR.* 2nd, 90. (Original not seen, Abst.
in *Helminth. Abs.* **25** (1956). No. 931v)
Nolf, L. O. (1932). *Amer. J. Hyg.* **16**, 288.
Oldham, J. N. (1935). *J. Helminth.* **13**, 13.
Oldham, J. N. (1937). *In* "Papers on Helminthology Published in Commemoration
of the 30 Year Jubileum of K. J. Skrjabin" (Schulz, R. E. S., and Gnyedina,
M. P. eds.), Academy of Agricultural Sciences, Moscow.
Onions, T. G. (1955). *Quart. J. micr. Sci.* **96**, 495.
Oostenbrink, M. (1950). "Het aardappelaaltje (*Heteroderera rostochiensis*Wollenweber),
een gevaarlijke parasiet voor de eenzijdige aardappelcultur." Wageningen:
H. Veenman and Zonen, 230 pp. (Original not seen. Abs. in *Helminth. Abs.* **19**,
(1950). No. 141).
Ouden, H. Den (1960). *Nematologica Suppl.* II, 101.
Parker, J. C. and Haley, A. J. (1960). *Exp. Parasit.* **9**, 92.
Passano, L. M. (1960). *In* "Physiology of Crustacea" Vol. I. (T. H. Waterman ed.),
Academic Press, New York.
Passey, R. F. and Fairbairn, D. (1955). *Canad. J. Biochem. Physiol.* **33**, 1033.
Passey, R. F. and Fairbairn, D. (1957). *Canad. J. Biochem. Physiol.* **35**, 511.
Payne, F. K. (1922). *Amer. J. Hyg.* **2**, 254.
Payne, F. K. (1923a). *Amer. J. Hyg.* **3**, 547.
Payne, F. K. (1923b). *Amer. J. Hyg.* **3**, 584.
Peacock, F. C. (1957). *Nematologica* **2**, 114.
Peacock, F. C. (1959). *Nematologica* **4**, 42.
Peacock, F. C. (1961). *Nematologica* **6**, 85.
Peters, B. G. (1928). *J. Helminth.* **6**, 1.
Poole, J. B. (1956). *Canad. J. comp. Med.* **20**, 169.
Prasad, D. (1959). *Canad. J. Zool.* **37**, 305.
Quanjer, H. M. (1927). *Tijdschr. PlZiekt.* **33**, 137.
Raski, D. J. (1950). *Phytopathology* **40**, 135.
Raven, B. and Schuurmans Stekhoven, J. H. (1934). *Zool. Anz.* **106**, 17.
Rees, G. F. (1950). *Parasitology* **40**, 127.
Reesal, M. R. (1951). *Canad. J. Zool.* **29**, 109.
Refuerzo, P. G. and Albis-Jimenez, F. S. (1954). *Amer. J. vet. Res.* **15**, 440.
Rhoades, H. L. and Linford, M. B. (1959). *Science, Lancaster, Pa.,* **130**, 1476.
Rhoades, H. L. and Linford, M. B. (1961). *Proc. helm. Soc. Wash.* **28**, 51.
Roberts, F. H. S., O'Sullivan, P. J. and Riek, R. F. (1952). *Aust. J. agric. Res.* **3**, 187.
Rogers, W. P. (1940a). *J. Helminth.* **18**, 183.
Rogers, W. P. (1940b). *Parasitology* **32**, 208.
Rogers, W. P. (1948). *Parasitology* **39**, 105.
Rogers, W. P. (1955). *Exp. Parasit.* **4**, 21.

176   W. P. ROGERS AND R. I. SOMMERVILLE

Rogers, W. P. (1958). *Nature Lond.* **181**, 1410.

Rogers, W. P. (1960). *Proc. roy. Soc. Ser. B.* **152**, 367.

Rogers, W. P. (1961a). "The Nature of Parasitism". Academic Press, New York.

Rogers, W. P. (1961b). *J. Helminth. R. T. Leiper Suppl.*, 151.

Rogers, W. P. and Sommerville, R. I. (1957). *Nature, Lond.* **179**, 619.

Rogers, W. P. and Sommerville, R. I. (1960). *Parasitology* **50**, 329.

Rohde, R. A. (1960). *Proc. helm. Soc. Wash.* **27**, 160.

Rose, J. H. (1955). *J. comp. Path.* **65**, 370.

Rose, J. H. (1957). *J. Helminth.* **31**, 17.

Rose, J. H. (1959). *Parasitology* **49**, 439.

Roughton, F. J. W. and Booth, V. H. (1938). *Biochem. J.* **32**, 2049.

Rowan, W. B. (1956). *Exp. Parasit.* **5**, 118.

Salle, A. J. (1961). "Fundamental Principles of Bacteriology". McGraw-Hill, New York.

Sandstedt, R. and Schuster, M. L. (1962). *Phytopathology* **52**, 174.

Sasa, M., Shirasaka, R., Tanaka, H., Miura, A., Yamamoto, H. and Katahira, K. (1960). *Jap. J. exp. Med.* **30**, 433.

Schanzel, H. (1958). *Sborn. vys. Sk. zemedelsk. les. Fak., Brno, Ser. B.* **6**, 213.

Schwabe, C. W. (1957). *Amer. J. Hyg.* **65**, 325.

Scott, J. A. (1929). *Amer. J. Hyg.* **10**, 125.

Seamster, A. P. (1950). *Amer. Midl. Nat.* **43**, 450.

Shepherd, A. M. (1960). *Nematologica* **5**, 103.

Silverman, P. H. and Campbell, J. A. (1958). *Parasitology* **49**, 23.

Simmonds, R. A. (1958). *Exp. Parasit.* **7**, 14.

Sledge, E. B. (1959). *Nematologica* **4**, 356.

Smith, P. E. (1953). *Amer. J. Hyg.* **57**, 194.

Soliman, K. N. (1953). *Brit. vet. J.* **109**, 364.

Sommerville, R. I. (1954). *Nature, Lond.* **174**, 751.

Sommerville, R. I. (1957). *Exp. Parasit.* **6**, 18.

Sommerville, R. I. (1960). *Parasitology* **50**, 261.

Soulsby, E. J. L., Sommerville, R. I. and Stewart, D. F. (1959). *Nature, Lond.* **183**, 553.

Sprent, J. F. A. (1946a). *Parasitology* **37**, 192.

Sprent, J. F. A. (1946b). *Parasitology* **37**, 202.

Stannard, J. N., McCoy, O. R. and Latchford, W. B. (1938). *Amer. J. Hyg.* **27**, 666.

Steiner, G. (1939). *Congr. int. Microbiol.* 434.

Stephenson, W. (1942a). *Parasitology* **34**, 246.

Stephenson, W. (1942b). *Parasitology* **34**, 253.

Stephenson, W. (1944). *Parasitology* **35**, 167.

Stewart, M. A. and Douglas, J. R. (1938). *Parasitology* **30**, 477.

Stoll, N. R. (1940). *Growth* **4**, 383.

Stoll, N. R. (1959). *Ann. N.Y. Acad. Sci.* **77**, 126.

Stoner, R. D. and Hankes, L. V. (1955). *Exp. Parasit.* **7**, 99.

Stoner, R. D. and Hankes, L. V. (1958). *Exp. Parasit.* **7**, 145.

Švarc, R. and Zmoray, I. (1960). *Helminthologica* **2**, 133.

Tarshis, I. B. (1958). *Proc. helm. Soc. Wash.* **25**, 99.

Taylor, A. and Whitlock, J. H. (1960). *Cornell Vet.* **50**, 339.

Taylor, A. E. R. (1960). *Exp. Parasit.* **9**, 113.

Taylor, D. P. (1962). *Proc. helm. Soc. Wash.* **29**, 52.

Tetley, J. H. (1937). *N.Z. J. Sci. Tech.* **18**, 805.

Thomas, H. A. (1959). *Proc. helm. Soc. Wash.* **26**, 55.

Thomas, R. J. and Stevens, A. J. (1960). *Parasitology* **50**, 31.
Thorne, G. (1923). *Dep. Circ. U.S. Dep. Agric.* 262.
Thorne, G. (1961). "Principles of Nematology". McGraw-Hill, New York.
Tracey, M. V. (1958). *Nematologica* **3**, 179.
Triffitt, M. J. (1930). *J. Helminth.* **8**, 19.
Triffitt, M. J. and Oldham, J. N. (1927). *J. Helminth.* **5**, 133.
Turner, A. W. and Hodgetts, V. E. (1955). *Aust. J. agric. Res.* **6**, 115.
Turner, J. H. (1953). *J. Parasit.* **39**, 589.
Turner, J. H. (1961). *J. Parasit.* **47**, 30.
Twohy, D. W. (1956). *Amer. J. Hyg.* **63**, 165.
Veglia, F. (1915). *Third and Fourth Reports, Director of Veterinary Research, Dept. Agric. Union. of South Africa*, 347.
Vinovev, V. G. (1957). *Zool. Zn.* **36**, 617.
Wald, G. (1960). *Circulation* **21**, 916.
Wallace, H. R. (1954). *Nature, Lond.* **173**, 502.
Wallace, H. R. (1955a). *J. Helminth.* **29**, 3.
Wallace, H. R. (1955b). *Ann. appl. Biol.* **43**, 477.
Wallace, H. R. (1956a). *Ann. appl. Biol.* **44**, 274.
Wallace, H. R. (1956b). *Nature, Lond.* **177**, 287.
Wallace, H. R. (1958). *Nematologica* **3**, 236.
Wallace, H. R. (1959a). *Ann. appl. Biol.* **47**, 350.
Wallace, H. R. (1959b). *Tech. Bull. Minist. Agric., Lond.* No. 7, H.M.S.O.
Wallace, H. R. (1960a). *Nematologica* **5**, 315.
Wallace, H. R. (1960b). *Ann. appl. Biol.* **48**, 107.
Wallace, H. R. (1961a). *Helminth. Abstr.* **30**, 1.
Wallace, H. R. (1961b). *Nematologica* **6**, 222.
Waterman, T. H. and Chase, F. A. (1960). *In* "Physiology of Crustacea". Vol. I. (T. H. Waterman, ed.). Academic Press, New York.
Weerdt, L. G. van. (1960). *Nematologica* **5**, 43.
Weinstein, P. P. (1952). *Exp. Parasit.* **1**, 363.
Weinstein, P. P. and Haskins, W. T. (1955). *Exp. Parasit.* **4**, 228.
Weischer, B. (1959). *Nematologica* **4**, 172.
Wertejuk, M. (1959). *Acta parasit. polon.* **7**, 315.
Wharton, R. H. (1957). *Ann. trop. Med. Parasit.* **31**, 278.
Widdowson, E., Doncaster, C. C. and Fenwick, D. W. (1958). *Nematologica* **3**, 308.
Wieser, W. (1953). *Medd. Våxtskyddsanst. Stockh.* **65**, 1. (Original not seen. Abs. in *Helminth. Abs.* **22**, (1953) No. 230).
Wieser, W. (1955). *Proc. helm. Soc. Wash.* **22**, 106.
Wigglesworth, V. B. (1954). "The Physiology of Insect Metamorphosis". Cambridge University Press, Cambridge.
Wilson, P. A. G. (1958). *J. exp. Biol.* **35**, 584.
Winslow, R. D. (1954). *Ann. appl. Biol.* **41**, 591.
Winslow, R. D. (1955). *Ann. appl. Biol.* **43**, 19.
Winslow, R. D. (1956). *J. Helminth.* **30**, 157.
Winslow, R. D. (1960). *In* "Nematology" (Sasser, J. N. and Jenkins, W. R., eds.) University of North Carolina, Chapel Hill.
Yoeli, M., Alger, N. and Most, H. (1958). *Amer. J. trop. Med. Hyg.* **7**, 247.
Zmoray, I. and Švarc, R. (1960). *Helminthologica* **2**, 209.

Parasitic Bronchitis

D. POYNTER

Parasitology Department, Allen and Hanbury's Ltd.,
Ware, Hertfordshire, England

I.	Introduction	179
II.	The Parasite	179
III.	The Parasite in the Pasture	181
IV.	Pathology	187
V.	The Treatment of Husk	194
VI.	Naturally Acquired Immunity......................................	195
VII.	Passive Immunization	196
VIII.	Active Immunization	197
IX.	The Measurement of Helminth Immunity...........................	199
X.	Vaccination	201
XI.	The Mechanism of Immunity	206
XII.	Conclusion	208
	Acknowledgement	209
	References	209

I. INTRODUCTION

The bovine disease known as parasitic bronchitis (husk or hoose) is caused by the nematode *Dictyocaulus viviparus*. As long ago as 1744 Ruysch noticed worms living in the air passages of cattle and indeed the cow was the animal in which nematode lungworms were first recorded.

In 1756 Nichols correlated the presence of bovine lungworms with a distinct disease which occurred in a epizootic form in England. Camper reported the disease in 1803. It has been observed and described on several occasions since.

Needless to say most of the early work centred upon the treatment of the disease rather than upon any real attempt at solving the problems of the epidemiology and aetiology of the condition.

II. THE PARASITE

Dictyocaulus viviparus lives as an adult in the larger air passages of the lungs. The female worms lay eggs which are passed up the trachea and down the oesophagus. On their way through the gut the eggs hatch to produce first stage larvae and these are passed out with the dung. Once voided the first stage larvae progress through the second stage to reach the third infective stage which under optimum conditions takes about 7 days. The third stage infective larvae when ingested by a susceptible bovine

I

animal, penetrate the wall of the alimentary tract and are carried in the lymph vessels through the mesenteric nodes to the thoracic duct. They thereby enter the jugular vein and so reach the heart. They leave the heart by way of the pulmonary artery and so eventually attain the pulmonary capillaries. They rupture these fine capillaries and reach the alveoli. They gradually ascend into the bronchioles and pass through the fourth larval stage. By the time they attain the larger air passages they are in the young adult stage and it is at this stage that a considerable amount of growth occurs so that the worms become relatively large reproductive adults.

There has been a considerable amount of controversy with regard to the actual details of the life cycle of this parasite. In the past people have been inclined to assume that details of the migratory route as discovered for *Dictyocaulus filaria*, a parasite of sheep, can be taken as also applying to *Dictyocaulus viviparus*. This, however, is not so and relatively little direct work has been carried out on the migratory route of *D. viviparus*. Soliman (1953) pointed out that information on the development of the parasitic phases of the life cycle of this parasite was incomplete, and that more observations were desirable. His work on guinea-pigs using doses of 7000 infective larvae showed them to be present in the lymphatic nodes within 24 h, and in the lungs within 3 days. In seventeen field cases of bovine parasitic bronchitis he was able to find larvae in the mesenteric lymph nodes of ten. He refers only to finding third stage larvae and although giving no figures on his recoveries he states that they were very variable.

Jarrett *et al.* (1957a) in a paper devoted largely to the pathology of husk, stated that it was the fourth stage larvae that left the lymph nodes to migrate to the lungs. They infected calves with 5000, 100 000 and 240 000 larvae but made no mention of finding lung lesions until 5 days later. On the other hand, Douvres and Lucker (1958), working with guinea-pigs, recovered third stage larvae from the lung 18 h after administering doses between 120 000 and 450 000 larvae. Poynter *et al.* (1960) working on guinea-pigs also found that in this animal larvae were able to reach the lung within 24 h. Larvae were found travelling through the lymph nodes during the first 2 days after the infection, but they were not found at later times. Livers of the guinea-pig were also carefully examined with consistently negative results showing that larvae penetrating into the gut mucosa entered the lymphatic vessels.

Poynter *et al.* (1960) produced evidence to show that larvae could reach the lungs of calves within 24 h and confirmation of the lymphatic migration was also obtained.

In an attempt to provide some quantitative estimate of the numbers of larvae which reached the lung after a given amount of time, an experiment was performed in which 20 000 larvae were given to a calf. The animal was killed 48 h after dosing, a very careful dissection was performed in which the lungs and lymph nodes were removed. The lung was found to contain 3151 larvae whilst 1082 larvae were teased out of the lymph nodes. It is obvious then that the majority of larvae recovered from the calf had reached the lung within 48 h. The vast majority (942 of) larvae recovered from the lymph nodes were in the draining of the small intestine. It seems then that the main site of larval penetration is indeed the small intestine.

No conclusive evidence has, however, been presented to establish that *Dictyocaulus viviparus* is capable of infecting the unborn calf. Kasparek (1900) reported that calves only $1\frac{1}{2}$ to 8 days were being infected with lungworms. Porter and Cauthen (1942) checked this observation by attempting to infect a calf pre-natally by feeding infective larvae to the pregnant dam. Although the cow received a total of 30 600 infective larvae over a period of 1 month, and was definitely clinically infected, the calf did not shown any symptoms of lungworm, nor were larvae detected in its faeces on daily examination for the first 2 months of its life. Another interesting observation made was that despite daily examination no lung worm larvae were observed in the faeces of the cow. Soliman (1953) finally resolved the pre-natal controversy by direct field observation. He examined twenty-six foetuses from cows suffering from husk and two bull calves born to cows suffering from husk. Not a single lungworm was found. He also carried out faeces examination on sixty heifers born whilst their dams were suffering from parasitic bronchitis, and again reported negative findings. Apart from the early observations of Kasparek (1900) there has never been any suggestion of pre-natal infection with *Dictyocaulus viviparus*. Further, no aspect of the epidemiology of the condition requires this hypothesis to explain any unusual observation.

Parasitic bronchitis is widespread in Great Britain but it is generally accepted that it is in the wetter western areas of the island that the disease reaches the most serious proportions.

Cunningham *et al.* (1956) working in central and S.W. Scotland carried out a survey of knackeries and farms in an attempt to find the incidence of the disease in animals of various ages. About 1500 pairs of bovine lungs were examined as a result of which it was found that 31% of young cattle which had completed their first season at grass were affected as opposed to only 3.8% of the older age groups. The farm survey showed that cattle could harbour lungworms for up to 6 months in the absence of reinfection.

III. THE PARASITE IN THE PASTURE

It has for a long time been realized that there is a close connection between husk, the pasture and the management of stock on the pasture.

Workers at the Central Veterinary Laboratory of the Ministry of Agriculture have contributed much to our knowledge of the epidemiology of parasitic bronchitis both in the way of field investigation and direct experimentation.

There is no doubt that lungworm larvae in the faeces and on the pasture suffer a heavy mortality. Michel (1959) stated that as many as 98% of the larvae might be killed during the first fortnight. Rose (1956) showed

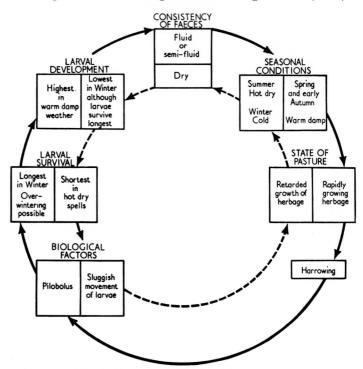

Fig. 1. Summary of the ecological factors affecting the free-living stages of *D. viviparus*; Those factors which are linked by the clockwise arrows are advantageous to the parasite. those factors linked by the anti-clockwise arrows are disadvantageous.

that the proportion of non-infective larvae reaching the infective stage was determined largely by climatic factors. The rate of development of the larvae depends on the temperature. At 25°C larvae may only take 3 days to reach the infective stage whereas at 5°C such development may take 26 days. At 0°C development is not entirely suspended so that it may proceed throughout the British winter.

There is still some controversy about whether or not the infective larvae of *D. viviparus* are able to overwinter on the pasture. A history of husk outbreaks in Southern England suggested to Taylor (1951) that disease-producing infestations were able to survive on a pasture for periods of nearly a year. Michel and Parfitt (1955) as a result of direct experiments concluded that the concentration of larvae on the herbage fell away quickly in spring and early summer but that the larvae could persist for 4 months in autumn and early winter. They stated that it was possible for the infestation of pastures to disappear completely during the winter months but pointed out that they did not wish to imply that larvae would not live through the winter in any circumstances. Later Michel and Shand (1955) in presenting their observations on seventeen husk outbreaks stated that consideration tended to confirm the view that the larvae did not survive on the ground over the winter. They write of there being considerable circumstantial evidence that the ultimate source of infection is in the form of larvae passed by carrier animals and not larvae that have persisted on the ground through the winter. Further, they state that the indications were that the larvae did not persist on the ground even for as long as 5 months. It is salutary to realize that although Michel and Shand (1955) carried out a most exhaustive survey of the outbreaks, they were still forced to write: "The conclusion seems to be inescapable that as yet no recommendations can be formulated with confidence."

Porter (1942) stated that the larvae of *D. viviparus* lived for 1 week but not for 6 or 7 weeks. In Germany, Wetzel (1948) concluded that the larvae did not survive the winter on pasture, and Stableforth (1953) in a review of work at Weybridge said that the larvae survived for only a month in spring and summer and up to 3 months at other times. Direct experiments on the survival of lungworm larvae were carried out by Jarrett *et al.* (1954) who set out to determine whether or not larvae could survive the winter under the field conditions obtaining in the West of Scotland. They fenced off three plots of ground and heavily contaminated these with infected faeces. After periods of 6 months and 13 months had elapsed, the plots were subsequently grazed by young susceptible calves. Animals from each group were found at post-mortem examination to be infected. The results of further experiments were published by Jarrett *et al.* (1955b). Six heavily infected field cases of parasitic bronchitis were turned onto four plots during August and September 1953. The plots were then closed until the following summer when young calves reared indoors were put onto them. On three plots it was demonstrated that larvae had survived since lungworms and/or lesions attributable to them were seen in the susceptible animals. Later, Allan and Baxter (1957) found that *D. viviparus* larvae persisted for 7 months on a pasture in Northern Ireland. In contrast, Soliman (1952) in Southern England failed to infect susceptible animals by grazing them on a pasture which had been naturally infected 2 months previously but Swietlikowski (1959) working near Warsaw observed that larvae were able to survive the winter on the pasture. It is difficult in work of this nature to known how much significance to attach to negative findings. Enough has, however, been demonstrated to show that *D. viviparus* may survive through a winter on the pasture. It must also be realized that the infection persists in cattle and that the carrier animal is also a hazard.

The infective larvae of *D. viviparus* are very inactive. Other species of nematode larvae are able to migrate from the faeces in which they are passed but Michel and Rose (1954) found that only a negligible proportion of the *D. viviparus* larvae in a faecal pat reached the herbage. The very small number that did were found very close to the faeces. This led to the conclusion that they would not have been picked up by grazing animals which are known to avoid faeces. It appeared, then, as if it was the dissemination of faeces containing larvae which made these available to the grazing animal and not the active movements of the larvae themselves. The term translation has been used to express the movement of larvae from the faeces to the pasture and it has become apparent that this process of translation is of great importance in the transmission of infection. Michel and Parfitt (1955; 1956) demonstrated that the concentration of larvae on the herbage determined the size of the infection in a susceptible calf subsequently grazing that herbage. Spedding and Michel (1957) suggested that the mechanical spreading of faeces was important in the process of translation. Rose and Michel (1957) later carried out experiments to investigate the effect on translation of such factors as the consistency of the faeces, mechanical agencies, climatic conditions, age of faeces and and larvae and the possible role played by birds. It was concluded that the number of larvae reaching the herbage was influenced to an appreciable extent by the consistency of the faeces. Far more larvae were recovered from plots onto which fluid or semi-fluid faeces were dropped than from the plots contaminated with solid faeces. This was mainly due to the greater ease with which semi-fluid faeces could be spread. It was concluded that when animals pass diarrhoeic faeces, which are usually spread over a wide area, far more larvae will reach the herbage than when the animals pass drier faeces which are deposited as a pat. It was further demonstrated that the mechanical spreading of the faecal pats was an effective means of distributing larvae over the herbage. More larvae were recovered from the plots over which the faeces were spread either by means of a small fork or using a cow's foot than from those in which the faeces were in the form of a pat. In comparing the results of similar experiments conducted at various times during the year, Rose and Michel (1957) observed marked differences in the numbers of larvae recovered from the herbage. The supposition was therefore made that climatic factors, in addition to mechanical spreading, played a part in distributing larvae over the herbage. The state of the spread faeces and the rate at which they disintegrated varied. During the winter the spread faeces and herbage

were perpetually wet except when frozen. One month later no spread
faeces could be seen on the herbage but a large number of larvae were recovered. In the spring and autumn the faeces were moist for most of the
time. They underwent gradual disintegration which was not as rapid as
that seen during the winter and fewer larvae were recovered from the
herbage. During the summer the faeces were dry within a few hours of being spread and no visible disintegration was observed. It was at this time
that the smallest numbers of larvae were recovered from the herbage.

Rose and Michel (1957) also found that in the winter and late autumn
pats up to 3 weeks old were still wet enough to allow them to be spread.
It was also noted that at these times considerable numbers of larvae could
be recovered from the pasture. During the spring and autumn the pats
partially dried out and spreading became difficult although broken pieces
of the pat could be scattered; under these conditions some larvae reached
the herbage. In the summer the pats dried so quickly that spreading was
impossible but larvae did however survive in the pats. It may therefore
be taken that a faecal pat can serve as a reservoir of infection.

Birds do not seem to be of any great practical significance in the spread
of larvae or of faeces containing larvae.

Experiments on the grazing behaviour of cattle in relation to faeces
(Michel et al., 1956) showed that the cattle will graze contaminated herb
age unless the faeces are conspicuous.

It is interesting to note that the optimum conditions necessary for
translation are not those required for larval development and survival.
Although maximum numbers of larvae were found in the winter these
were usually non-infective or dead; in the spring and autumn all the living
larvae recovered were infective, but larvae recovered from the herbage
in the summer were dead (Rose and Michel, 1957).

Michel and Parfitt (1956) demonstrated a correlation between the
rate of growth of the herbage and the amount of translation. Rapidly
growing herbage leads to loose dung and also supplies a moist micro-
climate which keeps the dung in a condition in which it may be spread
easily. This moist microclimate in the herbage favours the survival of
larvae in small amounts of faeces. It is also of note that the temperatures
which produce rapid herbage growth also contribute to rapid larval development. It has already been mentioned that the early larval stages are
more susceptible to death from low temperatures than the infective stage
and it therefore follows that in the winter when the time for larval development is prolonged, the larvae will remain for longer periods of time in a
more susceptible form. Translation will therefore be at a minimum.

The factors required for the survival of infective larvae are not the
same as those necessary for their development. Survival is greatest at
lower temperatures. It has been estimated (Michel et al., 1959) that in

spring and summer a decline in population from 100 to 1 would take about 30 days, whilst in autumn and winter the same reduction would take 60 – 90 days.

The overall effect of the above factors is to produce a seasonal fluctuation in the numbers of lungworm larvae on the pasture. During spring and early summer the conditions for translation are good so that herbage infestation may be high although the larvae themselves are short lived. At the height of summer, pasture infestations are usually low. During the autumn, conditions are good for both the development and survival of lungworm larvae. In winter, although existing infestations survive well, little larval development occurs, so that few infective larvae arrive on the herbage.

In 1960 Rose published the results of a series of experiments designed to determine the relative importance of climatic conditions, the distribution of faeces over the herbage and the grazing behaviour of the bovine animal in relation to the transmission of lungworm infection. It was shown that the climatic factors were of primary importance by virtue of their direct influence on the rate of development and survival of the lungworm larvae. It was found that, during the winter, transmission is negligible since only a small proportion of larvae become infective and consequently the distribution and grazing behaviour are unimportant. However, when climatic conditions are suitable for the development and survival of larvae the distribution of the faeces and the grazing behaviour of the animals become important.

Michel and Parfitt (1956) carried out an experiment utilizing a small paddock which was infested with *Dictyocaulus viviparus*. A susceptible calf was added to the paddock every 5 weeks. It was shown that there is a close relationship between the intensity of the disease and the mean herbage count during the first 9 days that the calf is exposed to infection. Michel and MacKenzie (1956) had already concluded that the infections in their experimental animals were not referable to larvae which the animals themselves had passed, and that the relevant part of the infection process occupied but a short space of time. The salient point of this work was to show that cattle do not produce on the pasture an infestation dangerous to themselves since they are refractory to infection by the time larvae which they have passed are infective and available on the herbage. Michel (1957a) later showed, however, that these considerations did not apply in a situation where abrupt changes in the rate of uptake of larvae were possible.

In Belgium Gregoire and his colleagues (Gregoire *et al.*, 1960; Gregoire and Pouplard, 1961) claim that by rotating cattle on nine plots so that the animals remain for 4 days on each plot husk can be prevented. This system is based on the assumption that the larvae of *D. viviparus* require

4 days in which to reach the infective stage and that the survival rate of the larvae is 4 weeks or less. It has already been mentioned that these assumptions do not necessarily apply.

Although much work has gone into a study of the epidemiology of husk, Michel (1957b) has stated: "The control of husk must be based on acquired resistance to the parasite." It was pointed out that it is difficult to make recommendations for the prevention of husk and that it is necessary to ensure that every animal acquires and retains an adequate resistance. Although considerable advances have been made towards an understanding of the problem, specific recommendations on control measures are not yet warranted.

Recently a factor has been discovered which may aid considerably our understanding of the translation of larvae from the faeces to the pasture. Robinson (1962) noted that when bovine faeces were spread on trays and kept under controlled conditions of temperature and humidity there often occurred an abundant development on the faeces of the conspicuous sporangiophores of *Pilobolus* spp. (Phycomycetes: Mucorales). It was also observed that the fungus developed at the time that *D. viviparus* larvae in the faeces reached the infective form and migrated to the surface of the faecal pat. *Pilobolus* is characteristic in that the whole sporangium containing the ripe spores undergoes a violent discharge to be spread on the surrounding herbage. On faecal surfaces containing the infective larvae and the fungus it was noted that there was an increase in the motility of the larvae when the illumination was increased. The normally quiescent larvae began to move actively and, on meeting the sporangiophores, attached to them and migrated to the upper surface of the sporangium. Having attained this situation the larvae became coiled and as many as fifty have been seen on the top of a single sporangium. In the field the fungus has been observed to propel the larvae a distance of 10 ft.

The spores of *Pilobolus* must pass through the gut of a herbivore before further development occurs. Robinson (1962) concluded that if the association between *Pilobolus* spp and *Dictyocaulis viviparus* was widespread in the field, then it must represent a significant factor in the epidemiology of parasitic bronchitis. Since a survey of *Pilobolus* in Britain showed it to be present in over 95% of samples examined with a range from the North of Scotland to the Isle of Wight (Robinson *et al.*, 1962) there seems every indication of its significance in the epidemiology of husk.

An attempt to summarize the various factors which affect the fate of the free-living stages of *D. viviparus* on the pasture is made in Fig. 1.

IV. PATHOLOGY

During recent years active attention has been turned by many workers to a study of the clinical and pathological aspects of parasitic bronchitis.

Joest (1908) was one of the first to attempt any classification of the lesions found at post-mortem examination. He recognized three stages which were described as acute alveolar emphysema, interstitial emphysema and commencing pneumonia, and well established pneumonia.

In 1922 Daubney investigated an outbreak of lungworm disease on the experimental farm of the United States Bureau of Animal Industry. He provided an accurate account of the macroscopic and microscopic changes observed. It was not until 1957 that a true appreciation of the development of the disease was established. This was due to the work of Jarrett, McIntyre, and Urquhart (1957a), who experimentally studied the changes produced in young calves by single doses of larvae calculated to give rise to sub-lethal and lethal disease. By slaughtering calves at various times after infection the serial pathology of the condition was established and the lesions apparent correlated with the clinical condition of the animal. These workers were able to reproduce all the lesions seen in the naturally occurring disease.

Jarrett *et al.* (1960b), whose work has provided a basis for our understanding of the clinical and pathological aspects of husk, divided the disease into four stages according to the time of initial infection. These stages are 1. the penetration phase, days 1–7; 2. the pre-patent phase, days 7–25; 3. the patent phase, days 25–55; 4. the post patent phase, days 55–70.

The penetration phase is of minimum clinical significance. At our own experimental farm we infected over 300 calves with *Dictyocaulus viviparus* and did not observe any disease during the first 7 days. During this phase larvae having travelled through the lymphatic vessels attain the lung. Poynter *et al.* (1960) observed that even 36 h after infection larvae may be recovered from the lung. The lungs of such animals showed numerous petechial haemorrhages which were associated with the escape of larvae from the capillaries into the alveoli, such lesions are rapidly resolved and do not produce any clinical effect.

The pre-patent phase, days 7–25, is that phase during which clinical effects are first detected. During this phase there is an intense eosinophilic exudate into the lungs, with the result that the small bronchi and bronchioles become blocked. Such blockages lead to the collapse of alveoli distal to the block, since the air in the alveoli is absorbed into the blood and no more air can enter to take its place. Such damage need not however be permanent since if the blockage is removed the alveoli may again attain their normal function.

In heavily infected or particularly susceptible animals there is, at about 10–14 days from infection, a marked increase in respiratory rate which may in the course of 4–5 days double, so as to reach 70–80 per min. Coughing now becomes more noticeable. Should no complications supervene there may, at about 21 days from dosing, be a check to the progress of the disease which is associated with a regression of the primary bronchial lesions.

It must be appreciated that several complications are likely to appear during the pre-patent phase so that deaths occur. The main complications which may be seen during the course of the disease are pulmonary oedema, emphysema and secondary bacterial infection. During the patent phase of the disease there are of course present in the lung adult reproducing nematodes (Fig. 2) which give rise to eggs. Many of

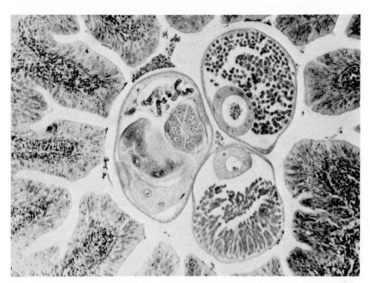

FIG. 2. Transverse section of an adult female *D. viviparus* in a bronchiole.

these eggs are aspirated into the actual lung tissue. The presence of these eggs and their hatched first stage larvae brings about the reaction in which macrophages and multi-nucleate foreign body giant cells attempt to engulf the nematode material (Fig. 3). This produces a marked consolidation of lung lobules and primary parasitic pneumonia is established. Jarrett *et al.* (1960b) state that a great deal of the clinical effect is caused by this lesion. We have found that out of ninety-seven calves infected with *D. viviparus*, forty-three cases of the foreign body reaction were seen. At this stage too the respiratory rate undergoes an increase so that it may rise to over 100 per min; loss of appetite occurs; a reduction in growth is seen and coughing is frequent. Ausculation reveals harsh bronchial breathing.

The post-patent phase of the disease is often one of gradual recovery in that the respiratory rate decreases, weight gain is resumed and the frequency of coughing lessens.

Peacock *et al.* (1962) have had opportunity to observe 250 calves each of which received a dose of sixty to seventy larvae per lb body weight. Of these eighteen died in the pre-patent phase of the disease,

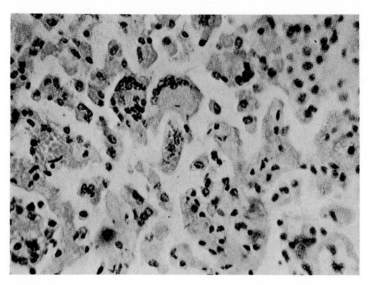

FIG. 3. Foreign body reaction associated with nematode material in the lung.

thirteen died during the first week of patency, twenty-three during the second week of patency and ninety-eight died in the post-patent stage. These figures show that the post-patent stage may be dangerous. Death is usually due to the spread of a lesion the aetiology of which is unknown. This lesion is referred to as alveolar epithelialization and it is one in which the cells of the alveolar walls become thick and cuboidal (Fig. 4). This epithelialization may spread to involve whole lobes of the lung.

Jarrett *et al.* (1960b) list several complications which may be seen either during or after husk. During the disease pulmonary oedema is the frequent cause of a sudden clinical deterioration. The alveoli become filled with fluid (Fig. 5). This may evaporate to leave behind a protein-containing hyaline membrane (Fig. 6) which is deposited on the alveolar walls. Emphysema may occur when bronchioles rupture and air finds its way into the septa of the lung. Large bullae may be formed in this manner. Emphysema affects the contraction of the lung. During the course of husk secondary bacterial infection may occur (Fig. 7), and it is for this reason that antibiotics are routinely used in severe husk cases.

Calves are sometimes left after a husk attack with a chronic cough. This may be due to the development of bronchiectasis in which the bronchi of a lobe fail to clear themselves of exudates so that they become

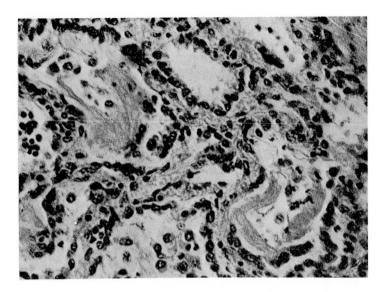

FIG. 4. Alveolar epithelialization.

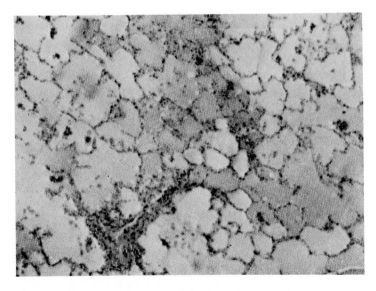

FIG. 5. Alveoli filled with fluid in pulmonary oedema.

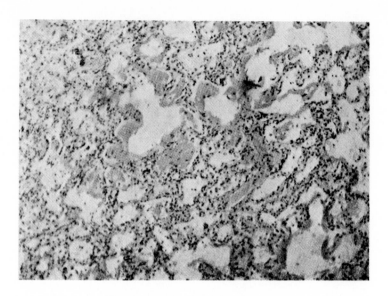

Fig. 6. Formation of hyaline membranes.

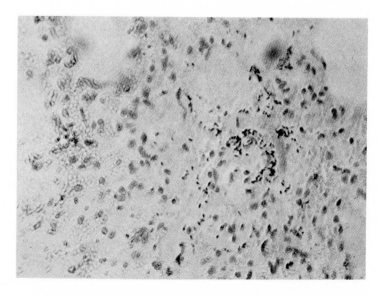

Fig. 7. Secondary bacterial infection in a husk-affected lung.

infected with bacteria. The bronchi dilate and eventually a given lobe becomes full of pus. Pulmonary fibrosis is another lesion often seen in recovering cases but it is probably not of great clinical significance.

No account of recent developments in parasitic bronchitis would be complete without mentioning a syndrome known as "fog fever". This was described by Hudson (1951) as occurring in adult cattle and a feature of the syndrome was pulmonary oedema. It was suggested that it might be due to an allergy associated with lungworms. Michel (1953) showed that a proportion of fog fever cases are undoubtedly the consequence of lung-worm infestation. If fog fever is defined as a rapidly developing pul-monary oedema then it becomes clear that it may have a variety of causes. Michel (1954) was able to produce the syndrome by using larvae but he states that it can be caused by the specific pneumonia referred to by Jarrett *et al.* (1953), the experimental administration of very large numbers of *Ascaris lumbricoides* (Taylor, 1953), or the London fog.

Simpson *et al.* (1957) also studied the histopathology of husk by experi-mentally infecting calves. The lesions observed were similar to those described above. It was also noted that nodules of lymphoid tissue were present in the lungs of two resistant calves killed following challenge.

Skovronski (1959) studied the levels of sugar, inorganic and acid soluble phosphorus and lactic acid in the blood of six calves experi-mentally infected with *D. viviparus* and in thirty naturally infected calves. In the experimental infections the biochemical changes developed at the same time as the clinical symptoms and all levels were depressed. In calves naturally infected, the sugar and phosphorus levels were low but the level of lactic acid remained normal.

Ugrin (1959) also studied some of the facets of parasitic bronchitis, being interested in the clinical symptoms and gaseous exchange. He observed an increase of respiratory rate, an increase of oxygen intake, increase of momentary ventilation of the lungs and a reduction of respira-tory coefficient.

Fisher and McIntyre (1960) found that in parasitic bronchitis there was a greatly increased respiratory rate accompanied by a smaller increase in ventilation rate, indicating shallower respiration. No marked decrease from normal was found in the plasma pH but the plasma CO_2 content was significantly above normal indicating a compensated respiratory acidosis.

It is accepted that helminth infections are often associated with eosino-philia and parasitic bronchitis is no exception. Weber and Rubin (1958) reported rises at 15–17 days after exposure and further rises at 25–52 days. Djafar *et al.* (1960) also reported peaks of eosinophilia and found a lower eosinophil response in animals that eventually died than they did in survivors. Cornwell (1962) reported eosinophil responses to normal and irradiated larvae. After challenge vaccinated calves developed an eosinophilia four times as great as that produced by irradiated larvae. The actual function of the eosinophil is still the subject of active work (Archer, 1960) but it is worth noting that Spiers (1958) has suggested that it may have a part to play in antibody formation by becoming sensitized to the antigen and phagocytosed by the reticulo-endothelial antibody producing cells.

It is thus evident that many advances have been made in the pathology of husk the majority of which have concerned the histopathology of the condition.

V. THE TREATMENT OF HUSK

In 1955 Taylor and Michel remarked that with regard to husk, "the need for an effective treatment is so great it is reasonable to leave no stone unturned". Up until this time many substances had been tried against husk and some no doubt hastened the death of calves receiving them.

In 1957, Walley (1957a, b, and c) announced the development of cyanacethydrazide, a drug which was received with enthusiasm since it showed promise of providing a major advance in the treatment of husk. Extensive trials were carried out in calves, sheep goats and pigs. Action was shown against worms present in the air passages but no action was found on migrating larvae. One interesting and new facet of this anthelmintic was that it could be administered orally, subcutaneously or intramuscularly. Groves (1958) reported favourably on the drug when he used it in the field against husk. O'Donoghue (1958) in Canada also found it useful as did Trace (1958) in the U.S.A. However, other workers such as Rubin and Tillotson (1960), Swanson et al. (1959), Allan (1957), Gripper (1957), Enigk et al. (1958), Enigk and Duwel (1959), and Guilhon and Petit (1958) obtained results which were not so promising. A critical appraisal of the drug was carried out by Colglazier and Enzie (1961) who concluded that the treatment of experimental infections of D. viviparus in calves was of little or no value. Further they noted no clinical improvement in the treated animals. The chemical was used in accordance with recommended procedures. Attention was drawn to the fact that parasitic bronchitis may for several reasons be self-limiting and it was suggested that this may have led to erroneous conclusions with respect to the influence of specific medication on the course of lungworm infections.

Diethylcarbamazine has also been prominent in the treatment of husk and its introduction is due to the work of Parker (1957), Parker and Roberts (1958), and Parker et al. (1959). Parker and Vallely (1960) summarized their findings by stating that in several experiments, both with naturally and artificially infected calves, diethylcarbamazine was effective in treating husk. Rubin and Tillotson (1962) also carried out experiments using diethylcarbamazine and confirmed its therapeutic effect. They reported that the drug was more effective against worms that had been in the host approximately 2 weeks than against either recently ingested larvae or mature lungworms. In all, four groups of calves were treated at various times during an experimental infection. One group received no treatment, another was treated early in the infection, another in the intermediate stage and another in the late stage. The outstanding gross feature observed in the lungs of the calves at necropsy was the minimal pathological changes in those given intermediate treatment as compared with those of all the other groups. Diethylcarbamazine then affects worms of about 2 weeks old but has no effect on very young lungworms. More work is needed to assess its activity, if any, on adult worms. Parker et al. (1959) reported it successful under field conditions but Rubin and Tillotson (1962) obtained an inconclusive result which was suggestive of some activity. In any event, Parker and Vallely (1960) recognize that the compound is most effective against immature worms. There is no doubt that if animals do get parasitic bronchitis, diethylcarbamazine is likely to be of value.

Rubin and Tillotson (1962) state that "a satisfactory anthelmintic to control D. viviparus in cattle should have a high degree of activity against all stages of development within the host, from the recently ingested infective larvae to the sexually mature worms. This range of activity is needed, since one must assume that under natural conditions of exposure, an infective animal would most likely be harbouring all stages of the parasite by the time a diagnosis is made and treatment initiated."

The same authors also pointed out that neither cyanacethydrazide nor diethylcarbamazine possesses all the qualities desired for treating husk. They further draw attention to the fact that since continual medication of animals subject to exposure is impractical because many of the harmful effects of lungworm are produced by forms not susceptible to anthelmintics, satisfactory chemical measures for the prevention of verminous bronchitis seem impossible to attain. They conclude, "probably one should seek to control this disease by biologic rather than chemical means."

VI. NATURALLY ACQUIRED IMMUNITY

It has long been known that a strong acquired immunity to husk exists. Such was the experience of Taylor (1951), Wetzel (1948), Gregoire (1951), Jarrett et al. (1955a) and Swanson et al. (1955). Porter and Cauthen (1942) carried out experiments on reinfection. One calf aged 138 days was susceptible to reinfection but this procedure failed in one yearling and in another the worms matured slowly and lived for only a short time. Michel (1955) observed that when calves that had recovered from an experimental lungworm infection were reinfected, the second infection did not

K

become patent but that immature worms might persist in the lungs for some months. Rubin and Lucker (1956) also showed the development of immunity to reinfection but noted that calves appear to vary inherently in their capacity to acquire resistance. A similar observation was made by Weber (1958). Weber and Lucker (1959) undertook some experiments to determine whether or not calves initially given much smaller doses of normal infective larvae would acquire enough resistance to withstand a subsequent heavy, but not necessarily lethal exposure to infection. Of six calves four were each given 500 larvae and two 1500. Two and a half to three months from the end of patency each calf was challenged with 25 000 larvae. Five calves out of six had acquired a strong resistance, though not a complete immunity against patent reinfection with *D. viviparus*. These resistant calves surpassed the controls in respect of weight gain and also suffered a minimum of respiratory distress. Jarrett *et al.* (1959a) carried out an experiment on ten 2-month old calves in which the animals each received 2500 infective larvae; 160 days later each calf was dosed with a further 4500 larvae, and after a lapse of a further 150 days 13 000 larvae were administered to each calf. The calves were killed and subjected to post-mortem examination 32 days after the last infection. Every animal developed a patent infection as a result of the first dose of larvae; four developed patent infections as a result of the second exposure, whilst only three developed patent infections as a result of the third exposure, the numbers of worms found being 165, six and twelve respectively and all of these being small or immature. A further experiment by the same workers showed that immunity also developed when calves were infected with twenty-five doses of 300 infective larvae, the doses being separated by intervals of 2 or 3 days and extended over a period of 62 days.

It is apparent that there is ample field and experimental evidence to show that the infection of calves with *D. viviparus* confers a high degree of resistance to a subsequent reinfection. It must, however, be realized that there is a variation of response between one animal and another so that some will be better immune than others whilst some may never develop a great degree of immunity.

VII. PASSIVE IMMUNIZATION

In 1955 Jarrett *et al.* (1955a) carried out an experiment on the passive immunization of calves against *Dictyocaulus viviparus*. Up until this time little work had been conducted on passive immunization in helminth infections. Success had been reported by Miller (1934) and Campbell (1938) working with *Cysticercus fasciolaris* in rats and by Kerr (1935) in the case of *Cysticercus pisiformis* in rabbits. Sarles and Taliaferro (1936, 1938) reported significant reductions with *Nippostrongylus* in the rat as did Lawlor (1940) with *Strongyloides* in the rat. Other systems in which passive transfer has been tried are with hookworms in dogs (Otto, 1938) and mice (Kerr, 1938), in filariasis of cotton rats (McFadzean 1953) and schistosome infections of mice (Stirewalt and Evans, 1953).

Jarrett *et al.* (1955a) obtained immune serum from six recovered field cases of parasitic bronchitis which were further infected with doses ranging from 50 000 to 200 000 larvae. The complement fixing antibody of the sera showed a typical secondary response after the experimental infection and only one calf developed respiratory symptoms, the other being completely resistant. At the time when the level of complement fixing antibodies in the sera was judged to be at its peak the animals were bled and a total of 23 l of serum obtained. The globulin fraction of the serum was separated and injected intraperitoneally into five calves each 10 weeks old. Each calf received 500 ml of immune serum daily on 3 consecutive days and was infected with 4000 larvae 2 days later as were five control calves. The animals were slaughtered 30 days after infection and their worm burdens estimated. The number of worms found in the immunized group was considerably less than that found in the control group and there were also differences in the associated lung damage seen in the two groups. The main conclusions which could be drawn as a result of this work were that in parasitic bronchitis there are present humoral antibodies which are detectable and measurable by a complement fixation test; serum containing these antibodies conferred a considerable degree of protection against a single challenging infection of *D. viviparus*.

Rubin and Weber (1955) tested various dosages of immune sera against a challenge of 50 000 larvae which was known to be consistently fatal to non-immunized animals. Six calves were used of which five were given intravenous injections of immune serum at rates between 0.1 ml–5.0 ml/lb body weight. The two calves which received the highest doses of immune serum survived but the others died 33, 37 and 48 days after infection. The control calf died on the 23rd day. This experiment also suggests that the passive transfer of protective substances had occurred.

VIII. ACTIVE IMMUNIZATION

Jarrett *et al.* (1960a) experimented in actively immunizing calves against parasitic bronchitis by using as an antigen freeze dried adult *D. viviparus* collected from the bronchi of experimentally infected calves. The material was prepared as a water in oil emulsion and each 100 ml of emulsion contained 1 g of dried lungworm, 0.625 g of heat killed *Mycobacterium phlei*, 50 ml of 0.85% NaCl, 50 ml of low viscosity liquid paraffin and 2 g of "emocithine".

The first experiment did not show the intramuscular injection of such material to have any effect on a subsequent challenge with 4000 infective lungworm larvae. Further experiments were however carried out in which the efficacy of vaccination was determined against smaller challenge doses and a challenge of small repeated doses of infective larvae. In the group challenged with 2000 larvae as a single dose and that challenged with 2000 larvae administered as 200 per day on alternate days, there was stated to be a significant degree of protection as judged by the quantitative reduction in worm burden. There was, however, no appreciable difference in the amount of damage suffered by the lungs. In the group given 500 larvae as a single challenge dose and that given 500 larvae administered as 50 per day on alternate days, the reduction in worm burden just failed to be of significance. If then the injection of adult lungworm material had evoked any appreciable immunity it is perhaps surprising that such immunity withstood a challenge of 2000 but not 500. Jarrett *et al.* (1960a) stated that although a reduction in the number of worms developing from a challenge infection was sometimes obtained the method seemed of little practical value.

Other work using injectable dead lungworm material in an attempt to obtain immunity has been carried out by Wade *et al.* (1961) in guinea-pigs and rabbits. These workers concluded that guinea-pigs given injections of lyophilized third-stage lungworm larvae emulsified with Freund's complete adjuvant harboured 50% as many worms 8 days following a challenge infection with viable larvae as did the control guinea-pigs given injections of isotonic sodium chloride adjuvant emulsion. Injections of adjuvanted lyophilized mature lungworms produced guinea-pigs with lung burdens 61% those of the controls. However, a perusal of the results shows that in the experiment a group of guinea-pigs given saline alone had fewer worms than any other group and it is therefore obvious that the results are not significant. Significance is, however, claimed for the results in rabbits. Since, however, the maximum lungworm burden was fourteen and since a challenge of 20 000 larvae was given it is apparent that Wade *et al.* (1961) did not readily get the infection to take in their rabbits, a fact which does prejudice their results.

It should be noted at this point that a certain amount of caution is necessary when utilizing the guinea-pig as a host for *D. viviparus*. The early experiences of our group have already been published (Poynter *et al.*, 1960) but further work (Silverman *et al.*, 1962) has shown that the guinea-pig may be stimulated to produce resistance against *D. viviparus* by the injection of helminth material from a variety of sources. Results have been obtained with lyophilized *Strongyloides papillosus* and other helminths which are as good as those seen with lyophilized *D. viviparus*. It seems as if the guinea-pig is capable of responding to a non-specific factor common to these two helminths. It should also be mentioned here that patent infections are not usually seen in the guinea-pig so that it must constantly be kept in mind that the experimental system is one in which natural immunity plays a part.

Wade *et al.* (1962) vaccinated calves with an antigen prepared from lungworms and third stage larvae. No immunity was observed in animals 2 months old at the time of infection. In three calves 8 months old at the time of first infection, an average of thirty-seven lungworms was recovered 35 days after challenge with 18 000 whereas the average control lungworm burden was 187. The worms taken from the vaccinated animals also weighed less and were of a shorter length. There is then evidence of an acquired resistance having developed.

It is perhaps worth noting at this point that Wade and his colleagues (1958, 1961, 1962) consistently used more larvae than the Glasgow workers to get the same clinical effect. It has been suggested that the conditions under which larvae are cultured may affect their infectivity. This may be related to the fact that the larvae used by Glasgow are reared to the third stage in the faeces whereas those at Florida are reared to the third stage in water.

IX. The Measurement of Helminth Immunity

There is still no serological test which is known quantitatively to detect a protective circulating antibody against a parasitic worm.

Jarrett *et al.* (1959a) used a heated adult whole worm antigen in a complement fixation test of the 50% haemolysis unit type to study the immunity resulting from experimental infection. It was noted that with primary infections the antibody response was first detected at 30–35 days and reached a peak at 80–100 days. After holding at this level for about 1 month it then declined to a low level at 150–200 days. Challenge of the calves when the titre had declined produced a rapid rise in antibody titre characteristic of a secondary response, a peak being seen at 3–4 weeks.

Weber (1958) in the U.S.A. used an adult whole-worm antigen prepared by a low temperature method and a complement fixation test of the serum dilution type, employing as the end-point complete inhibition of haemolysis and two full units of complement. Twelve days after infection an initial antibody response was detected and the titre rapidly reached a peak 4 days later. The titre was then maintained at a high level until the 63rd day. Such a response was seen in calves exposed for the first time and in those re-exposed on one or more than one occasion.

Michel and Cornwell (1959) used ten pairs of calves to compare the level of acquired resistance to reinfection with *D. viviparus* and levels of complement fixing antibody. It was found that the antibody titres required considerably longer to develop than did resistance to reinfection and no correlation between the two measurements could be demonstrated. They concluded that the lack of correlation between titre and protection suggested that complement fixing antibodies as measured by a test using a heated adult worm antigen are not themselves protective nor can that level be used as a reliable measure of an animal's ability to prevent the establishment of worms. They did not deny the possibility that the antibody levels measured by the procedure they used might prove to be some other manifestation of resistance.

Cornwell and Michel (1960) further investigated the complement fixing antibody response of calves to the nature of experimental *D. viviparus* infection. The results obtained for single doses of larvae corresponded closely to those obtained by Jarrett *et al.* (1959a). Little confirmation of Weber's (1958) results was obtained but it was pointed out that his antigen was prepared in a dissimilar manner. The results of the exposures to natural infection did not show any great differences from those obtained in the calves given a single dose of larvae. The continuous intake of larvae from the herbage produced a fairly uniform titre in the middle range. If the herbage infestation fell then the C.F. titre fell. However if an increase in pasture level occurred then the titre also rose in a manner typical of a secondary response. Cornwell and Michel (1960) suggested that their results showed that the development of antibodies is related to the time elapsing since the initial exposure and not to the clinical severity of the disease, the fate of the calf, or the worm burden at post-mortem. It was further suggested that the stimulus to antibody production which the heated whole worm antigen detects may be the arrival and development of immature worms in the lung.

Cornwell (1960a) later studied the complement fixing antibody of calves to the X-irradiated vaccine. The titres resulting from the first dose were low whilst the second produced a variable rise in titre. A similar result was recorded by Poynter *et al.* (1960) who also noted that after challenge almost all calves show a very rapid increase to a higher level than that seen after vaccination. In older animals the titres rose faster and reached greater heights than those seen in younger calves. It was also stated that the relationship between the complement fixation titre and the actual immunity of a given animal was not absolute. Immunity could develop before the rise in the C.F. titre and persist as the C.F. titre was falling as was noted in the case of hyperimmune animals. Cornwell (1960a) noted that he found no evidence of irradiated larvae developing to maturity but he did suggest that the antibody response may be due to irradiated larvae which succeeded in becoming established in the lungs before being eliminated.

Cornwell (1960b) also followed the C.F. titre of nineteen calves which were vaccinated with a double dose of irradiated larvae and subsequently exposed to challenge. The challenge stimulated an early rise in titre. In 1961, Cornwell again reported wide variations in individual calves.

The only conclusion that can at present be reached is that the C.F. test cannot be relied upon to reflect the immune status of a given calf.

X. VACCINATION

There is no doubt that the most significant advance in the field of parasitic bronchitis is the discovery and development of a vaccine which prevents the disease. Husk is the only helminth disease for which a vaccine exists and its basis lies in the biological effect of X-irradiation on infective larvae.

One reason for the failure of the dead infective material to stimulate sufficient active immunity in the calf was thought to be that the defensive reaction might depend upon substances which were only elaborated by living worms. Sharp (1959) describes how in their efforts to make a vaccine the Glasgow workers "cast widely around for a method of treating the larvae themselves whereby we could use them in a weakened form to induce strong immunity without producing the disease". The method eventually adopted was X-irradiation. Early experiments indicated (Jarrett et al., 1960a) that irradiation at less than 20 000 r did not produce a sufficient degree of alteration of the larvae. Experiments were therefore conducted at 20 000, 40 000 and 60 000. One of the first factors to be determined was the level of irradiation which prevented the larvae producing a patent infection. It was found that the irradiating dose of 60 000 r was too high. The larvae were so inactivated that they evoked no immunity to a subsequent challenge. At 20 000 and 40 000 r however, the larvae were partially inactivated so that they produced no appreciable disease and yet evoked immunity to a subsequent challenge. It was thus established that one dose of 4000 larvae irradiated at 20 000 or 40 000 r enabled calves to resist a subsequent challenge of 4000 normal larvae given 50 days later. Such immunizing doses did however produce mild pulmonary complications. In calves killed 35 days after infection with larvae irradiated with 20 000 and 40 000 r lesions were found at autopsy which were responsible for clinical signs recorded during the 35 days.

The Glasgow workers carried out a trial (Jarrett et al., 1958a) in which they estimated the utility of vaccination as a field procedure. They artificially infected a number of calves which were then allowed to graze on a pasture which was subsequently grazed by groups of vaccinated and control calves. Forty-two bull calves were used, fifteen acting as carriers, fifteen as vaccinates and twelve as controls. Each member of the vaccinated group received 1000 larvae irradiated at 40 000 r. Fifty days later the group was turned out to graze a paddock previously infested by five carriers and grazed by a further ten carriers and twelve controls. It was estimated that the concentration of larvae on the herbage was 1300 per sq. ft. The mean number of larvae passed per g of faeces was consistently higher in the control group, a maximum of some 700 larvae per g being recorded whilst the highest mean figure for the vaccinated group was about 200 larvae per g. The figures published showed that the larval output of the controls was significantly greater than that of the vaccinates both in the number passed at any one time and in the length of patency. The respiratory rates of the control group, a reliable index of respiratory disease, were much higher than those of the vaccinates. It is, however, mortality which provides a really critical test of the value of a vaccine against parasitic bronchitis. Of the twelve control calves, ten died but of the fifteen vaccinates only three died. No reason was found for the failure to protect three of the vaccinates.

In view of the very heavy challenge and the fact that the immunizing dose was only 1000 larvae per calf the degree of protection afforded was very good indeed. This was confirmed by the fact that when the surviving vaccinates were killed there were virtually no pulmonary lesions.

A further field trial (Jarrett et al. 1958b) involved forty commercial farms with a past history of parasitic bronchitis. A total of 1088 calves were involved in the trial and on each farm half were vaccinated and half left as controls. Once again the vaccination involved one dose of 1000 larvae irradiated at 40 000 r. Parasitic bronchitis broke out on six farms where 62% of the controls died but only 6% of the vaccinates.

It was then shown under both experimental and field conditions that one dose of 1000 D. viviparus larvae irradiated at 40 000 r could protect the vast majority of calves from a lethal challenge. Such a procedure did not however completely prevent the disease when the vaccinated animals were exposed to high levels of challenge. Consequently further work was undertaken by Jarrett et al. (1959b) on double vaccination with irradiated larvae. The vaccine was given to three groups of ten calves in two doses (40 000 r); all calves were given 1000 larvae as the first dose (day 0), and 4000, 2000 and 1000 respectively as the second dose (day 42). Another group received only the first dose of vaccine, i.e. the 1000 dose. All groups including a control group were challenged with 10 000 larvae (day 93) and a further control group was challenged with 5000 larvae so as to guard against excessive mortality in the 10 000 challenge group preventing assessment of worm burden. In all the doubly vaccinated groups there was no rise in respiratory rates after challenge but in the singly vaccinated group and the control groups there were marked increases. The animals were killed 125 days after the beginning of the experiment. The calves in the doubly vaccinated groups gained approximately 18% in weight during this time, those in the singly vaccinated group gained 7.6%, whilst the challenge controls gained only 5%. In all the doubly vaccinated groups no lungworms were found. The singly vaccinated group harboured a mean of 820 worms, which is perhaps surprisingly high since the control group challenged with 10 000 larvae had 879 worms. However, with respect to this control group, it is noted that it was impossible to assess the total number of worms present as many were immature and were visible only on histological examination. Further, the lesions in the singly vaccinated group were of a less permanent nature than those observed in the control group. In any event it was apparent that the two dose vaccinating schedules had yielded very good degrees of protection indeed.

A pasture trial utilizing the double dose vaccination procedure was carried out by Jarrett et al. (1961). Ten calves were used, five of which were given two doses of vaccine at a 30 day interval. Each dose of vaccine consisted of 1000 third stage larvae which had been subjected to 40 000 r of irradiation. The other five calves acted as controls. Twenty days after the second dose of vaccine, all calves were turned out on to a pasture which was known to be heavily contaminated with D. viviparus larvae deposited there by a group of forty calves of whom thirty-eight had died. Thus a natural heavy challenge was available. One control calf died after being on the pasture 18 days. The respiratory rates of both groups increased and by days 18–20 were almost 70 per min. However, the respiratory rate of the vaccinated group then fell so that by day 48 the mean rate of the vaccinates was 45 per min, whilst the controls still registered 83 per min. No patent infections were seen in the vaccinates. At post-mortem examinations carried out 70 days after being put on to the pasture 1767 adult lungworms were found in the lungs of the four surviving control animals but no adults were found in the lungs of the vaccinates, although 125 immature forms were recovered. It was also apparent that the vaccinates gained more weight than the controls. A mean weight gain of 58% was seen in the vaccinates during the course of the trial whereas the controls gained only 38%. During the last 4 weeks the controls were experiencing a real check in weight gain since they gained a mere 0.7%, whilst the vaccinates gained 9%. This experiment showed that the X-irradiated vaccine was of great value under practical farming conditions.

Other groups of workers in many parts of the world have confirmed the efficacy of the X-irradiated lungworm vaccine. In England, Poynter et al. (1960) have given an account of their early work on the commercial aspects of producing the vaccine. During this work they had occasion to perform several protection tests, the results of which have never been published. Table I shows the results obtained in their last three protection tests and it will be seen that in every case a good degree of protection was obtained.

K*

In France, Pierre *et al.* (1961) reported the results of a protection test carried out utilizing a similar vaccination schedule. It was found that two of the control animals died and that the survivors had at post-mortem examination a mean lungworm burden of 1766, whereas the

TABLE I

The lungworm burdens recovered from calves in experiments with
X-irradiated vaccine

	Trial 1 Challenge; 4000 larvae.		Trial 2 Challenge; 30 larvae/lb body weight.		Trial 3 Challenge; 30 larvae/lb body weight.	
	Vaccinates	Controls	Vaccinates	Controls	Vaccinates	Controls
	0	148	1	209	0	1563
	0	49	119	1054	7	1627
	51	153	103	1935	1	348
					0	196
	1	240			12	
Total	52	791	223	3198	20	3734
Mean	13	158	74	1066	4	933

Each dose of vaccine comprised 1000 larvae irradiated at 40 000 r and each animal received two doses separated by an interval of 28 days. The animals were challenged 21 days after the second dose of vaccine.

vaccinates had a mean of only sixty-six worms and all survived. There was also a significant difference in the weight gains of the groups. The mean weight gain in the vaccinates being 10.2 kg and that of the controls 1.33 kg.

Englebrecht (1961) in the U.S.A. has also carried out a protection test using two doses of 1000 larvae irradiated at 40 000 r. The average lungworm burden in the vaccinates was 3.8, whilst the controls had a lungworm burden of 636.

Olson (1962) in Sweden vaccinated animals on six farms where husk had previously occurred. In assessing the result one farm had to be eliminated since no infection was present, but in the remaining farms it was stated that the results of vaccination were very good. It was also noted that when vaccinated and unvaccinated animals grazed together on infected pasture, the vaccinates were adequately protected since their symptoms were slight and transitory. Such a procedure is not, however, recommended as normal husbandry.

Van Eck *et al.* (1960) carried out a field trial with the X-irradiated lungworm vaccine. They reported good results both as regards the safety of the vaccine and its immunizing value. At the same time as clinical cases of lungworm infection manifested themselves on non-vaccinated neighbouring farms, the animals on vaccinated farms were troubled at most with a cough, which lasted a few days.

In Denmark, Larsen (1961) made observations on 284 vaccinated and 590 unvaccinated calves but no symptoms of verminous bronchitis developed in either group.

In Great Britain the vaccine has been used under practical farming conditions for 4 years. Jones and Nelson (1960) attempted some evaluation of the 1st year's field use of the vaccine and reported favourable results. In 1961, Nelson *et al.* presented the results for 1960 which was a bad "husk year". The vaccine was used on 8000 farms and on twenty-eight evidence of parasitic bronchitis was observed in vaccinated calves. In seven of twenty-eight farms this affected only one animal and on six farms the situation was confused by other respiratory diseases. On the other fifteen farms more than one animal was involved and of these farms eleven had animals showing marked clinical symptoms. In every farm in which marked clinical symptoms occurred there was a history of parasitic bronchitis. It was concluded that the extremely low incidence of reported cases of husk amongst vaccinated animals amply demonstrated the efficacy of the vaccine.

Lucker and Vegors (1960) reported an experiment in which they attempted to immunize calves by giving them each 4000 X-irradiated infective larvae exposed to 40 000 r. Eighteen weeks after vaccination the calves were challenged with 15 000 normal larvae each. Another group of calves immunized with normal larvae was also included. At 5 weeks after challenge the control group was found at post-mortem examination to have an average lungworm burden of 800, the group given X-irradiated larvae as an immunizing infection had 738 and the group immunized with normal larvae had thirty-seven. It is apparent then that the one dose of X-irradiated vaccine evoked no protection. The reason for this is obscure. It is obvious that the resistance in the group immunized with normal larvae had not waned. Lucker and Vegors do not give any details of the X-irradiation procedure they employed whereas it is known that all the workers who have reported successful results have utilized a technique similar to that originally described by Jarrett *et al.* (1960a).

It is then general experience that protection against lungworm disease will result from two oral doses of 1000 *D. viviparus* larvae irradiated at 40 000 r.

In practice calves are vaccinated when aged 2 months or over. Each receives two oral doses of irradiated larvae and there is a 4 week interval between doses. It is recommended that the calves be housed during the course of the immunizing schedule and for 2 weeks afterwards in order to provide conditions and time for the immunity to be acquired.

The work conducted at the Glasgow Veterinary School has thus led to the production of a safe and effective vaccine against parasitic bronchitis.

There is no doubt that the vaccine is already playing a part in the prevention of the disease. Its introduction has, however, posed many interesting questions which were highlighted by Taylor (1960). It must be confessed that at present we do not really know how long the artificially acquired immunity lasts. In the field, resistant animals are no doubt often meeting larvae which upon ingestion serve to further stimulate their resistance. A complete withdrawal from infection will no doubt mean a decrease in resistance but during this time the animal will get older and there have been suggestions that an age resistance may also operate. How the immunity obtained from the vaccine compares to that obtained by grazing infected pastures is also unknown. The vaccine should give a calf a sufficient degree of resistance so that it can graze an infected pasture but there is no doubt that the calf's immunity will be strengthened by the normal larvae it obtains from the pasture. It is during its first period on an infected pasture that the calf is most susceptible and vaccination will give protection for this period.

Cornwell (1959) and Cornwell and Berry (1960) reported that vaccinated calves subjected to natural infection could develop patent infections and act as carriers in transferring infection from one pasture to another. The main purpose of vaccination is to prevent disease and it is a fact that challenged animals may harbour small lungworm burdens which produce no disease but do produce larvae. Cornwell and Berry (1960) stated that in any control measures based on vaccination all calves must be dosed; a sound recommendation.

Taylor (1960) also drew attention to possible batch variation in the vaccine. There are many control procedures employed to prevent such variation and they have been recorded by Poynter and Terry (1962). Since the vaccine has only a short life the approach is to make sure that every batch compares closely to batches known by direct tests to give good protection. The tests employed include; tests for the absence of pathogens in the calves producing larvae for the vaccine and in the vaccine itself; physical and chemical checks carried out on the X-irradiation procedure; checks on the viability of the larvae; checks on the invasiveness and attenuation of the larvae undertaken in guinea-pigs and retrospective safety tests on the vaccine which are carried out in calves. At present there have, during 4 years production, been no untoward occurrences which would incriminate any one batch as being in any way atypical.

XI. The Mechanism of Immunity

Jarrett et al. (1957b) in one of their earlier publications on the X-irradiated vaccine concluded that irradiated larvae migrated as far as the mesenteric nodes and there died after exerting their immunogenic effect. They also observed (Jarrett *et al.*, 1959b) that the respiratory rates of calves rose after the first dose of vaccine, and later reported (Jarrett *et al.*, 1960a) that a small number of adult worms could develop from the irradiated larvae. Poynter *et al.* (1960) also reported finding worms in the lungs of three out of sixty-two calves given 1000 irradiated larvae each; the numbers were, however, very low, being three, nine and thirteen. It has already been mentioned that Cornwell (1960a) suggested that the antibody response might be due to irradiated larvae which succeed in becoming established in the lungs before being eliminated. He advanced the hypothesis that the differing degree to which larvae became established in the lungs was reflected in the variable C.F. titre and degree of immunity. It does not, however, seem reasonable to suppose that the few adult worms which were known to reach the lungs could be responsible for the provocation of immunity. The position was clarified by Poynter *et al.* (1960) who found the irradiated larvae migrated to the lungs in the same way as normal larvae. They also observed that in the resistant calf normal larvae migrated directly to the lungs where they are subjected to the immune reaction of the host. No evidence was found that the larvae were held up during their passage through the mesenteric nodes.

To determine whether or not the mesenteric nodes do prevent larvae migrating to the lung Poynter *et al.* (1960) performed an experiment in which a resistant calf was given 20 000 irradiated larvae. The conditions which it had been suggested could prevent larvae migrating to the lung were firstly a dose of X-irradiation of 40 000 r and secondly the status of the immune calf. The animal was killed 48 h after dosing and 3151 larvae were recovered from the lungs. All the thoracic and mesenteric lymph nodes were dissected and 541 larvae found in half of them. It was therefore concluded that there were 1082 larvae migrating in the lymph nodes. Thus it was shown that the majority of X-irradiated larvae recovered from an immune calf had reached the lung.

Knowing the X-irradiated larvae reach the lung and knowing that they do not become adult it is apparent that at some time during their maturation the effects of X-irradiation become apparent. Poynter *et al.* (1960) using guinea-pigs produced evidence to show that X-irradiation either affected the change between the fourth or fifth stages or affected the worms after their change into the fifth stage. There are some worms which escape the effects of X-irradiation but only very few. We have to date slaughtered 169 calves all of which have received 1000 irradiated larvae and we have only found worms in the lungs of four. X-irradiated larvae attain the lung and progress until the transition between fourth and fifth larval stages at or just after which they are disposed of. Work was also conducted in immune guinea-pigs and it was found that complete larval suppression occurred at the same time. The behaviour of the normal larva in the resistant animal does then compare closely to the behaviour of the irradiated larva in the susceptible animal.

Cornwell (1962) has recently taken a stage further the observation of Wade and Swanson (1958) that typical lungworm infections could be produced by the subcutaneous injection of first and third stage larvae. He has shown that the fourth stage larvae given parenterally are able to produce immunity in the calf. This would seem to suggest that the third stage larvae were of minimal importance in exerting an immunogenic effect.

Simpson *et al.* (1957) reported that nodules of lymphoid tissue were present in the lungs of two resistant calves killed following challenge.

Jarrett *et al.* (1960b) also reported that in immune animals fibrous and lymphoid nodules may develop around dead larvae. We have observed lesions in vaccinated animals (Fig. 8) which are similar to this and have

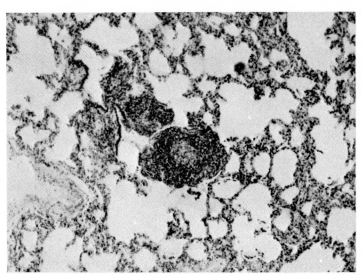

Fig. 8. A lymphoid nodule which has developed in the lung of a calf following vaccination.

also observed lymphoid nodules developing around verminous material in the lungs of resistant animals. The function of these lymphoid nodules is not known but it is possible that they might be concerned in the local production of a protective antibody.

XII. Conclusion

An account has now been given of the recent advances made in the study of *Dictyocaulus viviparus* and parasitic bronchitis. Due to the activities of many workers in many countries it may be said that in no other nematode disease has such progress been achieved. The Weybridge workers and others have provided a sound knowledge of the ecology of the parasite and the epidemiology of the disease. The Glasgow workers have been responsible for elucidating further aspects of the epidemiology, for providing a detailed account of the pathology and clinical aspects of the condition and also for studying the immunology of the disease and discovering a method of vaccination. Progress has also been achieved by commercial houses in the development of compounds showing some activity against lungworms, and also by the large-scale production of the X-irradiated vaccine.

ACKNOWLEDGEMENT

I wish to thank my colleagues at Allen and Hanbury's Ltd., for their helpful discussion.

REFERENCES

Allan, D. (1957). *Vet. Rec.* **69**, 894.

Allan, D. and Baxter, J. T. (1957). *Vet. Rec.* **69**, 717–8.

Archer, R. K. (1960). *Vet. Rec.* **72**, 155.

Campbell, D. H. (1938). *J. Immunol.* **35**, 202–16.

Camper, P. (1803). Oeuvres d'Hist. Naturelle, III. Paris.

Colglazier, M. L. and Enzie, F. D. (1961). *Proc. Helm. Soc. Wash.* **28**, 86–91.

Cornwell, R. L. (1959). *Vet. Rec.* **71**, 562.

Cornwell, R. L. (1960a). *J. Comp. Path.* **70**, 494–8.

Cornwell, R. L. (1960b). *J. Comp. Path.* **70**, 499–513.

Cornwell, R. L. (1961). *J. Comp. Path.* **71**, 191–200.

Cornwell, R. L. (1962). *J. Comp. Path.* **72**, 170–80.

Cornwell, R. L. and Berry, J. (1960). *Vet. Rec.* **72**, 595–8.

Cornwell, R. L. and Michel, J. F. (1960). *J. Comp. Path.* **70**, 482–93.

Cunningham, P. M., Jarrett, W. F. H., McIntyre, W. I. M. and Urquhart, G. M. (1956). *Vet. Rec.* **68**, 141–3.

Daubney, R. (1922). *J. Comp. Path.* **25**, 108–17.

Djafar, M. I., Swanson, L. E. and Becker, R. B. (1960). *J.A.V.M.A.* **136**, 200–4.

Douvres, F. W. and Lucker, J. T. (1958). *J. Parasit.* **44** (Sect. 2), 28–9.

Englebrecht, H. (1961). *J. Parasit.* **47**, (Sect. 2) 21.

Enigk, K. and Duwel, D. (1959). *Deutsch. Tierarztl. Wchnschr.* **66**, 379–82.

Enigk, D., Duwel, D. and Federmann, M., (1958). *Deutsch. Tierarztl. Wchnschr.* **65**, 122–5.

Fisher, E. W. and McIntyre, W. I. M. (1960). *J. Comp. Path.* **70**, 377–84.

Gregoire, C. (1951). *Ann. Med. Vet.* **95**, 481.

Gregoire, C. and Pouplard, L. (1961). *Ann. Med. Vet.* **105**, 3–7.

Gregoire, C., Pouplard, L., Cotteleer, C., Rase, F. and Jaumin, J. (1960). *Ann. Med. Vet.* **104**, 181–90.

Gripper, J. N. (1957). *Vet. Rec.* **69**, 635.

Groves, T. W. (1958). *Vet. Rec.* **70**. 219–21.

Guilhon, J. and Petit, J. P. (1958). *Bull. Acad. Vet. de France.* **31**, 255–7.

Hudson, J. R. (1951). *Vet. Rec.* **64**, 701.

Jarrett, W. F. H., McIntyre, W. I. M. and Urquhart, G. M. (1953). *Vet. Rec.* **65**, 153–5.

Jarrett, W. F. H., McIntyre, W. I. M. and Urquhart, G. M. (1954). *Vet. Rec.* **66** 665–76.

Jarrett, W. F. H., Jennings, F. W., McIntyre, W. I. M., Mulligan, W. and Urquhart G. M. (1955a). *Vet. Rec.* **67**, 291–6.

Jarrett, W. F. H., McIntyre, W. I. M., Urquhart, G. M. and Bell, E. J. (1955b) *Vet. Rec.* **67**, 820–4.

Jarrett, W. F. H., McIntyre, W. I. M. and Urquhart, G. M. (1957a). *J. Path. Bact.* **73** 183–93.

Jarrett, W. F. H., Jennings, F. W., McIntyre, W. I. M. and Mulligan, W. (1957b) *Vet. Rec.* **69**, 1329–40.

Jarrett, W. F. H., Jennings, F. W., Martin, B., McIntyre, W. I. M., Mulligan, W. Sharp, N. C. C. and Urquhart, G. M. (1958a). *Vet. Rec.* **70**, 451–4.

Jarrett, W. F. H., Jennings, F. W., McIntyre, W. I. M., Mulligan, W. and Urquhart G. M. (1958b). *Proc. Roy. Soc. Med.* **51**, 743–4.

Jarrett, W. F. H., Jennings, F. W., McIntyre, W. I. M., Mulligan, W., Thomas B. A. C. and Urquhart, G. M. (1959a). *Immunology*, **2**, 252–61.

Jarrett, W. F. H., Jennings, F. W., McIntyre, W. I. M., Mulligan, W., Sharp, N. C. C and Urquhart, G. M. (1959b). *Amer. J. Vet. Res.* **20**, 522–6.

Jarrett, W. F. H., Jennings, F. W., McIntyre, W. I. M., Mulligan, W. and Urquhart G. M. (1960a). *Immunology* **3**, 145–51.

Jarrett, W. F. H., Jennings, F. W., McIntyre, W. I. M., Mulligan, W., Sharp, N. C. C and Urquhart, G. M. (1960b). *Vet. Rec*, **72**, 1066–8.

Jarrett, W. F. H., Jennings, F. W., McIntyre, W. I. M., Mulligan, W. and Sharp N. C. C. (1961). *Amer. J. Vet. Res.* **22**, 492–4.

Joest, E. (1908). *Ztschr. Infektionskr. Haustiere* **4**, 201–15.

Jones, B. V. and Nelson, A. M. R. (1960). *Vet. Rec.* **72**, 2395.

Kasparek, T. (1900). *Arch. Tier. Berl.* **26**, 70–3.

Kerr, K. B. (1935). *Amer. J. Hyg.* **22**, 169–82.

Kerr, K. B. (1938). *Amer. J. Hyg.* **27**, 60–6.

Larsen, M. E. (1961). *Nordisk Vet*, **13**, 259–70.

Lawlor, H. J. (1940). *Amer. J. Hyg.* **31**, 28.

Lucker, J. T. and Vegors, H. M. (1960). *J. Parasit.* **46**, Sect. 2, 39.

McFadzean, J. A. (1953). *Amer. J. Trop. Med. Hyg.* **2**, 85–94.

Michel, J. F. (1953). *Nature, Lond.* **171**, 940.

Michel, J. F. (1954). *Vet. Rec.* **66**, 381–4.

Michel, J. F. (1955). *J. Comp. Path.* **65**, 149–58.

Michel, J. F. (1957a). *Vet. Rec.* **69**, 1118–21.

Michel, J. F. (1957b). *Agriculture* **64**, 224–8.

Michel, J. F. (1959). *J. Roy. Agric. Soc.* **120**, 28–44.

Michel, J. F. and Cornwell, R. L. (1959). *Vet. Rec.* **71**, 912–3.

Michel, J. F. and MacKenzie, R. E. (1956). *Emp. J. Expt. Agric.* **24**, 61–74.

Michel, J. F. and Parfitt, J. W. (1955). *Vet. Rec.* **67**, 229–35.

Michel, J. F. and Parfitt, J. W. (1956). *Vet. Rec.* **68**, 706–10.

Michel, J. F. and Rose, J. H. (1954). *J. Comp. Path.* **64**, 195–205.

Michel, J. F. and Shand, A. (1955). *Vet. Rec.* **67**, 249–66.

Michel, J. F., Ollerenshaw, C. B. and Rose, J. H. (1956). Quoted by Rose and Miche (1957).

Michel, J. F., Rose, J. H. and Spedding, C. R. W. (1959). Quoted by Michel (1959)

Miller, H. M. (1934). *Amer. J. Hyg.* **19**, 270–7.

Nelson, A. M. R., Jones, B. V. and Peacock, R. (1961). *Vet. Rec.* **73**, 153.

Nicholls, F. (1756), *Philosophical Transactions XLIV*. Part I. London.

O'Donoghue, J. G. (1958). *Can. J. Comp. Med.* **22**, 237–9.
Olson, A. (1962). *Med. Vet. Sver.* (1962) 123–4, 127–9.
Otto, G. F. (1938). *J. Parasit.* (Suppl.) **24**, 10.
Parker, W. H. (1957). *J. Comp. Path.* **67**, 251–62.
Parker, W. H. and Roberts, H. E. (1958). *J. Comp. Path.* **68**, 402–10.
Parker, W. H. and Vallely, T. F. (1960). *Vet. Rec.* **72**, 1073–8.
Parker, W. H., Roberts, H. E., Vallely, T. F. and Brown, F. T. (1959). *Vet. Rec.* **71**. 509–11.
Peacock, R., Manton. V. J. A., Poynter, D. and Terry, R. J. (1962). Unpublished information.
Pierre, M., Euzeby, J., Malher, G. and Jeannin, A. (1961). *Bull. Soc. Sc. Vet. de Lyon* **63**, 69–81.
Porter, D. A. (1942). *Proc. Helm. Soc. Wash.* **9**, 60–2.
Porter, D. A. and Cauthen, G. E. (1942). *Amer. J. Vet. Res.* **3**, 395–400.
Poynter, D. and Terry, R. J. (1962). *Proc. 7th Int. Cong. Biol. Stand.* In Press.
Poynter, D., Jones, B. V., Nelson, A. M. R., Peacock, R., Robinson, J., Silverman, P. H. and Terry, R. J. (1960). *Vet. Rec.* **72**, 1078–90.
Robinson, J. (1962). *Nature, Lond.* **193**, 353–4.
Robinson, J., Poynter, D. and Terry, R. J. (1962). *Parasitology.* (In Press).
Rose, J. H. (1956). *J. Comp. Path.* **66**, 228–40.
Rose, J. H. (1960). *J. Comp. Path.* **70**, 475–81.
Rose, J. H. and Michel, J. F. (1957). *J. Comp. Path.* **67**, 57–68.
Rubin, R. and Lucker, J. T. (1956). *Cornell Vet.* **46**, 88–96.
Rubin, R. and Tillotson, A. J. (1960). *Amer. J. Vet. Res.* **21**, 1040–5.
Rubin, R. and Tillotson, A. J. (1962). *Amer. J. Vet. Res.* **23**, 42–48.
Rubin, R. and Weber, T. B. (1955). *Proc. Helm. Soc. Wash.* **22**, 124–9.
Ruysch, F. (1744). *Thesaurus Anotomicus.* Amsterdam.
Sarles, M. P. and Taliaferro, W. H. (1936). *J. Infect. Dis.* **59**, 207–20.
Sarles, M. P. and Taliaferro, W. H. (1938). *J. Parasit.* (Suppl) **24**, 35.
Sharp, N. C. C. (1959). *Agriculture* **66**, 241–5.
Silverman, P. H., Poynter, D., Terry, R. J. and Podger, K. (1962). *J. Parasit.* (In Press).
Simpson, C. F., Wade, A. E., Dennis, W. R. and Swanson, L. E. (1957). *Amer. J. Vet. Res.* **18**, 747–55.
Skovronski, R. V. (1959). *Sbornik Nanchniken Trudov Lvovski Zorveterinarni Institut* **9**, 227–32.
Soliman, K. N. (1952). *Brit. Vet. J.* **108**, 167–72.
Soliman, K. N. (1953). *J. Comp. Path.* **63**, 75–84.
Spedding, C. R. W. and Michel, J. F. (1957). *Parasitology.* **47**, 153–9.
Spiers, R. S. (1958). *Nature, Lond.* **181**, 681.
Stableforth, A. W. (1953). *Vet. Rec.* **65**, 709.
Stirewalt, M. A. and Evans, A. S. (1953). *Proc. Helm. Soc. Wash.* **20**, 15–19.
Swanson, L. E., Wade, A. E., Dennis, W. R. and Stone, W. M. (1955). *Florida Agric. Exp. Sta. Ann. Rep.* 1955. 158–9.
Swanson, L. E., Wade, A. E., Senseman, V. F. and Djafar, M. I. (1959). *Amer. J. Vet. Res.* **20**, 777–83.
Swietlikowski, M. (1959). *Acta. Parasit. Polonica.* **7**, 249–305.
Taylor, E. L. (1951). *Vet. Rec.* **63**, 859–73.
Taylor, E. L. (1953). *B.V.A. Publication* **23**.
Taylor, E. L. (1960). *Vet. Rec.* **72**, 684–8.
Taylor, E. L. and Michel, J. F. (1955). *Vet. Rec.* **67**, 612–3.

Trace, J. C. (1958). *Calif. Vet.* **11**, 19–20.

Ugrin, I. N. (1959). *Sbornik Nanchniken Trudov Lvovski Zorveterinarni Institut* **9**, 233–40.

Van Eck, G., Kruize, J., Paul, S., Reinders, J. S. and Wilson, J. H. G. (1960). *Tijdschr. Diergeneesk.* **85**, 1089–1101.

Wade, A. E. and Swanson, L. E. (1958). *Amer. J. Vet. Res.* **19**, 792–3.

Wade, A. E., Swanson, L. E. and Fox, L. E. (1961). *Amer. J. Vet. Res.* **22**, 123–7.

Wade, A. E., Swanson, L. E., Fox, L. E., Simpson, C. F. and Malewitz, T. D. (1962). *Amer. J. Vet. Res.* **23**, 277–83.

Walley, J. K. (1957a). *Vet. Rec.* **69**, 815–24.

Walley, J. K. (1957b). *Vet. Rec.* **69**, 850–3.

Walley, J. K. (1957c). *J. Amer. vet. med. Ass.* **131**, 539–44.

Weber, T. B. (1958). *J. Parasit.* **44**, 244–5.

Weber, T. B. and Lucker, J. T. (1959). *Proc. Helm. Soc. Wash.* **26**, 132–7.

Weber, T. B. and Rutin, R. (1958). *J. Infect. Dis.* **102**, 214–8.

Wetzel, R. (1948). *Monatsh Vet. Med.* **3**, 141–8.

Experimental Trichiniasis

JOHN E. LARSH, Jr

Professor of Parasitology, Schools of Public Health and Medicine,
University of North Carolina, Chapel Hill, and Professor of Parasitology,
School of Medicine, Duke University, Durham, North Carolina, U.S.A.

I.	Introduction	213
II.	Anatomical and Physiological Alterations in Hamsters, Rats and Mice	215
	A. Hamsters	215
	B. Rats	221
	C. Mice	237
III.	Summary and Forecast	280
	References	282

I. Introduction

The great German scientists, Leuckart and Virchow, are credited with unravelling the main features of the complicated life history of *Trichinella spiralis* (Schwartz, 1960). The presence of both intestinal and extra-intestinal phases made this a monumental task, but both workers were fascinated by this unique parasite. Nevertheless, it is doubtful whether these brilliant minds and those of many other outstanding early workers could have predicted that, for more than a century, this parasite would hold fascination for ever-increasing numbers of investigators. Despite this unusual sustained popularity, even today with a vast array of modern research tools at hand, many important aspects concerning the parasite and the disease it produces are unknown. One might predict, therefore, that as long as such challenges exist there will continue to be large numbers of reports, making it desirable to have periodic reviews indicating recent advances.

The period of the present survey extends from about 1950 to the present. A selected few earlier reports are included, especially to bridge certain gaps not covered by recent studies and, in some cases, to correct or modify conclusions inconsistent with present knowledge. The papers selected to illustrate advances in various areas were those that appeared to be among the best examples available to the reviewer. Since in many cases, due to space limitations, only a few examples could be used, the failure to list a particular paper or papers should not be misconstrued.

Since this review deals with experimental infections, only a few *in vitro* studies that seem to provide data of practical value to the present experimentalist are mentioned. This approach, therefore, eliminates from consideration certain significant advances in recent years. The most important are those dealing with the chemical composition and metabolic activities of larvae, and detailed antigenic analyses and serologic studies. Fortunately, most of these have been included in recent reviews (Kagan, 1960; Sadun, 1960).

The most popular hosts for experimental studies, in order of popularity based on numbers of papers, have been mice, rats, and hamsters. Rabbits and guinea-pigs have been used much less in recent years; most of the papers dealing with the former concern serologic studies. Due to considerations of space, this report will be limited specifically to mice, rats, and hamsters, but certain reports of work in rabbits will be included.

The infection produced by *T. spiralis* is very complex and, considered in a broad sense, is little understood even today. To advance our knowledge, more information is needed concerning the physiology of both the parasite and the host. In recent years biochemical studies of larvae under various conditions have been fruitful in providing information concerning chemical composition, certain metabolic pathways, excretory products, and so forth. However, the time has not arrived when such data can be used directly to explain the many complex interrelationships of the parasite and the host. Therefore, at present, our best approach is to note carefully all anatomical and/or physiological alterations in the host at precise periods during an infection. Not forgetting the many non-specific chain reactions involved, we may in time unravel the mysteries of their precise mechanism, especially if the chemical studies continue to provide basic data concerning the life needs and host-toxic metabolites of the parasite. With this in mind, the paper deals with many of the known host alterations after contact with this parasite. In a broad sense most of these can be tied in with immunity. However, in an attempt to emphasize the scope of our problem, alterations will be listed under the separate body systems involved. Following this, the varied aspects of acquired immunity *per se* will be presented. However, before considering these various host alterations, it is important to recall the pertinent details of the life cycle in each host, since there are differences among hosts in the precise location of adult worms, their longevity, the period of larvapositing, and so forth. Moreover, certain of these details are of vital concern in experimental designs. Therefore, this section will precede the consideration of the various host alterations. A brief concluding section will include a general summary and a forecast by the reviewer of certain problems likely to be pursued in the future and thus be included in the next review of the subject

Other points concerning the approach should be mentioned. For the reader to evaluate the experimental work, he must know certain important details of the experimental design, such as relative age of host, dose(s) of larvae used for infection, necropsy periods, treatments used, and so forth. Where certain of these are omitted, it can be assumed they were not given in the paper cited. To avoid inclusion of unnecessary details, animals more than 3 months old will be designated "old" or "adult". Younger ages, if known, will be given. Most of the studies involved precise quantitative measurements and the results were analyzed by various popular statistical tools. Thus, the use of the word "significant" is restricted entirely to its statistical connotation. Finally, due to the extensive and varied list of advances to be presented, the customary section on "Discussion" has been omitted. This material is included under each topic, including the comments, if any, of the reviewer.

II. ANATOMICAL AND PHYSIOLOGICAL ALTERATIONS IN HAMSTERS, RATS AND MICE

A. HAMSTERS

1. *Pertinent Details of the Life Cycle*

Both the golden hamster (*Mesocricetus auratus*) and the Chinese hamster (*Cricetulus barabensis*) have been employed in experimental studies in recent years. Their responses to the parasite are not always similar, either in type or degree. Therefore, it is important to consider them separately. In old (17 weeks) golden hamsters, penetration into the duodenal mucosa can be demonstrated within 2 h after an infection with 100 larvae (Boyd and Huston, 1954). The recovery is very high for the first 2 h, but falls to 55% at 24 h. During the next 5 days large numbers of adults are lost, so that only 23% are found on the 6th day when the sex ratio is 1.6 (F/M). The remaining worms are eliminated by 15 days postinfection. After an infection with 500 larvae, the results are strikingly similar, except that much smaller percentages of the dose are recovered during the first 2 h, and at 6 days the percentage is about one-half as high (about 12%). After both infections, there appears to be a significant loss of worms between 24 h and 6 days, and almost all of the remaining worms are lost within the next 9 days. The males are eliminated more rapidly than the females. There is a suggestion that age of the host is a factor in the number of worms that persist for 6 days after infection, since much greater numbers (32 and 34%, respectively, after infecting doses of 250 and 500 larvae) are found at a similar period (7 days) in hamsters 11 weeks of age (Sadun and Norman, 1956).

In animals about 8 weeks old, circulating larvae can be recovered from the heart between 3–22 days postinfection, but they are not seen in the cheek pouch until 16 days (Humes and Akers, 1952). By this time they apparently are distributed throughout the musculature, since large numbers can be recovered after artificial gastric digestion (Boyd and Huston, 1954). At 15 days, about 3000 larvae can be recovered from an infection with 100 larvae. This appears to be the maximum number involved, since there is little change in numbers recovered 3, 4, and 5 weeks after infection. However, after infection with 500 larvae, there is slight progressive increase, from about 55 000 at 15 days to about 62 000 at 5 weeks. As would be expected in the younger hamsters, with much greater adult worm burdens at 7 days, the numbers of muscle larvae are considerably greater (Sadun and Norman, 1956). In fact, with the same infecting dose (500) the younger animals harbor more than twice the number of larvae (about 161 000).

It is of interest that reduced body temperature during hibernation of golden hamsters may have striking effects against the parasite. If hibernation occurs soon after infection, and even if it lasts only a short time (48–72 h), the very low body temperature (5–7°C) will prevent completely the development of *T. spiralis* (Chute, 1961). Later in the infection longer periods of hibernation appear to be necessary to produce demonstrable interference, as measured by numbers of muscle larvae. Also, there is some evidence that hibernation at later periods after infection, if prolonged, may bring about destruction of muscle larvae.

In adult Chinese hamsters, male and female worms, normal in size and appearance, can be found in the small intestine from 3–26 days after infection with 100 larvae, but no worms are present at 40 days (Ritterson, 1957). Despite the presence of adults, relatively few muscle larvae are seen in pressed diaphragm preparations or after artificial gastric digestion of large portions of the carcass between 14–112 days postinfection.

2. *The Excretory System*

Striking changes are noted in the urine of golden hamsters (8–10 weeks old) that survive an infection with *T. spiralis* (Bernard, 1961a). After an initial polyuria of 3 weeks, most animals show oliguria for many weeks. In general, the uric acid and creatine excretion are elevated, while the creatinine excretion is reduced. The urinary uric acid/creatinine ratio (UA/C) is elevated on days 7 and 15 postinfection and again throughout the period between 30 and 60 days. The amount and type of exercise do not alter the excretion of creatine and creatinine. While the trauma produced by the adult worms in the intestine cannot be overlooked, it would appear more likely that the larval phases of infection are responsible for producing the changes in the UA/C ratio. At first thought, these alterations would appear to be due entirely to renal and metabolic changes produced by secretions of the pituitary-adrenal complex in response to stress, since such changes are known to cause decreased tubular resorption of urate. However, various doses of ACTH, and cortone acetate,. fail to produce similar changes in uninfected hamsters (Bernard, 1961a). Although these and other factors may be contributory to a small degree, in this case it would appear that the striking tissue catabolism in response to the larvae is the principal cause of the excess urate excretion. It is likewise probable that the increased creatine excretion can be traced to the muscular tissue where the striking pathology would be expected to diminish these stores. If this were the case, the fall in creatinine would be a logical sequence of the pathologic process. However, chronic starvation, if prolonged, could be a contributory factor.

3. *The Endocrine System*

In infected golden hamsters (8–10 weeks old), various alterations are noted in the adrenal glands by histochemical methods at certain periods postinfection (Bernard, 1961b). During the first 2 weeks, the alkaline glycerophosphatase reaction is slightly more intense, nonspecific dehydrogenase activity is increased significantly during the 2nd and 3rd week, and there is a significant elevation in ascorbic acid 6 weeks postinfection. The glands are heavier during the period 3–9 weeks postinfection. Concentration of cortical sudanophilic lipids is greater in more severe cases than in those less severely affected, and controls, but birefringence activity does not change.

In infected Chinese hamsters, there is a loss of lipid in the outer zone of the adrenal cortex as early as 3 days after infection, and 2 days later it cannot be demonstrated histochemically by Sudan black B (Ritterson and Mauer, 1957). There is a renewal in lipid content in the adrenals by 14 days, which is most marked in the inner zone, and the normal diffuse pattern is evident by 26 days postinfection. The rapid loss of lipid is related to stress produced by the early development of the adult worms in the intestine, and recovery of lipid content takes place when the larvae are migrating to and invading the muscles. Although generalized myositis, moderate to severe, occurs in this host between 14 and 40 days (Ritterson, 1957), this stress situation fails to be reflected in the adrenal lipid changes, at least within 26 days. No histopathology is noted in the glands during 112 days of infection, and adrenal weight/body weight ratios do not appear to bear any relationship to the status of the infection. Spleen weight/body weight ratios, however, average higher during the migratory phase (14–26 days) of the infection.

4. *The Cardiovascular System*

a. The heart. Various electrocardiographic abnormalities have been reported in human trichiniasis at various periods after infection. In old golden hamsters, the only experimental host tested as far as is known, atrioventicular blocks are observed during the acute stage of a lethal infection (Bernard and Sudak, 1960). This abnormality, not reported previously, is due probably to histopathologic changes produced by the larvae. These changes, noted by earlier workers, could have altered the conduction pathways in the area of the atrioventicular node. Intra- venticular blocks are also noted in a number of hamsters with older infections, as reported and unexplained in human trichiniasis (prolonged QRS duration). While the effects of old age *per se* can be ruled out in the hamsters, the causation of this abnormality has not been elucidated.

b. The vascular system. By careful preparation, to minimize trauma and maintain the tissue at body temperature, the cheek pouch of the golden hamster offers a means to observe *T. spiralis* larvae *in vivo* for extended periods (Humes and Akers, 1952). In hosts 6–9 weeks old, vascular changes are observed as early as 3 days when large numbers of leukocytes appear to become "sticky" and roll slowly along the endo- thelium while the main stream of erythrocytes and platelets occupies the central area of the vessel. By 6–11 days postinfection, leukocytic pave- ments (mural thrombi) occur, preventing entirely the flow of blood in some venules occluded completely by this process. This evidence of an inflammatory reaction is reminiscent of the agglutination and margina- tion of red blood cells in certain malarial infections. The vascular changes produced by *T. spiralis* occur in venules and veins, but not in arterioles of the cheek pouch, and persist for about 36 days postinfection. In the meantime, in the infected striated muscle fibers, a network of small vessels of venous nature, formed by enlargement of existing vessels and/ or growth of new vessels (probably mostly capillaries), is noted with unobstructed blood flow. Especially in early stages, the vessels of the network appear to be sinusoidal in character. These presumably arise from one or more arterioles that branch off at oblique angles. From the vicinity of the coiled larvae, these vessels drain into one or more venules. This increased vascular supply, noted as early as 19 days, lasts for more than 280 days.

c. Blood. In the golden hamster (8–10 weeks old), changes occur in the leukocytic response after an infection with 225 *T. spiralis* larvae (Bernard, 1961c). Both circulating and tissue eosinophils are increased moderately, the former reaching a peak between 16–19 days post- infection and returning to a normal level about 1 week later. The peak eosinophilia occurs about 1 week after the first circulating larvae invade the musculature, but is not associated with the intensity of infection as indicated by weight loss. There is no appreciable change in the absolute leukocyte count, but, as indicated by differential counts, there is an absolute lymphocytopenia and neutrophilia. Between 4–12 days post- infection, the normal lymphocyte/neutrophil ratio (2:1) becomes altered to the extent that the neutrophils are dominant. The return to normal range is variable, occurring between 20–70 days. The blood also may carry circulating antibodies, which will be mentioned below.

5. *The Muscular System*

The spontaneous nocturnal activity of old golden hamsters is altered after infection with 225 *T. spiralis* larvae (Bernard, 1959). Decreased activity is first noted about 5–7 days postinfection when the adult worms presumably are destroying intestinal tissue. During the next 2 weeks normal, or hyperactive, activity is noted. This is during the time when larvae are known to be in the peripheral blood and muscle invasion is underway. At about 30 days postinfection activity practically ceases, and fails to reach the normal range until at least 9 weeks postinfection. This period corresponds presumably to the time when the infected muscle fibers are being destroyed and the permanent cyst is formed. At any rate, inflammatory reactions in tongue muscles of this host are at a peak at 5–6 weeks postinfection. In view of the long duration of drastically curtailed activity, it is clear that the pathological and/or physiological consequences of the muscle phase of infection are being experienced by this host. Activity suppression in this host after infection has been confirmed by others (Goodchild and Frankenberg, 1960).

Intact cysts, from golden hamsters infected for 50–65 days, exposed at 37°C for 4–6 min to collagenase show swelling of the cyst wall. The increasing plasticity is revealed by the lively motions of the contained larvae, which escape within 15–25 min after the cyst is exposed to the enzyme (Ritterson, 1959a). Soon thereafter the cyst wall is digested gradually. Free larvae appear to be unaffected by the enzyme for a period of at least 24 h. Heat-inactivated collagenase, trypsin, pancreatin, and hyaluronidase are not active, but 1% sodium hypochlorite ("Clorox") causes rapid (1–3 min) dissolution of the cyst wall. Stained preparations reveal structures in the cyst wall similar to those described for altered collagen isolated from tissues showing the Arthus reaction.

6. *Immune Responses*

Direct comparison of golden and Chinese hamsters leaves no doubt that the latter has a considerably greater degree of refractoriness to the muscle phase of the parasite (Ritterson, 1959b). In golden hamsters given fifty larvae at infection, all animals tested show muscle larvae by 14 days (diaphragm press) and maximum numbers recovered at 42 days are about 8000–11 000. On the other hand, in Chinese hamsters given twice as many larvae at infection few animals reveal muscle larvae and even after carcass digestion at 42–48 days only a few can be recovered. After these respective infections, adult worms can be demonstrated in both hosts at 14 days, and in the Chinese hamster some gravid females are still present at 21 days.

In golden hamsters at 14 days after infection with 50 larvae, larvae are seen within intact muscle cells without evidence of focal "round" cell response. However, diffuse neutrophilic infiltration of the tissue is evident at this time, and does not diminish noticeably until about 42 days postinfection. Later, after growth of the contained larvae, the muscle fibers show the characteristic basophilic degeneration and round cell infiltration that accompanies encapsulation. In view of the slowly-progressing degeneration of the host cell and growth of the parasite, indicating little, if any, intrinsic immunity, the golden hamster appears to provide a favorable environment for the larvae. If it may be assumed that most invaded host cells behave similarly, it is clear that this host has little natural immunity to this phase of infection. In Chinese hamsters at 14 days after infection with 100 larvae, degenerating muscle cells are seen with associated round cell infiltration. Eosinophilic degeneration of the contained larvae is seen. Later, the round cell foci become progressively smaller as the unsuccessfully-invaded fibers degenerate. Intact, non-parasitized muscle is the final outcome. It is clear, therefore, that this host fails to provide a favorable environment for the larvae. If it may be assumed that most invaded host cells react similarly, it is clear that this host has a striking degree of natural immunity to this phase of infection.

A wide variety of factors have been used in attempts to modify this strong immunity. Adrenalectomy, administration of ACTH, concentrated carcass extracts of golden hamsters, infection with *Leishmania donovani* (as a R-E cell blocking agent), and a massive infecting dose of *T. spiralis* larvae fail to alter the immunity (Ritterson, 1960). Methyl testosterone produces a demonstrable increase in the numbers of muscle larvae without affecting the inflammatory response, which appears to indicate that the action is related to its anabolic effect on muscle tissue. Prolonged feeding of a diet with 2% cod liver oil produces a significant ameliorization in the natural immunity (Ritterson, 1960).

Cortisone has a striking effect on this strong immunity of Chinese hamsters (Ritterson, 1959b). All those given cortisone daily and infected with 100 or 175 larvae show muscle larvae, the number being directly proportional to the dose of cortisone. Also, the longevity of the adult worms is prolonged. At 14 days postinfection, intact larvae are seen within muscle fibers, and the time of onset of fiber degeneration and subsequent local round cell infiltration is roughly similar to that in golden hamsters. However, cortisone appears to inhibit the early round cell response around invaded muscle fibers and thus permits survival of contained larvae. The diffuse neutrophil response is also present, if less intense, and varies in degree as to cortisone dosage. At later periods (21 and 28 days postinfection) typical intense inflammatory reactions are noted around apparently normal larvae, but these reactions and the diffuse neutrophil response are depressed markedly when larger doses of cortisone are used.

Incubation of washed muscle larvae for 24 h in the serum of uninfected Chinese hamsters or golden hamsters fails to yield circum-oral precipitates, and no such precipitates are visible after incubation in serum of the two separate hosts taken 12 days postinfection. However, precipitates occur in serum taken from the two hosts 19 days after infection (Ritterson, 1959b). Six-Mercaptopurine (0.1–0.2 mg daily) fails to affect the capacity to reject muscle larvae, despite its known inhibitory effect on antibody production (Ritterson, 1960). On the basis of these various observations, it is concluded that the Chinese hamster is innately resistant to the *T. spiralis* muscle phase, probably as a result of premature disintegration of the parasitized muscle fiber ("hypersusceptibility"). Thus, a suitable environment does not appear to be maintained long enough for the larvae to mature. Moreover, "natural" or early antibody response does not seem to be related to the refractoriness of this host, and the action of cortisone is suggested to be due to its effect in prolonging the structural integrity of the injured cells (Ritterson, 1959b).

B. RATS

1. *Pertinent Details of the Life Cycle*

The pre-adults undergo four molts to reach the adult stage in rats (Villella, 1958). Most of those developing into females undergo successive molts at 6, 12, 18, and 24 h postinfection, while those destined to become males molt 6 h later, at 12, 18, 24, and 30 h. Molting apparently takes place in the mucosa, since by 4 h postinfection almost all pre-adults have entered the tissue (Gursch, 1949). Most of the worms are found in the lumen about 24 h after infection, and between 30–48 h the males and females re-enter the mucosa. While copulation may occur during the lumen phase, it is more likely that this takes place after penetration. Male and female worms are seen partially or deeply embedded in the mucosa at 33 h, and at this time insemination has occurred in large numbers of females (Gould *et al.*, 1955). At 30 h, ovulation has occurred in about 6% of females, and by 32 h 72% show ova and 52% show sperms in the seminal receptacle (Wu and Kingscote, 1957). During insemination the anterior portions are embedded in the mucosa of villi, while the cloacal and vulval portions lie exposed between adjacent villi. Evidence indicates that insemination may occur more than once.

In old rats infected with 1280 larvae, about 47% are lost during the first 24 h (Gursch, 1949). Thereafter to the 9th day, the numbers of adult worms remain fairly constant. There appears to be a significant loss of worms between 9–12 days, after which all remaining ones are eliminated by 18 days. After an infection with 5000 larvae, the findings are similar, except that a greater loss occurs between 9–12 days and all remaining worms are gone by 15 days. Throughout both infections, there is a linear distribution of adult worms in the small intestine, the greatest numbers being found in the first quarter-section. Relatively few worms are found in the large intestine until the striking reduction occurs in the small intestine between 9–12 days. After this (10–13 days) the numbers in the large intestine increase greatly, but almost all are gone by 14 days. It appears, therefore, that this build-up in numbers is merely a reflection of the losses from the small intestine, and most are being eliminated without re-establishing. After an infection with 1280 larvae, the sex ratio (F/M) of adults in the entire intestine through day 9 is about 2.0, but for the remainder of the infection it decreases until on day 14 it is about 1.0.

Free larvae placed in Thiry-Vella fistulas of rats are able to complete the life cycle in this environment where all nutrients are obtained from the host tissues or exudates (Goodchild, 1957). As might be expected, the numbers of adults and larvae recovered are fewer, and the adult males and females are much smaller than those from rats with intact intestines. In fact, sexually mature males are not much longer than larvae. The depressed degree of infection may be due to physiological changes in the fistula (altered pH and oxygen tension, altered bacterial flora, accumulated mucus, etc.), suppression of larvapositing by difficulties encountered in the fistular vascular system, absence or reduced quantity of a factor favorable to sexual reproduction, or simply due to much smaller numbers of larvae produced by the dwarfed females. The larvae deposited in the muscles possess the usual infectivity, as shown by the fact that those recovered and fed orally to other rats produce the usual degree of infection.

In adult rats given 5000–6000 larvae, circulating larvae can not be found in large samples of heart blood between 52–110$\frac{1}{2}$ h after infection (Gould *et al.*, 1955). Small numbers can be demonstrated at 114 h, and between 114–144 h (4.7–6.0 days) the numbers demonstrated show a more or less progressive increase. At 144 h, the average number per ml of blood is eighteen. These data and the above information on the adult worms suggest that the most active larvapositing period is completed in about one week (between 4–11 days postinfection). Each female produces about 345 larvae (Edney *et al.*, 1953), as determined by twenty-two successful transplantations of single female worms. The numbers of larvae do not appear to vary as to strain of rat (white or hooded), sex, or age of host. Rather the variations from worm to worm appear to be due to inherent differences in reproductive potential.

Cytochemical studies reveal vitamin C in conspicuous quantities in muscle larvae (Bullock, 1951). It is found mostly in the mid-gut region of the intestine immediately behind the "cell body". None is present in the reproductive system. It occurs in larvae in infected rats 10–190 days postinfection, but is in maximum concentration between 14–30 days. It declines gradually and none is present by 338 days.

Electron micrographs of infected rat muscles at intervals after infection show in vivid detail the cuticle and other structures of the larvae, and surrounding areas (Themann, 1960).

2. The Cardiovascular System

a. The heart. The evidence indicates it is not unusual for the migrating larvae to invade the heart tissue early in the infection, but few have been found encysted there. Further, myocarditis, common in trichiniasis, is thought by most workers to be due to direct myocardial invasion of larvae and resulting mechanical damage rather than a cardiotoxic agent(s). Strong support for the view that the migrating larvae are responsible in some way for myocarditis was obtained recently by histopathologic studies in rats 5 weeks old infected with 4000 irradiated larvae (Zaiman et al., 1961). The irradiation treatment sterilized the developing adults and an average of only one muscle larva was found in ten control rats. In thirty-six animals infected with irradiated larvae, only one showed histological evidence of myocarditis, whereas fourteen out of eighteen given non-irradiated larvae at the same dose level exhibited myocardial lesions (and usual numbers of muscle larvae). Both focal and diffuse inflammatory infiltration was noted, consisting chiefly of mononuclear leukocytes, with occasional eosinophils and neutrophils. Myocardial fiber destruction was evident in advanced lesions. Further evidence that myocarditis is not due to toxic products from the intestinal parasites, but to activities of the migrating larvae has just been presented. Infection of one member of a pair of parabiotic rats (4–6 months old) with a dose of non-irradiated larvae (8000–64 000) results in myocarditis in 100% of those that survive for 8 days, whereas none of the "uninfected" parabionts, known to acquire very small numbers of muscle larvae under these conditions, has myocarditis (Maeir et al., 1962).

b. Blood. Serum samples obtained from young rats (average weight, 107 g) infected with a dose of larvae ranging from 1000–6000 show certain changes when analyzed electrophoretically (Kagan and Goodchild, 1961). The total serum protein values increase from the normal range (4.6–6.4 grams %) to 9.2–12.8 grams %. The percentages of the individual proteins remain fairly constant over a period of 62 days postinfection, but at specified periods certain changes are noted. For example, during the first 15 days albumin shows a slight increase (from about 30–40%), and during the next 10 days gamma globulin increases somewhat (from about 15–22%). On the other hand, alpha-1 (10%), alpha-2 (20%), and beta (27%) globulins remain at near normal levels. The A/G ratios vary from 0.4–0.7. Rabbits show a pattern more typical in an infectious process (Seniów, 1960). There is, by the microelectrophoresis method, a significant difference between the mean values for albumin and the various globulin fractions after an infection "of intense degree". The mean value for albumin changes from about 62% before infection to about 46%. The reduction is noted by 7 days, reaches the lowest value at about 75 days, and there is little increase by 167 days postinfection. Gamma globulin changes from about 14–24% during infection. It shows a striking increase by 7 days, increases very little to reach the peak level at 75 days, and decreases very little by 167 days. The combined alpha fractions change from about 13–20%, and the beta fraction shows the least significant change, from 11–9.9%. The A/G ratios change from 1.6–0.8.

At 6½ months after an infection of rats with 1200 larvae, the total serum proteins, albumin, albumin polysaccharide, and the A/G ratio are within the normal ranges (Weimer et al., 1958). However, there is at this time a significant elevation in total globulin, globulin polysaccharide, total serum glycoprotein, hemoglobin, and hematocrit. It is, therefore, clear that the increase in total serum glycoprotein is due to the increase in the polysaccharide moiety of the globulin fraction. Hemoconcentration, as indicated by the increased hematocrit value, probably explains the increased hemoglobin value, but in the absence of an increase in total serum protein does not appear to be a factor to account for the other elevated values. Reinfection with 1500 larvae does not appear to produce significant differences in the values noted after the first infection, at least when measurements are made 6 weeks after reinfection. Since increased protein synthesis has been one of the factors suggested for serum glycoprotein increase, it is interesting that there is considerable evidence for this in mice. Larvae encysted for long periods contain a high level of RNA (Zarzycki, 1960), and they incorporate a high percentage (85–92%) of labeled amino acids, fed to the host, into protein (Hankes and Stoner, 1958).

Antibodies appear in the serum of rats as early as 14 days postinfection and can be detected by use of the hemagglutination test (Kagan and Bargai, 1956). Their concentration, in general, is in proportion to the size of the infecting dose of larvae. The microprecipitin test, utilized by

Oliver-Gonzalez (1940, 1941) in the early *in vitro* studies on the effect of antiserum on adult worms and larvae, has been in recent use in experimental studies with rats. Tests with serum from rats infected from 30–300 days show precipitates around body openings of adults and/or larvae (Chute, 1956). Serum from rats 80 days after an infection with 1500 larvae produces oral precipitates in 10% of adult worms and 2% of larvae incubated in the antiserum for 18–20 h at room temperature. Ten days after reinfection with 1500 larvae, these percentages increase to 98 and 4, respectively, and after an additional reinfection in 10 days, they are 100 and 22, respectively. Circulating antibodies, demonstrable by the microflocculation reaction using a larval antigen, are present in a large percentage of rats 6 months after infection with about 1200 larvae, and in most cases titers rise after reinfection (Markell and Lewis, 1957).

It is of great interest that the appearance of precipitin antibodies in rabbits occurs soon after certain maximum physiological alterations are noted (Aikawa *et al.*, 1951). In most cases, clinical edema, related directly to the intensity of infection, first occurs between 5–10 days postinfection, and there is a significant increase in the fluid space available for dilution of thiocyanate ions. Maximum alterations occur a few days later, followed by detection of precipitins by the ring-precipitin test, suggesting the direct or indirect role of an antigen-antibody reaction. In any case, the changes indicate injury and a resultant increased permeability of the vascular tree, probably in capillary walls, resulting in loss of crystalloids from the circulation into the interstitial spaces. Changes in body weight in certain cases may mean an increased cellular permeability to water and ions. A significant drop in hematocrit without evidence of intravascular hydration indicates red blood cells also are lost from the vascular tree. Some may be hemolyzed, as suggested by clinical jaundice in some animals. Since the severity of the reaction determines the extent of increased membrane permeability, circulating red blood cells would be expected to be lost only in the most severe cases.

In young rats given 3000 larvae at infection, there is a marked increase in the number of circulating eosinophils (Pollay *et al.*, 1954). Within 4 days these cells increase from normal (0 to about 4%) to about 11% and by 12 days postinfection the level has reached about 20%. They continue to increase slightly for about another week. Lower peaks (about 11%) in young rats have been noted by others between 10–30 days after one infection (Lord, 1958). On the other hand, a poor eosinophil response (from about 0.5% to about 3%) has been noted in rats 2.5 months old infected with a dose of larvae, ranging from 500–2500 (Larsh and Nichols, 1949). Reinfection with 2000 larvae 30 days after the first infection failed to elevate the level within 25 days.

3. *The Muscular System*

The histopathology of the voluntary muscle system after infection with *T. spiralis* was described in early studies, but the residual effects of the damage have been difficult to appraise.

Infected rats are unable to match the running ability of controls and in the attempt lose considerably more weight (von Brand *et al.*, 1954). Significant differences are noted during the early stages of infection (2–3 weeks) and at various periods (6 weeks to 12 months) during the late stages. Weight loss appears to be due chiefly to the loss of water. The fact that the working ability of rats, with moderate or heavy infections, is significantly impaired many months after infection indicates clearly that there is a residual effect. This effect can not be attributed exclusively to the diseased state of the voluntary muscles, regardless of its importance, since it is influenced by all bodily functions that affect the muscles directly or indirectly, such as circulation, respiration, water balance, and so forth. Considering the greater prevalence of subclinical and mild clinical cases, more information is needed on the effects of light infections.

Histochemical studies of rat muscles show no evidence of phosphatase activity in uninfected fibers, but by 12 days postinfection large amounts of alkaline phosphatase are found in degenerating muscle tissue that becomes associated with the inner cyst wall of fully encysted larvae (Bullock, 1953). The alkaline enzyme releases phosphate from glycerophosphate and yeast nucleic acid substrates, but not from lecithin. This infection does not appear to have any effect upon the amount or distribution of acid phosphatase. The pathological effect of importance is the basophilic, granular degeneration, evident 1–2 days after fiber invasion, since this results at the time of encystment in the formation of Nevinny's "basophilic halo" or the so-called inner cyst wall. The alkaline phosphatase activity appears a few days after the basophilic degeneration sets in, or 4–5 days after fiber invasion, and persists undiminished for the remainder of the infection. It is, in fact, still present after 555 days when calcification is well under way. Basophilia, indicating a tissue pH considerably below 9.0, likewise remains throughout infection. It appears to be due to the increase in cytoplasmic ribonucleic acid (RNA). Neighboring uninfected fibers, often showing other pathologic changes, give no evidence of phosphatase content.

A vital role of phosphatase in the function of the eosinophils in this phase of the infection is indicated by the presence of phosphatase-positive cells only in perivascular infiltrates and in cellular infiltrates near infected fibers. In eosinophils located at a distance from the parasites or blood vessels, the enzyme is absent, as it is from all other cells involved in the inflammation (macrophages, lymphoctyes, plasma cells and others). Cellular reactions in rats in the region of parasitic destruction may be demonstrated over a long period of time (more than 130 days in some cases), but the tissue reaction usually subsides after about 60 days postinfection. Phosphatase-positive eosinophils, seen as early as 8 days, appear to persist as long as the tissue eosinophilia.

The Evans blue histochemical technique shows no evidence of change in the diaphragm between 4 days and 17 months after infection, hence penetration into muscle fibers does not produce changes in host glyco- protein (Lewert and Lee, 1954). This suggests the absence of enzymes for this purpose. Intense staining with this dye reveals areas where water-soluble (alcohol-insoluble), carbohydrate-containing protein is present. Penetration enzymes of certain parasites produce immediate changes in the glycoprotein of the acellular constituents of connective tissue, resulting in a more soluble or depolymerized state. Such altera- tions presumably soften the acellular material, making it a much less effective barrier to penetration. Host glycoprotein alterations in the Trichinella-infected muscle can be revealed by the Hotchkiss histo- chemical method. However, these, in later stages, are degenerative or reparative host responses to invasion, and cannot be attributed to penetration activities of the larvae. Prominent, swollen fibers can be seen 6–20 days after infection and the sarcolemma is Hotchkiss positive. These fibers are thicker and more prominent than those of neighboring un- infected fibers. The fiber itself contains a considerable amount of Hotchkiss-positive material. The area of altered fibers is metachromatic with toluidine blue, as in areas of connective tissue formation or of protease action on such tissue. These areas correspond to those with increased alkaline phosphatase activity (Bullock, 1953). The external acellular capsule that forms around the larvae contains glycoprotein. With increasing age of infection, the Hotchkiss staining intensifies and the capsule is metachromatic as revealed by toluidine blue. The meta- chromasia is still present 5 months or more after infection, but is less pronounced. The Hotchkiss staining decreases after 10 months, but is still visible after calcification begins at the poles of the capsule.

Despite their great power to penetrate the intestinal mucosa and many other tissues, the various stages of *T. spiralis* apparently do not possess enzymes, found in certain other parasites, that facilitate penetration. In addition to the apparent absence of enzymes to produce immediate alterations in host glycoprotein, *in vitro* studies have shown that the pre-adults (living, homogenates, and extracts) lack collagenase activity (Lewert and Lee, 1954). Moreover, action against a gelatin substrate (gelatinolytic activity) is negative in living larvae and extracts, and homogenates show no "tryptic" activity by the Anson technique. However, a type of "spreading factor" can be demonstrated in the skin by concentration and spreading of intravenous Evans blue after intra-dermal injection of larval extract. The nature and degree of this spreading differs from that produced by hyaluronidase. Therefore, as shown with other parasites, "spreading" can be caused by other non-related substances, and enzymes other than hyaluronidase can act on polysaccharide-containing protein.

4. *The Gastrointestinal System*

In old rats, histologic sections of the small intestine reveal that some larvae penetrate the mucosa within 2 h, and after 4 h of infection almost all have entered (Gursch, 1949). Many appear to enter the tissue by lodging securely between villi and then penetrating into glandular tissue. Histochemical observations with Evans blue vital stain support the evidence for rapid penetration without the aid of specific enzymes for this purpose (Lewert and Lee, 1954).

Immediate changes in the glycoprotein of the acellular constituents are not apparent in the intestinal mucosa, but distribution of the dye provides other information. Evidence of penetration can be found within 20 min after inoculation of free larvae into the stomach when blue villi can be seen scattered throughout the duodenal mucosa. Sections reveal that this colour is due to accumulation of dye in the expanded lacteal. By 2 h postinfection, the lymphatics of the submucosa, as well as those of the tunica propria of the villi, retain dye in their lumina. By 4 h, and more pronounced at 16 h, the local lymph nodes of the intestine and also the mesenteric nodes show deeper staining than in uninfected controls. By 24 h, blue-staining material is seen in the vicinity of the developing worm, but this can not be distinguished from the mucoid secretion of the intestine, which also stains at this time. The muscularis probably is a barrier to deeper penetration, since many parasites reach this area and turn about. In any case, with the pre-adults, and later the adult males and females, burrowing about in the mucosa, cell contents and tissue fluids are released and extensive irritation of the mucosa is evident (especially vascular hyperemia, necrosis, and edema). Therefore, during the intestinal phase of infection, striking signs and symptoms of this pathologic process may appear, provided the intensity reaches a certain level. In young rats given 3000 larvae, there is anorexia (revealed by reduced feed consumption), diarrhea, marked weight loss, and greatly reduced physical activity. These signs decrease in time except the reduced activity, which may follow a progressive course (Pollay *et al.*, 1954).

5. *Immune Responses*

The relative natural immunity of rats has been known for many years

(Gould, 1945). This host is regarded as being very susceptible to an initial infection and, therefore, exhibits very little natural immunity. Until recently no evidence indicated a significant difference in virulence of *T. spiralis* "strains" for rats. However, in Kenya, a "strain" from humans shows exceptionally low infectivity when administered to rats (Forrester *et al.*, 1961). In any case, few tests have been reported in recent years to show the effect of various factors on the establishment and early maintenance of *T. spiralis* before acquired immunity comes into play. The nature and character of acquired immunity in this host were established early by the studies of McCoy and others (Gould, 1945). In recent years there has been continued interest in this phase of immunity and a variety of tests have been made.

  a. Immunity after a stimulating infection(s). A single small stimulating infection (80, 160, 320 or 640 larvae) produces immunity within 14 days, which varies in degree depending on the number of larvae in the stimulating infection (Fischthal, 1943). The two highest doses produce an absolute immunity, since no muscle larvae result from a massive challenging infection (10 000 larvae). There is evidence that the immunity wanes after a comparatively short period. Old rats challenged 20 days after a stimulating infection harbor much smaller female worms, with strikingly fewer eggs and larvae, thn non-immunized rats. These values are not as striking in the case of rats challenged 30 or 54 days after the stimulating infection, but are still smaller than those for worms from controls (Semrad and Coors, 1951).

  It is clear, therefore, that rats develop rapidly a striking acquired immunity after a single stimulating infection, which is not true in mice as will be seen later. As early as 14 days, the immunity is strong enough to eliminate within 7 days almost all of the adult worms from a massive challenging infection, which prevents any increase in the number of muscle larvae (Fischthal, 1943). Moreover, as early as 20 days after a single stimulating infection, the immunity is strong enough to inhibit significantly the development of worms from the challenging infection. Thus, prior to the significant loss of worms (about 6–8 days post-infection), the females show marked stunting and contain much smaller numbers of eggs and larvae (Semrad and Coors, 1951). These latter effects would appear to be due to the direct action of specific antibodies.

  In recent years many studies have been made, testing the immune response of parabiotic rats (Zaiman, 1953; Zaiman and Rubel, 1953; Zaiman *et al.*, 1953; Boyd and Petersen, 1954; Zaiman and Stoney, 1954; Zaiman *et al.*, 1954; Zaiman and Safholm, 1955; Zaiman *et al.*, 1955a; Zaiman *et al.*, 1955b). Infection of one member of the pair results in the transfer of immunity to the "uninfected" twin even in cases where separation by surgery is performed 5 days after the immunizing infection.

L

Likewise, uninfected mates combined surgically with immunized mates 4 weeks after the latter receive a second stimulating infection are protected against a challenging infection. Transferred immunity is demonstrable in the recipient for as long as 11 months after immunization of the donor with non-irradiated larvae, and for as long as 5 months when the donor is immunized with larvae irradiated to prevent sexual maturity of the developing adult worms. As would be expected, the degree of immunity in the recipient is intermediate between that of the donor and previously uninfected controls.

The transfer of immunity to uninfected parabiotic rats supports the mounting evidence that this immunity is general in nature and not limited by prior stimulation to local intestinal sites. However, considering the long duration of the transferred immunity, it is not likely to be passive in nature, resulting from transferred protective substances via the combined circulatory systems. Rather, it appears that antigenic substances are thereby transferred, resulting in the activation of the recipient's cells and the subsequent development of active immunity. The fact that only a few days of parabiosis are required supports this contention. It is entirely unlikely that antibody production has reached the level necessary for effective transfer within this brief period. On the other hand, it is known that large amounts of antigen are present in the circulation for several days after infection (Bozicevich and Detre, 1940). Large quantities must be excreted in the urine, since uroprecipitation tests are positive as early as 3 days postinfection (Zapart, 1960). On the other hand, transferred antigens would not seem to be the explanation for the immunity acquired by the "uninfected" parabionts combined surgically with donors 4 weeks after the donors receive a second stimulating infection. It is more likely, in this case, that transferred antibodies are responsible. This probability of a passive immunity should be tested by infecting certain of the "uninfected" parabionts at intervals.

b. The production of artificial active immunity. Six injections of 30 000 intact, killed larvae given at intervals for 14 days offer significant protection to 1000 living larvae given 5 days after the last injection (Chute, 1956). This can be demonstrated within 5 days postinfection by a great reduction in the number of adults in the small intestine. Injections of excretion-secretion antigens collected from incubated larvae appear to engender immunity, but the degree is less in that the average numbers of worms, while reduced, do not differ significantly from the numbers in controls. However, the numbers of muscle larvae are reduced significantly. Moreover, injections of rabbit antiserum between 16–26 days after infection with 2000–2500 larvae reduce the size of muscle larvae recovered 35 days postinfection.

Therefore, both somatic and metabolic antigens from first-stage larvae produce an active immunity in rats, which after a challenging infection reduces the number of adult worms in the small intestine and/or the number of muscle larvae. It is interesting that these antigens produce host cell sensitivity within 2 weeks, which may persist for many months (Briggs, 1961). Mast cells from infected rats show metachromasia and cell disruption with release of granules when exposed *in vitro* to these antigens, and the release of biologically active amines is associated with the cell injury.

The reduced numbers of muscle larvae are due obviously to the reduction in numbers of females, but even when the latter fails to occur reduced numbers of larvae may result from direct deleterious action(s) against the females that lower their reproductive potential (Semrad and Coors, 1951). However, despite all effects against the adults, larvapositing proceeds under these conditions. It is worth noting, therefore, that rabbit antiserum has a stunting effect against the larvae when given early in the muscular phase (Chute, 1956). The presence of an extra-intestinal defence raises many questions, which cannot be answered satisfactorily without further work. There is great need for studies on this phase alone, as have been made separately on the pre-adult and adult stages in mice. Nevertheless, with present information it is safe to state that, regardless of the effectiveness of such a defence, its role in the total immunity of the host must be considered a minor one. Under usual circumstances, it would be called into play only when the intestinal phase is unable to check the females. In untreated rats this appears to be limited to the initial infection, since after reinfection most adult worms are eliminated before larvapositing can occur (Fischthal, 1943; Gould *et al.*, 1955).

c. *The stage(s) responsible for acquired immunity.* Larvae exposed to 6000 r ^{60}Co or 10 000 r ^{60}Co and used to infect rats in doses of 3700 produce a striking degree of immunity, as measured by the number of adults present 6–10 days after a challenging infection with 3700 non-irradiated larvae (Gould *et al.*, 1955). However, larvae exposed to 18 000 r ^{60}Co fail to produce immunity in this way, but using larvae counts as the measure they appear to offer some protection. After use of larvae exposed to 10 000 r ^{60}Co and reinfection with non-irradiated larvae, very few muscle larvae are found, due to the presence of few adults in the small intestine after 4 days. This dose of irradiation with ^{60}Co produces sterility in the developing adult worms, so that the immunizing properties are those related to the pre-adults and sterile adults without an assist from migrating and encysting larvae. On the other hand, only part of the pre-adult stage is responsible after exposure to 18 000 r ^{60}Co, since this dose prevents most larvae from maturing into adults.

These results confirm the evidence that all three phases of the life cycle (pre-adults, adults, muscle larvae) are not required to produce an effective immunity. It is clear that the pre-adults and adults combined are sufficient to produce a high-grade immunity. Also, the pre-adults alone appear to produce a measurable degree of immunity, but, by comparison with that from the two combined stages, it is feeble. It should be noted that the doses of radiation required to separate these phases appear to differ greatly according to the source. It requires about 10 000 r ^{60}Co to produce partial or complete sexual sterilization in developing worms, and about 18 000 r ^{60}Co to prevent most larvae from maturing into adults. Although the roentgen rays from a 200 kV unit are less penetrating, much smaller doses of X-ray are needed to produce these effects, about 3500 r for sterility, and about 5000–6000 r for prevention of maturation (Gould et al., 1953). However, the important point to keep in mind is the amount of energy absorbed by the larvae during exposure, not the measure of the external dose beam. Early attempts to express this factor of absorbed energy were made by stating the dosage in "rep" (roentgen-equivalent-physical), but this has been improved in recent years by the determination and use of "rad" (radiation-absorbed-dose). When rep is used, it is interesting that dosages of ^{60}Co (2500–3000 rep) needed to produce sterility in certain other parasitic larvae more nearly approximate those expected from a X-ray source (Villella et al., 1961). Moreover, work in mice has shown that the β-rays of ^{32}P will sterilize all developing T. spiralis larvae exposed to 4000 rad and will prevent maturation of those exposed to 6000 rad (Hartung and Becht, 1960). These results, therefore, suggest that the X-ray doses used in the past probably will be found to be similar to the rad values needed to produce various effects against the larvae.

Irradiation provides a valuable tool for immunity studies and will probably continue to be used for separation of life cycle stages. It is, therefore, important, if direct comparisons of different studies are to be made available, that careful attention be given to the selection of proper doses based on the newer concepts of absorbed energy (rad). In recent years, some appear to have selected X-ray doses far in excess of those needed to fulfill the conditions of the experimental design, apparently misled by the comparatively large doses of ^{60}Co needed to accomplish the same ends. Even when doses are expressed in rep, ^{60}Co requires about three times the dose of X-ray to sterilize or prevent maturation (Gould et al., 1957). Moreover, some fail to check the establishment and maintenance of irradiated larvae after inoculation. Unless "viability controls" are used, and counts of pre-adults or adults (according to the dose of irradiation employed) are made at a specified time(s) after infection, there is no assurance that the quantity of stimulation is that expected or desired. It is obvious that indirect evidence alone, obtained by worm counts after a challenging infection with non-irradiated larvae, is not acceptable in quantitative immunological work.

d. Factors that modify acquired immunity. Provided the environment is not altered to the extent that conditions are unfavorable to provide the needs of the parasite, modifying the immunity of the host is an effective device to reveal factors that influence it. The ultimate goal of such manipulations is to shed light on the mechanism involved in the operation of acquired immunity. A number of factors have been studied in this connection, some in rats, but more in mice to be discussed later.

1. CORTISONE. Adult rats infected with 1220 larvae and given daily cortisone injections from the time of infection for 30 days harbor slightly more muscle larvae than controls $6\frac{1}{2}$ months postinfection, and those given cortisone for 60 days have significantly more larvae than controls (Markell and Lewis, 1957). At $6\frac{1}{2}$ months after infection, antibodies in low titer are demonstrable in some rats of all groups by the larval microflocculation test. Upon reinfection 5 months after the first infection, and without further cortisone treatment, both cortisone-treated groups have significantly more larvae than controls 6 weeks later, and antibodies, detected in some rats of all groups, are present in low titer. Untreated controls exhibit absolute immunity to the challenging infection as measured by the number of larvae recovered, but no immunity is evident in the cortisone-treated rats.

At $6\frac{1}{2}$ months after infection, the rats given cortisone daily for 30 days after infection show a significant increase in certain serum constituents. Total serum globulin is increased, which produces a lower A/G ratio (Weimer *et al.*, 1958). Also, total serum glycoprotein is increased, due to an increase in the globulin polysaccharide, and the hematocrit value is increased. Six weeks after reinfection, there are also significant increases. Total serum albumin increases, which produces in this case a higher A/G ratio. Moreover, the increase in the total serum glycoprotein is due to increases in both the albumin and globulin polysaccharide. The hematocrit remains elevated. In the case of those given cortisone daily for 60 days postinfection, the values $6\frac{1}{2}$ months after infection show increases in total serum proteins, due to the increase in total albumin. The hematocrit remains elevated. After reinfection, the albumin value remains elevated, but the globulin fraction is reduced, producing a higher A/G ratio. The 60-day treated groups, therefore, are the only infected groups not showing a significant increase in total serum glycoprotein, and those reinfected are the only ones not to show a significantly increased hematocrit, indicating hemoconcentration. Also, the 30-day reinfected group is the only one to show a significant increase in albumin polysaccharide.

Young rats infected with 5000 larvae and given cortisone injections retain adult worms much longer and, as a consequence, have considerably greater muscle infections than controls (Markell, 1958). Between 5–8 weeks postinfection, when controls show no adults, the cortisone-treated rats still retain as adults more than 5% of the infecting dose of larvae, and even between 9–14 weeks there are more adults present than found in controls during the first 4 weeks. Between 9–14 weeks postinfection, the cortisone-treated rats harbor 9.7 times the number of larvae found in untreated controls.

These studies confirm previous work, showing that this steroid administered daily over a specified period interferes with acquired immunity to this parasite. In the present instance, injections began at the time of initial infection and, therefore, the results show the effect upon the development and maintenance of immunity. That it interfered drastically is evident by the retention of large numbers of adult worms for many weeks after all were gone from untreated controls. In view of this, it is surprising to note the failure of a 30-day treatment after initial infection to produce significantly more muscle larvae than in controls. However, a trend was noted in that the treated animals harbored larger numbers.

The serum changes noted $6\frac{1}{2}$ months after infection have not been explained. It is of interest, however, that the most consistent change from normal is significant increase in total serum glycoprotein. All infected and reinfected rats exhibited this increase, except those given cortisone for 60 days after the initial infection. Such an increase in glycoprotein is noted in a number of pathological and altered physiological states, in which inflammation or tissue destruction are noteworthy (*e.g.*, in advanced tuberculosis and certain advanced types of carcinoma). Most important, in *T. spiralis* infections in rats, Lewert and Lee (1954) have shown that infected muscles reveal striking glycoprotein alterations for long periods and the region comprising the external acellular capsule is positive for glycoprotein for more than 10 months (and it is of further interest that the inner cyst wall shows alkaline phosphatase reaction even after calcification is well under way; Bullock, 1953). This prompts the suggestion that inflammation, muscle fiber degeneration and reparative host responses may be involved in the present case, since these events are known to continue for many months in rats. However, despite the significant increase in numbers of muscle larvae, the 60-day cortisone groups failed to show the elevated glycoprotein response. Could this mean, as suggested by the work of Ritterson (1959b) in Chinese hamsters, that prolonged cortisone treatment increased the structural integrity of the muscle cells? If so, this might have minimized the alterations in host glycoprotein during larval encystment. Unless such treatment has a prolonged effect, which would be contrary to its rather brief

anti-inflammatory effect after injections are discontinued, this explanation would not seem to apply to the 60-day cortisone group reinfected
after 5 months, since cortisone was given only after the initial infection. On the other hand, the infection may take longer than 6 weeks to
produce a significantly elevated serum response.

On the basis of the apparent interference with the development of
acquired immunity after initial infection, it is difficult to explain the
significant increase in serum globulin in the 30-day cortisone group of
rats, especially when this value was not elevated in the untreated
controls. Further studies are needed to elucidate this and other serum
changes after infection. Regardless of the mechanisms, however, it is
clear that this infection elicits systemic effects as reflected in the distribution and concentration of serum proteins and glycoproteins and that
certain patterns are modified for long periods by prolonged cortisone
treatment.

2. CONCURRENT INFECTION. In rats 2 months of age given a subclinical infection with *T. spiralis* and 10 days later, during the migration
phase of large numbers of larvae, injected with encephalomyocarditis
(EMC) virus, there is a very high rate of crippling and death. These rates
are significantly greater than those in controls given the same virus doses
without *T. spiralis* (Kilham and Olivier, 1961). The rats with dual
infections begin to lose weight 3–5 days after virus inoculation, and virus
in various tissues can be isolated by this time. A striking feature is the
finding of virus in high titer in skeletal muscles containing larvae, and
the absence of virus in corresponding muscles from rats given only the
virus infection. A greater cellular response is noted in fibers with larvae
and virus than in those with larvae alone. These synergistic effects
operate 10–28 days after the *T. spiralis* infection and are influenced
within limits by the concentration of virus and the number of larvae
used for infection. There is a suggestion that physiopathologic changes
in invaded muscle fibers may favor virus multiplication. Interestingly
enough, no histologic evidence of damage to heart muscle is seen, despite
the common observation of myocarditis in Trichinella-infected rats
(Zaiman *et al.*, 1961; Maeir *et al.*, 1962).

Rats immunized against *Nippostrongylus muris* (1200, 4600, and 8100
larvae in three stimulating infections at 5-day intervals) show a significant reduction in muscle larvae after an infection with 1000 *T. spiralis*
(Louch, 1962). There is no cross reaction between serum antibodies produced in response to the two separate agents, as revealed by agar diffusion tests. A saline extract (lipid extracted) of *T. spiralis* gives a positive
reaction with blood from rats immunized with this agent, but is negative
with blood from uninfected rats or blood from those immunized with
N. muris. The mechanism whereby previous *N. muris* infections protect

against an initial infection with *T. spiralis* is not understood, but one possibility is a non-specific intestinal inflammation produced by *N. muris*.

3. WHOLE-BODY IRRADIATION. Rats exposed to small doses of irradiation (100 r 3 days prior to infection, 50 r 1 week postinfection, and 50 r 2 weeks postinfection) and given a small dose of larvae (340–400) show no interference with immunity as measured by the numbers of muscle larvae (Moskwa *et al.*, 1958). However, other observations show differences in the irradiated-infected rats when compared with controls. The body temperature per anus is subnormal (35.8–36.5°C at 1 and 2 weeks postinfection), the total white cell count is lower (20 000 mm 3, compared with 28 000 for non-irradiated, infected controls; irradiated, non-infected controls show 13 500), and signs of greater debilitation are obvious (reduced activity, appearance of fur, etc.). No difference is noted in skin sensitivity after injection of a larval extract. The failure to effect immunity confirms other studies with small radiation doses. As will be seen later, mid-lethal doses produce striking effects in mice.

e. The mechanism(s) of acquired immunity. Circulating hemagglutinating antibodies can be detected in the serum of rats about 14 days after a single infection (Kagan and Bargai, 1956), and the evidence indicates that precipitating antibodies in comparable titers appear somewhat later. The former are associated in time of appearance with gamma globulin increase, since a notable increase in this fraction is seen between 15–25 days postinfection (Kagan and Goodchild, 1961). However, the protective nature of the hemagglutinating antibodies has not been demonstrated. Precipitating antibodies, on the other hand, combine with antigenic material (presumably ES antigens) *in vitro* when incubated with adult worms or larvae, and certain ES antigen preparations are immunogenic (Chute, 1956). Striking actions against female worms, resulting in stunted development and smaller numbers of ova and larvae, can be demonstrated in immunized rats soon after reinfection (Semrad and Coors, 1951). Therefore, there is a strong suggestion that precipitating antibodies produce direct deleterious effects against the female worms. Male worms are likewise stunted in development, so such action must be directed against them as well (Semrad and Coors, 1951). In addition to this evidence for a humoral factor, it has been shown that migrating and encysting larvae are stunted when rabbit antiserum is administered to rats at a certain period postinfection (Chute, 1956).

There is also indirect evidence that cellular factors play an important role in this immunity in rats. Cortisone prevents the development of immunity apparently without interfering with the humoral response (Markell and Lewis, 1957). Based on the work in mice to be discussed in detail below, this steroid probably exerts its effect by preventing almost entirely the characteristic inflammatory response in the small intestine. When the cellular factors are thus inhibited, the adult worms persist for long periods and significant increases occur in the numbers of muscle larvae (Markell, 1958). The present evidence indicates, therefore, that both humoral and cellular factors are involved in the strong immunity demonstrated in rats. Considerably more information has been presented on these aspects from studies in mice, which will be discussed below.

C. MICE

1. *Pertinent Details of the Life Cycle*

After infection, the first phase of the parasite to engage the host is the pre-adult. This phase lasts only about 33 h, since the final molt of the male is completed about that time (Wu and Kingscote, 1957). A slender tube, presumably cuticle that lines the cloaca, is seen at the tip of this last molt. Free spermatozoa are formed about 26 h postinfection. Ovulation, an independent process from insemination, occurs at 37 h, and in some cases spermatozoa may be present in the seminal receptacle by this time. A similar slender tube is seen at the tip of the last molt of the female, presumably the cuticle lining the rectum.

In old mice given an initial infection with 200 larvae, a large percentage (63.6–95.2%) of the infecting dose can be recovered as adult worms during the first 11 days (Larsh *et al.*, 1952). During this period, relatively few worms are in the large intestine (1.1–10.9%); most are found in the anterior half of the small intestine (42.8–68.9%). Between 11–14 days, a highly significant reduction occurs in the small intestine (from 84.3% on day 11 to 27.1% on day 14), and very few (3.0%) remain in the anterior half. With this great loss from the small intestine, it is not surprising to note a significant increase in the large intestine (from 10.9% on day 11 to 34.5% on day 14). Despite this increase, it is not great enough to account for those lost from the small intestine, hence many apparently are eliminated from the body. After 14 days, there is a gradual loss of worms from the small intestine until by day 24 very few can be found (0.8%). The losses from the large intestine, with its much larger numbers during this period, are also gradual but at a slower rate, so that by day 24 there are still 9.0% present. This suggests temporary reattachment of certain worms lost from the small intestine, otherwise few would be expected after this long period. In rats the worms remain only a few days after being lost from the small intestine, so that few are found in the large intestine after 14 days (Gursch, 1949). In mice of about the same age as those above given twice the number of larvae at infection (400), a change in distribution of adult worms is noted earlier (Goulson, 1957, 1958). While the total numbers in the entire small intestine remain relatively constant for 11 days, as early as 9 days there are significantly more worms in the posterior half than in the anterior half. With the smaller (200) dose, this shift does not occur until several days later. It may be noted that the female worms recovered 7 days after an initial infection appear to be much larger (2.70–2.89 mm long) from mice (Campbell, 1955; Kim, 1957) than those (1.90 mm) from rats (Semrad and Coors, 1951). The size of the infecting dose may be the important factor, since a small dose (200) was used in mice and the rats were "heavily infected". Also, the distribution of adult worms in old rats is similar to that in mice, but the longevity is considerably less (Gursch, 1949).

Very similar findings as to the longevity of adult worms in the intestine have been reported by others (Rappaport, 1943b). In mice given about 215 larvae, there was little change in numbers during the first 10 days (66.3–82.2%), and the sex ratios (F/M) varied from 1.75 to 2.43. Reduced numbers were noted at 12 and 14 days (54.3–57.2%) when the sex ratios were 1.84–2.43; large numbers of worms were in the large intestine by this time. The greatest change was seen at 16 days (32.8%; sex ratio, 2.20; many of the females were in the large intestine). The specific age of these mice was not given, but implied from other reported experiments the average weight was 21.0 g. If this were true, these mice probably were much younger than those reported in the above experiments, which would explain the significant loss of worms at a somewhat later period (between 14–16 days, rather than between 11–14 days in the old mice reported above). This longer period compares favorably with that (between 15–17 days) seen in mice 5 weeks of age infected with 300 larvae (Larsh et al., 1956).

In young mice, about 1 month old, the distribution of adult worms in the small intestine is entirely different (Larsh and Hendricks, 1949). Five days after an infection with 300 larvae, of the total in the small intestine 30.5% are in the anterior half and the remaining 69.5% in the posterior half. At the same time, old mice, about 4.5 months old, given the same infection show 81.3% in the anterior half and 18.7% in the posterior half. It is obvious, therefore, that within certain limits age is a factor in the distribution of worms in the small intestine. By reducing drastically the intestinal emptying time of the young mice by an intraperitoneal injection of morphine sulphate, a significant reversal of the distribution can be obtained after an infection with 300 larvae (Larsh and Hendricks, 1949). By this procedure, 94.5% localize in the anterior half and the remaining 5.5% in the posterior half, compared with 29.9% and 70.1% respectively, in untreated controls. Thus, it appears that the main factor accounting for the difference in distribution of worms in young and old mice is the rate of intestinal emptying time, which is known to be significantly slower in old animals.

Mice (20–25 g) given a moderate infection (20 larvae per g of body weight) show no larvae in "teased-muscles" 5 days postinfection, but small numbers can be recovered on the following day (Phillipson and Kershaw, 1961). The numbers increase steadily to 15 days postinfection, after which there is little general increase. To avoid digestion of small larvae, a maceration method was used for recovery of larvae between 5–30 days postinfection; the alternative digestive method (17–30 days) revealed similar numbers. At the height of larval production, between 7–11 days postinfection, few larvae can be found in the blood, suggesting they leave the circulation rapidly. Larval development is slow and reaches a maximum about 24 days postinfection. However, by the 17th day, they are encysted, resist digestion in artificial gastric juice, and are infective for new hosts.

Encysted larvae in adult mice given a moderate infection (10 larvae per g of body weight) reveal interesting structures when viewed at great magnification, from 3500 to 49 000 × (Beckett and Boothroyd, 1961). For example, the ultrastructure of the stichosome indicates that the cells secrete very actively. It is, however, not clear whether a storage product (for material absorbed through the alimentary tract) or a digestive-juice precursor is formed. This structure is represented by a single row of uninucleate discoid cells adjacent to the esophagus. It extends from just posterior to the bulbous region of the esophagus almost to the mid-gut region. These cells can be seen in larvae as early as 6 days postinfection (Wu, 1955). Another example is the genital primordium. Even at great magnifications the cells have an indistinct outline, but each has a single nucleus and nucleolus. The cyst wall detail, nuclei of muscle cells, etc., and various heretofore unrecognized structures can be seen in electron micrographs.

At the time of penetration into diaphragmatic muscle fibers of mice (infected with about 40 larvae), desoxyribonucleic acid (DNA) and ribonucleic acid (RNA) are present in the cells of larvae in only small amounts, the latter being somewhat less (Zarzycki, 1960). By the middle of the 2nd week postinfection, DNA has decreased, RNA increased. The latter increases rapidly thereafter to a peak concentration by 15 days postinfection and persists at this level even after cyst formation. On the other hand, DNA level diminishes slowly after 2 weeks and presumably is absent after encystment. Since RNA functions primarily in the cell cytoplasm as a template in connection with synthesis of specific cellular proteins, these findings suggest that such synthesis is inhibited or proceeds at a slow rate until the larvae are well established in the muscle fibers.

Immature larvae (14 days), and even those encysted for long periods (56 and 180 days), exchange metabolites with the mouse host as proved by their incorporation of short-chain ^{14}C from the tissues of mice fed in the diet labeled amino acids (glycine-2-^{14}C and dl-alanine-2-^{14}C or glycine-1-^{14}C and dl-alanine-1-^{14}C) for a period of 7 days (Stoner and Hankes, 1955). Likewise feeding ^{14}C-labeled diets with more complex amino acids (dl-tyrosine-2-^{14}C and dl-tryptophan-2-^{14}C) reveals such an exchange (Hankes and Stoner, 1958). In this case, the larvae (in mice infected for 62 and 186 days) incorporate a high percentage (85–92) of their total ^{14}C content into protein (as precipitated by tungstic acid). In view of this, and the high level of RNA (Zarzycki, 1960), it is clear that protein synthesis is a very active process in encysted larvae. This has far reaching implications for further studies.

2. The Cardiovascular System

a. Blood. After an infection with 200 larvae, mice 2–3 months old show little variation in the total numbers of circulating white blood cells between 11 days prior to infection to 35 days postinfection (Yarinsky, 1961). On the day prior to infection, differential counts show 62.5% lymphocytes, 35.5% neutrophils, 1.5% eosinophils, and 0.5% monocytes. The percentages of lymphocytes decrease and those of neutrophils increase soon after infection until at 9 days postinfection there are more neutrophils. This reversal of the lymphocyte/neutrophil ratio remains in effect for at least 8 days. At 17 days postinfection, the percentages of lymphocytes and neutrophils are 39 and 54, respectively. Soon after this period, most counts show slightly more lymphocytes, but as late as 27 days postinfection the difference remains small. A low-grade eosinophilia (14.5%) is first noted 19 days postinfection and there is little change over the next 8 days. About the same degree of eosinophilia (10%) in this strain of mouse of the same age is noted during a similar period after different levels of infection, varying from 50 to 400 larvae in different mice (Larsh and Nichols, 1949); so there does not appear to be a dose response relationship within these limits. With the largest dose (400 larvae) eosinophilia (8%) is noted by 14 days (Coker, 1954, 1956a). In mice immunized with four stimulating infections (200 larvae each) and given a challenging infection with 200 larvae, many differences are noted. Leukocytosis is seen between the 3rd and 9th days postinfection, a reversal in the lymphocyte/neutrophil ratio occurs earlier (7 days, and lasts through 17 days postinfection), and eosinophilia (13.5–16.5%) occurs earlier (11 days postinfection; Yarinsky, 1961). With a larger challenging infection (400), eosinophilia (11.2%) is noted by 7 days and increases (23.8%) by 14 days (Coker, 1954).

Various serologic tests can be used to detect circulating antibodies, which will be discussed later in connection with the mechanism of acquired immunity.

3. The Muscular System

In old mice given an infection with 200 larvae, there is no evidence of inflammation in the musculature at 14 days postinfection despite the presence of tiny larvae (Coker, 1956c). At 21 days, there is an acute general myositis with participation by lymphocytes and other mononuclear leukocytes, as well as by neutrophils and eosinophils (Fig. 1). By

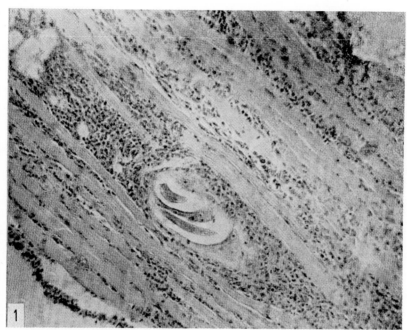

Fig. 1. Note the intense general myositis in an old mouse at 21 days after infection. Photograph taken by use of a compound microscope (10× ocular and objective). From Coker (1956c); by permission of the Editor, *J. Parasit.*

30 days, the general reaction has subsided partially, but there is a tendency towards greater consolidation around the larvae, which is most intense around dead ones (Fig. 2).

When mice infected (450 larvae given when mice were 6 weeks old) for 56 or 180 days are fed labeled diets for 6 days (*dl*-tyrosine-2-^{14}C and *dl*-tryptophan-2-^{14}C), the encysted larvae incorporate significant levels of ^{14}C activity (Hankes and Stoner, 1958). Incorporation of total ^{14}C into host muscle proteins is reduced in those with the oldest infection fed *dl*-tyrosine-2-^{14}C, as compared with muscle proteins from non-infected hosts. However, those fed the *dl*-tryptophan-2-^{14}C diet show a ten-fold increase in ^{14}C content of the total muscle proteins over that in non-infected muscle. This suggests a significant change in tryptophan metabolism in infected mice, since the non-infected muscle samples were from mice maintained on the same diet. Even the ^{14}C activity in the protein fraction of the serum shows a significant increase, compared with the level of activity in serum protein of the non-infected mice. Thus, the rate of tryptophan metabolism into protein apparently is much increased in mice infected for 186 days. In view of these various findings, it is interesting that a high percentage of human cases of trichiniasis fail to show by

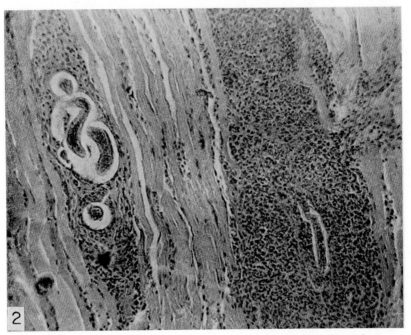

Fig. 2. Note the striking local myositis in an old mouse 30 days after infection, and especially the cellular accumulation around the dead larva. Photograph taken by use of a compound microscope (10× ocular and objective). From Coker (1956c); by permission of the Editor, *J. Parasit.*

paper chromatographic methods free tryptophan in serum samples, while, except for cystine, many other amino acids are detected in almost all cases (Kucharczyk, *et al.*, 1960).

Histochemical studies show that uninfected gastrocnemii of mice exhibit a moderate reaction for both sulphydryl and protein-bound amino groups, whereas infected fibers (5–28 days postinfection) exhibit a diminished activity (Beckett, 1961). The larvae show a concentration of both groups, which is the same or somewhat greater than that in surrounding muscle "breis" (semifluid material from the degenerated fiber). Within the larvae, the area of the genital primordium and cells comprising the "cell body" around the esophagus are sites of strongest reaction. Larvae and damaged muscle substance show considerable aminopeptidase activity. Normal muscle cells contain no histochemically demonstrable aminopeptidase, but mast cells, blood vessels, and nerves in the connective tissue give a positive reaction. These results, combined with those of Hankes and Stoner (1958), suggest strongly that the larvae cause chemical breakdown, and probably depletion of host muscle proteins, and it would seem that aminopeptidase is involved.

4. *The Gastrointestinal System*

Based on information from other hosts, it is likely that soon after infection the larvae enter the intestinal mucosa. At any rate, histologic sections show worms deep in the mucosa (Fig. 3) at 24 h postinfection (Larsh and Race, 1954). In some cases, they penetrate into the crypts of Lieberkuhn (Beresantev, 1962). During the first few days, they appear to develop and move about without evidence of a host response. Considerable tissue damage may occur, presumably due for the most part at least to mechanical factors. At 4 days in old mice a host response is evident in the form of a mild inflammatory reaction in the anterior half of the small intestine. This becomes progressively intense until a moderately severe reaction is reached at the peak of the acute phase, after which it subsides slowly and has the characteristics of a sub-acute (or chronic) phase. The details of this striking host response will be given later, since it is now known to be a characteristic manifestation of acquired immunity.

The intestinal damage gives rise to a variety of signs and symptoms. Depending on the age of the mice, their physical condition, and especially the number of larvae used for infection, there may be varying degrees of fever, diarrhea, anorexia (reflected in reduced feed consumption), body weight loss, activity reduction, apathy, and apparent changes in appearance of the fur. Certain of these are due, no doubt, to pathologic effects produced prior to the appearance of the characteristic host response. However, this response alone appears to place the animals under severe stress, since there does not seem to be any other explanation for the definite patterns of reduced feed consumption and body weight, at least after a moderate infection (200–400 larvae). No differences in daily feed consumption patterns are noted from those in uninfected mice until 5–7 days after infection. Between this time and before 14 days postinfection, there is a significant reduction (Larsh and Goulson, 1962). Soon thereafter near normal amounts are consumed, and by 20 days postinfection the daily intake usually compares favorably with that prior to infection. The reduced feed intake, and probably some interference with protein digestion (Rogers, 1941), leads to a precipitous weight loss (Yarinsky, 1961, 1962; Larsh and Goulson, 1962). Animals begin to lose weight between 6–9 days and minimum weights are noted by 13 days postinfection (Fig. 4). Soon thereafter steady gain is noted in all groups, unless they are under additional stress, such as produced by high doses of irradiation. These reductions are not noted early in the infection despite the extensive damage produced by the burrowing pre-adult and adult worms. On the other hand, both become evident at a time that coincides with the development of the acute inflammatory

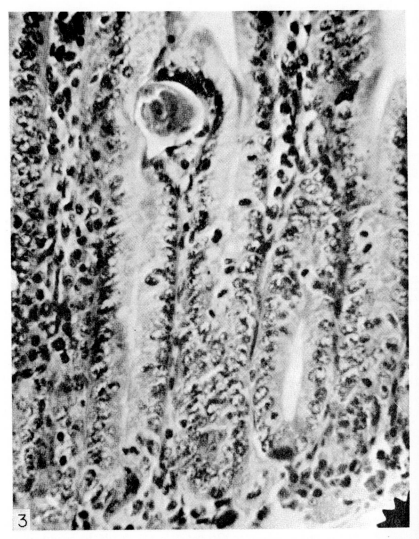

FIG. 3. Non-immunized old mouse 1 day after infection. Note the worm and absence of inflammation. × 348. From Larsh and Race (1954); by permission of the Publisher, *J. inf. Dis.*

response in the upper small intestine, and after the response has subsided considerably, during the later minimal stages of the subacute phase, feed consumption and body weight progress steadily to normal levels. Moreover, in strongly immunized mice, the same association is noted, but it occurs about 1 week earlier due to the much more rapid development of the inflammatory response.

5. *Immune Responses*

Mice were used very little in immunity studies until Culbertson (1942) demonstrated by quantitative methods that they develop a high degree of active immunity. Investigators found they offer many advantages in

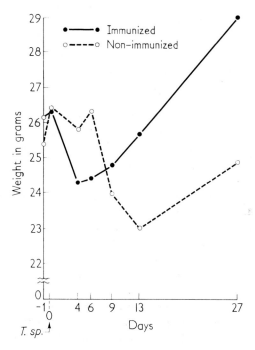

Fig. 4. Total-body weights of old immunized and non-immunized mice at certain intervals after a challenging infection with 200 *T. spiralis* larvae. From Yarinsky (1961); permission of the Graduate School.

large experiments due to their small size, and now they are the most popular host for immunity studies. A brief review of the early work was given by Larsh (1953a).

a. Immunity, serologic response, intestinal inflammation, and body weight loss produced by a single infection. As mentioned above, the vast majority of the larvae in an initial infecting dose can be recovered as adult worms during the first 11 days. By this criterion, mice have very

M

little natural immunity to this parasite. The adult worms in certain treated hosts have been shown to live for extremely long periods. Therefore, the significant loss of worms between 11–14 days postinfection in untreated old mice suggests that acquired immunity has begun to be manifested. Other evidence proves this point. On the second day postinfection, coproantibodies against the adult worms can be detected in low titer by using the precipitin-ring test (fecal suspensions containing the antibody overlaid with adult-worm antigens; Ivey, 1956). About 4 days after infection, a mild intestinal inflammation is observed in the anterior half of the small intestine (Fig. 5). This develops into an acute phase, which reaches the zenith about 8 days postinfection (Fig. 6) and then diminishes as it passes through a characteristic sub-acute (or chronic) phase (Fig. 7). This inflammatory response, even the characteristic cellular components involved, differs from that in highly immunized mice only in time and severity (Larsh and Race, 1954). Moreover, as mentioned above, it is associated with reduced feed consumption and body weight loss. In this connection, it is worth noting that in hamsters there is a rapid loss of adrenal cortical lipid during the period of these other effects (Ritterson and Mauer, 1957), as well as decreased physical activity (Bernard, 1959). These may well be other indications of stress produced by the inflammation. In any case, another factor to consider here is the appearance of circulating precipitins in low titer (1:2) about 7 days postinfection (Baughn, 1952 a,b). There is, therefore, in old mice an association of coproantibodies and circulating antibodies, intestinal inflammation, reduced feed consumption, and weight loss before a significant loss of adult worms occurs from, and only from, the proximal half of the small intestine (Larsh et al., 1952). There seems little doubt that the worm loss at this particular time is due to factors associated with acquired immunity. The fact that a shift in numbers occurs at 11 days after an infection with 400 larvae, so that greater numbers occur in the posterior half of the small intestine, suggests that the effects of acquired immunity are being manifested before it can be demonstrated by reduced numbers in the entire small intestine (Goulson, 1957, 1958). Finally, in old mice daily injections of cortisone (0.5 mg), from 2 days prior to an infection with 200 larvae until 14 days after infection (or to 30 days), prevent the usual loss of adult worms by 14 days (Coker, 1955). This action of cortisone is due probably to its almost complete inhibition of the intestinal inflammatory response, which will be discussed later. Here, its effect is presented only as further evidence that a delayed measurable acquired immunity develops after an initial infection. It is also interesting to note that at 7 days postinfection, the length and width (17.0 mm × 4.7 mm) of the spleen are much greater than the measurements (14.8 mm × 3.9 mm) at 14 days (Coker, 1956a). This may

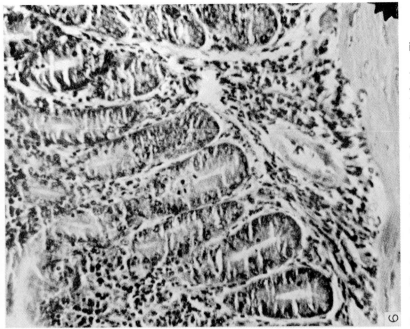

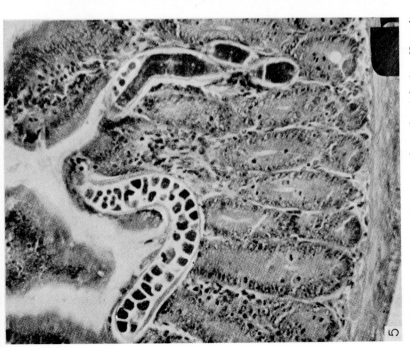

Fig. 6. Non-immunized old mouse 8 days after infection. The mucosa and submucosa are intensely inflamed and are infiltrated with polymorphonuclear leukocytes, plasma cells and lymphocytes. This represents the zenith of the acute phase. ×279. From Larsh and Race (1954); by permission of the Publisher, *J. inf. Dis.*

Fig. 5. Non-immunized old mouse 4 days after infection. Note the minimal inflammatory reaction. ×188. From Larsh and Race (1954); by permission of the Publisher, *J. inf. Dis.*

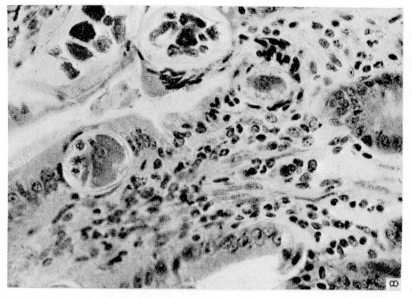

Fig. 8. Non-immunized young mouse 7 days after infection. Note the cross-sections of worms and the early polymorphonuclear leukocytic exudate adjacent to them. × 660. From Larsh *et al.*, 1956; by permission of the Publisher, *J. inf. Dis.*

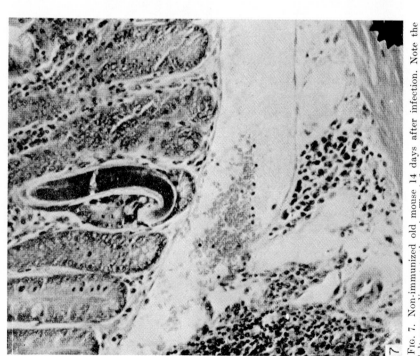

Fig. 7. Non-immunized old mouse 14 days after infection. Note the adult worm adjacent to the vein. The inflammatory reaction has subsided in this subacute phase. The cellular infiltrate consists of plasmacytes, lymphocytes and macrophages with a few polymorphonuclear leukocytes. The lymph node is mildly inflamed. × 162. From Larsh and Race (1954); by permission of the Publisher, *J. inf. Dis.*

be a further indication of stimulation and response of the defenses that occur prior to, or simultaneously with, the intestinal inflammation.

There is no difference in the worm burdens of old mice and young mice (1 month old) after an initial infection, and, therefore, no evidence of age immunity (Rappaport, 1943a; Larsh and Hendricks, 1949). Reduced worm burdens in old mice at 15 days postinfection are not due to age immunity, but more rapid development of acquired immunity than in young mice (Larsh et al., 1956). In the young mice, the intestinal inflammation is initiated at 7 days (Fig. 8) and the peak response is at 11 days (Fig. 9), both a few days delayed compared with old mice. The significant loss of worms occurs a few days later (15–17 days) than in old mice, but at 17 days subacute inflammation is still prominent (Fig. 10).

b. *Immunity and serologic response produced by a single stimulating (immunizing) infection.* Mice given a stimulating infection with 100 larvae and a challenging (test) infection of 300 larvae 35 days later show a significant loss of worms after 8 days (Rappaport and Wells, 1951). The sex ratios (F/M) are similar (about 2.0) throughout the intestine until about 17 days when females are lost more rapidly. However, both male and female worms are significantly stunted in size and the females contain relatively fewer embryos than those from controls given only the challenging infection. This inhibitory effect of the immunity on the females probably is reflected further by significantly reduced numbers of muscle larvae. As few as 50 larvae can produce immunity as measured by these various criteria, and it appears to be stronger after 12 and 30 days than after 60 days (Shikhobalova, 1952). On the other hand, mice 6 weeks old given a stimulating infection with 200 larvae and challenged with an infection of the same size 21 days later harbor about the same numbers of worms as controls 5 days after the challenging infection (Hendricks, 1950). As would be expected, the coproantibody titers (Ivey, 1956) and the circulating antibody titers (Hendricks, 1950) are higher at the time of the challenging infection (21 days after initial infection) than those noted above a few days (2–7) after initial infection.

The above examples are representative of many, showing that a single small stimulating infection may or may not produce an immune response of sufficient intensity to be manifested by a significant early loss of adults from a challenging infection. The age of the host, size of the two infections, the time interval between them, and the necropsy period selected are important factors. As shown above, it is evident by various criteria that both immunity, as measured by worm elimination and intestinal inflammation, and an antibody response can be demonstrated even after one small infection. The degree of the immunity at this time, however, is feeble compared with that shown by rats (Gould et al., 1955). After one stimulating infection in mice, the immunity remains comparatively

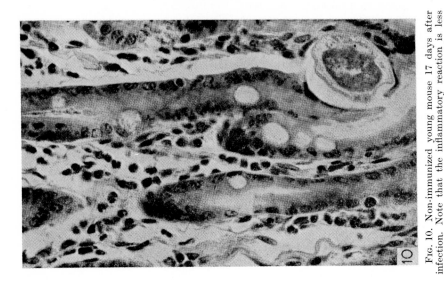

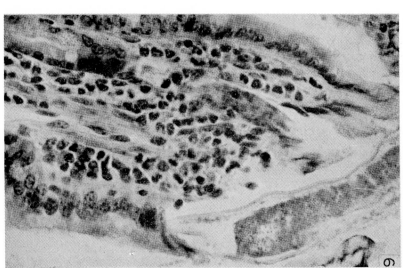

FIG. 10. Non-immunized young mouse 17 days after infection. Note that the inflammatory reaction is less intense despite the persistence of some worms within the mucosa. × 660. The reaction is in the subacute phase characterized by a mixture of mononuclear cells, especially lymphocytes and plasma cells. From Larsh et al., 1956; by

FIG. 9. Non-immunized young mouse 11 days after infection. In addition to the polymorphonuclear leukocytes, a few plasma cells and histiocytes are present at the zenith of the acute phase. × 660. From Larsh et al., 1956; by permission of the Publisher, J. inf. Dis.

feeble in degree, since the measurements made soon after the challenging infection are a reflection only of immunity produced by the initial infection. The major difference is in the response shown, under optimum conditions, by worm elimination several days earlier. After the initial infection, it requires about one week for the animals to develop acquired immunity of sufficient strength to produce demonstrable effects against the worms, and several additional days are required for significant worm elimination. On the other hand, at reinfection full advantage of the immunity provided by the first infection is taken at once and worm elimination, under certain conditions, can be executed several days earlier.

c. *Immunity, serologic response, intestinal inflammation, and body weight loss produced by multiple stimulating infections.* In old mice, two stimulating infections with 200 larvae each, separated by a 21-day interval, produce a significant reduction in adult worms 5 days after a challenging infection of the same size (Henricks, 1950). About the same degree of immunity is evident after three stimulating infections, but a fourth one produces more significant results. The circulating precipitin titers at 21 days after each of the four stimulating infections increase progressively, from 1:4 to 1:64 to 1:128 to 1:1024. Therefore, there is a striking inverse relationship between the numbers of adult worms recovered and the precipitin titers of the serum. Coproantibodies against the adult worms likewise appear to have a direct relationship with the development of immunity, since peak titers occur earlier after succeeding infections (Ivey, 1956). These results give indirect evidence of a causal relationship, but the protective nature of these particular antibodies has not been proved conclusively by transfer studies in mice.

As compared with non-immunized mice, there are striking differences in the longevity of adult worms in old mice given three stimulating infections (200 larvae each) before being challenged with 200 larvae (Larsh et al., 1952). For the first 6 days postinfection, the numbers of worms in the entire intestine are about the same as in controls (58.3–89.3%). However, on the 7th day, there is a dramatic reduction. This is due almost entirely to losses in the anterior half of the small intestine where few worms (6.5%) remain. The posterior half of the small intestine shows little or no change and contains 32.3%, and the entire large intestine contains its largest number (18.3%) at this time. The percentages for the two portions of the small intestine are similar to those noted in non-immunized controls about 1 week later, and the controls at that time also show peak numbers (34.5%) that will occur in the large intestine throughout infection. This latter percentage may mean that a larger number of those lost from the small intestine of immunized mice pass directly from the body. In any case, it is clear that in the presence of a strong acquired immunity, worms are lost in significant numbers from the small intestine about 1 week earlier than in non-immunized mice. In both groups, the elimination of worms from the posterior half of the small intestine occurs much later than from the anterior half. Due to this selective elimination, significant worm reductions can be demonstrated 5 days after the challenging infection in immunized mice, but the greatest difference in the entire small intestine occurs at 7 days. Therefore, this necropsy period is optimum for determining the degree of acquired immunity in mice of this age immunized and tested with similar doses of larvae.

Associated with the more rapid and effective elimination of adult worms in old immunized mice is a much more rapid and severe inflammatory response in the anterior half of the small intestine (Larsh and Race, 1954). Mild inflammation presumably develops immediately after the challenging infection, since it is present at 12 h and can be classified as minimal at 24 h (Fig. 11). The acute phase, with the polymorphonuclear leukocyte as the dominant cell, develops rapidly and reaches a zenith at 4 days (Figs. 12–13). Large areas of the mucosa and submucosa are involved, and the generalized reaction is no more striking in areas adjacent to worms than elsewhere (Fig. 13). Soon after the peak response, a mixture of infiltrating mononuclear cells (lymphocytes, macrophages, plasma cells) is seen, which characterizes the subacute (or chronic) phase (Fig. 14). Immediately after the challenging infection, there is a precipitous loss of weight in the immunized mice, which reaches the low point at 4 days (Fig. 4) (Yarinsky, 1961). Thereafter, there is steady gain in all those showing a normal immune response. Associated with this weight change is a great reduction in feed intake, which appears to account for most of the weight loss (Larsh and Goulson, 1962). Therefore, there is an association of a high titer of coproantibodies (Ivey, 1956) and circulating antibodies (Hendricks, 1950, 1951, 1952), a severely acute inflammation, reduced feed consumption and precipitous weight loss before most of the adult worms are lost from, and only from, the proximal half of the small intestine (Larsh et al., 1952). This combination of factors is the same as that noted about 1 week later in the presence of a feeble immunity acquired after a single infection. However, in the present case, the antibody titers are high prior to reinfection and there apparently is little or no lag phase after entry of the worms.

d. Stage(s) of the parasite responsible for acquired immunity. Until proved otherwise, the total immunity of a host must be considered to be due in part to all stages of the parasite engaged in the infection. In the case of T. spiralis, three separate phases (if not distinctly different stages) are involved: Phase 1, "pre-adults" used for infection; phase 2, adults whether fertile or sterile; and phase 3, migrating and encysting larvae. Early evidence indicated that the immunity was due mainly to

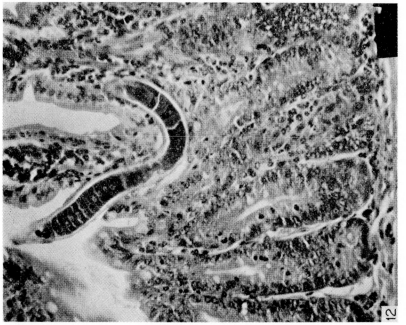

FIG. 12. Immunized old mouse 4 days after challenging infection, showing an invading adult worm and polymorphonuclear leukocytes throughout the mucosa. ×236. From Larsh and Race (1954); by permission of the Publisher, *J. inf. Dis.*

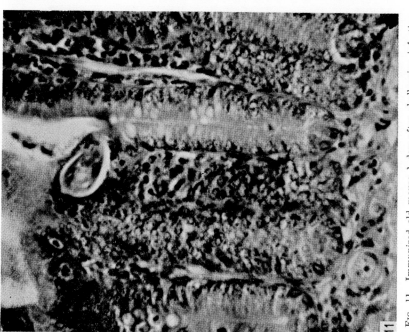

FIG. 11. Immunized old mouse 1 day after challenging infection. Note the worm and minimal inflammatory reaction. ×348. From Larsh and Race (1954); by permission of the Publisher, *J. inf. Dis.*

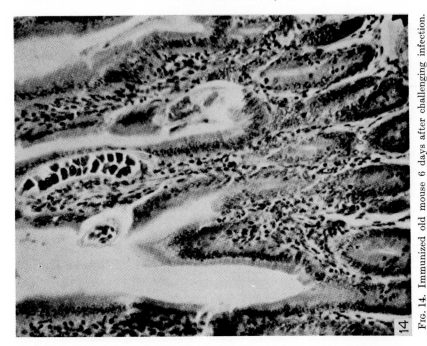

FIG. 14. Immunized old mouse 6 days after challenging infection. Note the adult worm and the mixed inflammatory infiltrate of the subacute phase, which consists of polymorphonuclear leukocytes, plasma cells, lymphocytes and a few macrophages. × 179. From Larsh and Race (1954); by permission of the Publisher, *J. inf. Dis.*

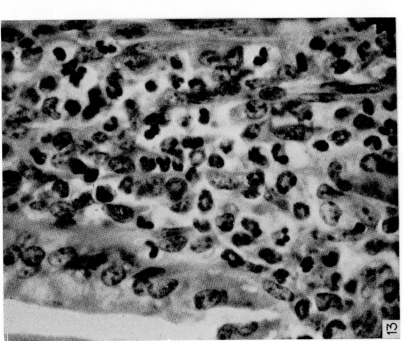

FIG. 13. Immunized old mouse 4 days after challenging infection. The cellular infiltrate is almost entirely polymorphonuclear leukocytic. This represents the zenith of the acute phase. × 721. From Larsh and Race (1954); by permission of the Publisher, *J. inf. Dis.*

the "intestinal forms" (phases 1 and/or 2), although the relative role in the total immunity could not be studied until a practical means for separating the phases was found. This was also provided by early studies, showing the effects of various doses of irradiation on infecting larvae. The use of antigenic substances from a single phase to produce an artificial active immunity provided another approach. These will be presented separately, since there are notable differences, presumably quantitative for the most part, between active immunity produced naturally as the result of infection and that produced artificially by vaccination.

Infections produced with larvae exposed to 3700 r of X-ray eliminate phase 3, since no muscle larvae can be demonstrated (Hendricks, 1951, 1952). Therefore, by using such irradiated larvae it is possible to compare the total immunity produced by phases 1 and 2 with that produced by all three phases (after use of non-irradiated larvae). In mice 6 weeks old, a single stimulating infection (200), with either irradiated or non-irradiated larvae, produces no demonstrable acquired immunity when measured by adult worms present 6 days after a challenging infection (200) with either irradiated or non-irradiated larvae. However, in old mice, additional stimulating infections (from 1 to 5 in different groups) with treated or untreated larvae produce acquired immunity, which in general varies in degree with the number of stimulating infections. It is of interest that those stimulated with non-irradiated larvae have a significantly greater degree of immunity than those stimulated with irradiated larvae, except after six stimulations when no difference is noted. Size of developing worms may be an important factor, since after irradiation (4000 r) both males and females are severely stunted (Gould et al., 1957). Both types of stimulating infections produce antibody titers related to the increasing numbers of infections. Precipitin titers against adult-worm antigens are about the same in both groups, but those against a larval antigen reach a higher titer in those stimulated with non-irradiated larvae. The type of larvae, treated or untreated, used for the challenging infection has no significant effect on the various antibody titers within 6 days. Kim (1956, 1957) verified in old mice the capacity of phases 1 and 2, without assistance from phase 3, to produce an acquired immunity after three stimulating infections (200 larvae each), but the number of adult worms and the degree of stunting was similar to those in mice stimulated with non-irradiated larvae. In additional tests, by using larger doses of irradiation from an X-ray source (5250 r and 7000 r), the infecting larvae were prevented from maturing into adults, thereby eliminating both phases 2 and 3. These resulting phase 1 pre-adult worms are immunogenic as shown by one or more measurements. After three stimulating infections, significant stunting of female worms, from a challenging infection with non-irradiated larvae, is produced, and there is more than a four-fold reduction in numbers of muscle larvae recovered from those stimulated with larvae treated with 5250 r.

Additional studies on phase 1 alone have shown that it can produce a strong immunity, which by certain measurements appears to compare in degree with that produced by all three phases (Larsh et al., 1959). By increasing the number of stimulating infections to 5 (200 each), irradiated (7000 r from a X-ray source) larvae produce about the same protection as non-irradiated larvae against a challenging infection with 500 non-irradiated larvae. Both groups harbor significantly fewer adults and muscle larvae than non-immunized controls. Considering the brief period of phase 1 in the life cycle (about 33 h, according to Wu and Kingscote, 1957), it might be expected that greater antigenic stimulation, and hence greater immunity would follow the use of non-irradiated larvae. Also, after this dose (7000 r) of irradiation, the phase 1 worms persist for a relatively brief period (Kim, 1956, 1957). At 7 days postinfection. for example, only 7.3% of an infecting dose of 200 irradiated larvae are still present, compared with 76.9% of adults from 200 non-irradiated larvae. Moreover, irradiation (6000 r) results in severe stunting of growth as early as 24 h postinfection (Gould et al., 1957). It is possible that irradiated larvae produce less host debilitation, thereby resulting in a proportionately greater response to a smaller quantity of functional antigens, or perhaps with the dose of non-irradiated larvae used antigenic paralysis is produced. On the other hand, a greater degree of immunity may, in fact, be produced by non-irradiated larvae and the failure to demonstrate it may be due to the tools used for measuring it. There is a suggestion of greater immunity in the present case in that those stimulated with non-irradiated larvae harbored fewer adult worms than those stimulated with irradiated larvae, but this difference (262.3 against 314.0) is not significant. Other evidence is provided by the antibody titers and studies of the intestinal inflammatory response in the two groups. The hemagglutinating titers were much higher (1:2560) in the mice immunized with non-irradiated larvae than in those given the irradiated larvae (1:640). Likewise, the inflammatory response of the former was much more intense and the zenith of the acute phase (4–6 days; Figs. 12–13) occurred earlier than that (8–10 days) noted in the latter (Fig. 15).

The β-rays of ^{32}P also can be used to separate phases of the life cycle for immunity studies (Hartung and Becht, 1960). Muscle invasion (elimination of phase 3) cannot be prevented by treating infecting larvae with 500, 1000, or 2000 rad, but striking interference follows the use of larvae treated with 3000 rad. Complete sterilization follows the use of larvae treated with 4000 rad, and after a 6000 rad treatment phases 2 and 3

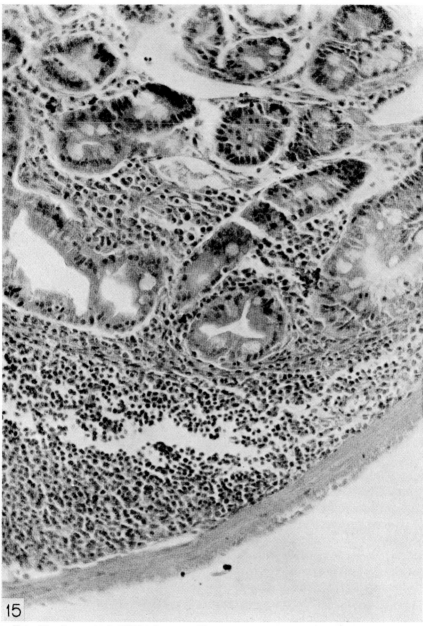

FIG. 15. Immunized (7000 r larvae) old mouse 10 days after challenging infection. Lymphoid tissue is seen in the submucosa. The mucosa shows considerable numbers of inflammatory cells, and the reaction represents the zenith of the acute phase. × 300. From Larsh *et al.*, 1959; by permission of the Publisher, *J. inf. Dis.*

apparently are eliminated, since the pre-adults survive in the intestine for only 5 days. Larvae treated with 4000 or 6000 rad are immunogenic when given to old mice as a moderate dose (500) 14 days prior to a challenging infection with the same number of non-irradiated larvae.

These studies show that phase 1 alone and phases 1 and 2 combined are immunogenic. Until direct comparisons of the separate phases can be made, it is not possible to evaluate accurately the relative role of the separate phases. It would appear from other studies that phases 1 and 2 combined give a greater degree of protection than either can provide separately. This would be expected if a common functional antigen occurs in both, as suggested in various studies. On the basis of these observations, it is evident that phase 3 is not needed to produce a high degree of immunity to reinfection. This does not, however, rule out this phase in the total picture of host immunity. If, as seems possible, the same functional antigen is present in and/or given off by all three phases, the above findings could be explained by assuming that the additional quantities of antigen(s) contributed by phase 3 simply are not required to produce the effects demonstrated.

There has been a recent controversy in regard to the hypothesis of a dual antibody basis for this acquired immunity (Oliver-Gonzalez, 1941; Hendricks, 1952; Ivey, 1956), which is based on certain qualitative antigenic differences between the adults and larvae. Some feel that the differences in vitro against the two stages at certain periods postinfection can be explained on a simple quantitative basis (Ross, 1952; Chute, 1956; Jackson, 1959). However, the most recent data leave no doubt that qualitative differences exist (Oliver-Gonzalez and Levine, 1962). By agar gel diffusion tests with antisera of rabbits given repeated infections, three bands of precipitate are seen when tested against the larval antigen (either extracts or metabolic products), and only two when tested against the adult extract antigen. There are also differences in location and non-coalescence of the bands formed against antigens of the two separate stages, and serum absorption with test antigens removes the homologous but not the heterologous antibodies.

Excretion-secretion antigens collected in vitro by incubating phase 1 or phase 2 worms are immunogenic (Campbell, 1954, 1955; Chipman, 1956, 1957; Ewert and Olson, 1960). After six injections (0.9 ml) of this ES antigenic material collected from phase 1 worms, there is not a significant difference in the number of adult worms present in mice (2.5 months old) 7 days after a challenging infection with 200 larvae, but there is at 30 days postinfection more than a 50% reduction in muscle larvae. After similar immunization with this antigen in old mice, there is an earlier loss of adult worms between 7–14 days, and they are significantly stunted (about 15% shorter). Using the same schedule, doses, and number of injections of ES antigens collected from phase 2 worms, no significant differences in numbers of adult worms are noted in old mice at 7 or 10 days after a challenging infection with 100 or 200 larvae. However, a significant reduction occurs in the number of muscle larvae after a challenging infection with 200 larvae. By using twelve injections of antigen, adult counts (10 days) are significantly reduced after a challenging infection with 100 larvae. However, after giving 200 larvae, only the larvae counts (30 days) are reduced significantly, as is the case after six injections of antigen.

Mice 5–6 weeks old given intraperitoneally in six divided doses a total of 0.9 ml of ES antigens (from phase 1 worms) harbor significantly fewer adult worms (13 days) and muscle larvae (30 days) than untreated controls after an infection with 200 larvae (Ewert and Olson, 1960), which confirms Campbell's (1954, 1955) observations. On the other hand, the same amount and schedule of sonicate antigens fail to produce immunity as measured in this way.

Other larval antigen preparations will produce an artificially acquired immunity in mice. For example, an aqueous extract from freshly-ground larvae or the acid-soluble protein fraction can be used (Shikhobalova, 1953). Intraperitoneal injections (0.2 ml given three times at 5–10 day intervals) protect against 250 larvae, as judged by fewer adults present, stunting of adults, and reduced numbers of muscle larvae.

Several conclusions are evident from two of these studies carried out under identical conditions (Campbell, 1954, 1955; Chipman, 1956, 1957). In the first place, as expected, the degree of immunity produced artificially is feeble compared with that produced naturally by infection. After six injections of antigen, it was not possible to demonstrate a significant reduction in numbers of adult worms at 7 days postinfection. To demonstrate more rapid loss of adults from the vaccinated mice, it was necessary to extend the necropsy period and/or reduce the size of the challenging infection, both calculated to favor the expression of a low-grade immunity. Nevertheless, in both cases a degree of immunity was evident even in the absence of a reduced adult worm population, as shown by reduced numbers of muscle larvae. The latter measurement, therefore, is more sensitive in the presence of a feeble immunity. It appears, however, to be mainly an indirect measure of the direct effects of the immunity against the females, causing stunting and a significant reduction in their reproductive potential. After twelve injections of antigen, it was possible to reduce the adults by 10 days postinfection, but only by using the smaller (100) challenging infection. This illustrates well the quantitative nature of the immunity. Although direct comparisons cannot be made when the total quantity of specific immunogenic materials is unknown, these findings do not differ a great deal from those noted after a single small stimulating infection given to produce immunity (Rappaport and Wells, 1951). For the same reason direct comparisons cannot be made to determine the potency of the ES antigens from the two separate phases. Nevertheless, the similarity of results is sufficient to suggest that the functional metabolic antigens from the separate phases may be similar. Now that a practical means is available for cultivating phases 1 and 2 *in vitro* (Kim, 1961), it should be possible to collect larger quantities of ES antigens, and make comparisons of the two separate stages by immunochemical methods.

e. *Factors that modify acquired immunity.* In all cases, it will be noted that the host is placed under varying degrees of stress in these attempts to alter immunity.

1. AN EXCESSIVE CHALLENGING INFECTION. After a single stimulating infection (100 larvae), mice show no demonstrable immunity to a large (800 larvae) challenging infection given 10 days, 36 days or 3.5 months later, as based on adult-worm counts (Rappaport and Wells, 1951). However, by more delicate measures (stunting of adult worms, and numbers of muscle larvae) immunity can be shown. By these means, the immunity is lowest after 10 days and highest after 36 days. A much more striking immunity can be demonstrated, including a significant loss of adult worms after 8 days postinfection, when a much smaller (300 larvae) challenging infection is given 35 days after this stimulating infection. It is clear, therefore, that immunity can be broken by an excessive challenging infection, which, based on adult-worm counts, can leave the false impression that no immunity exists. This illustrates again the quantitative basis of the immunity and probably accounts for the many early divergent views concerning the actual presence of immunity after certain schedules. Considering the vast amount of information to be obtained by using quantitative measures of immunity and other biologic phenomena, it is surprising to note the recent revival of the antiquated measure of survival and death after massive infections. At best this measure is of value only to indicate the virulence of the parasite under certain conditions, and, therefore, such data represent only a small fraction of the total measurable effects of immunity. With endpoints less complex than death, many effects may be profitably isolated and studied exhaustively. In the process a great deal may be learned of basic immunological mechanisms. Therefore, there would appear to be little, if any, need for the use of survival-death endpoints in modern experimental work in this field.

2. MISCELLANEOUS STRESS FACTORS. Male wild mice given an infection with 125 larvae and isolated individually in separate jars harbor very few adult worms 15 days later (Davis and Read, 1958). Of eleven mice, only three had worms at this time (3–18) whereas all eleven grouped

mice-harbored worms in usual numbers for this period (16–51). These grouped experimentals, daily on days 2–11 postinfection, were placed in groups of six in a large can and left there for about 3 h. Severe fighting begins at once, but by the 3rd day of grouping a social rank is obvious. Such effects of crowding in mice are known to lead to adrenal hypertrophy and a chain of physiological consequences. At necropsy 15 days after infection, the average adrenal weight of the isolated controls was 3.92 mg, and of the grouped experimental mice, 4.19 mg, which is not significant. However, at 30 days after infection, the adrenal weights differ significantly, being 4.24 mg for the isolated controls, and 5.08 mg for the experimental mice. Also, the experimentals at this time harbor considerably more muscle larvae (average, 1556 per g of muscle) than the isolated controls (1054 larvae per g of muscle). These results, showing that socio-psychological stress factors influence the development of acquired immunity, may have great significance in the evolution of vertebrate host populations, as well as the exploitation of new hosts by certain parasite species. The effect of stress in this connection has also been demonstrated in an inbred strain of laboratory mice (Robinson, 1961). Immunized experimental animals (one stimulating infection) given a challenging infection and exposed daily for at least 12 days to intermittent brief periods of stress (mild electrical stimulation, bright lights and a loud noise) harbor considerably more worms than immunized controls.

3. ALCOHOL. Alcoholic mice (5 weeks old when first treated) fail to develop the usual degree of acquired immunity to four stimulating infections (Larsh and Kent, 1949). In fact, those given a narcotizing dose of alcohol daily for 28 days before the first infection and at certain periods after each infection have about the same number of worms after a challenging infection as controls given only the challenging infection. It is of interest that those given the alcohol treatment only prior to the first infection are prevented from developing the degree of immunity noted in untreated controls, since the effects of alcohol are known to persist for only a brief period after discontinuing its administration. Alcohol also can interfere with the maintenance of acquired immunity produced in old mice prior to treatment, as measured by adult-worm counts 7 days postchallenge (Larsh and Fletcher, 1948). In this case, the interference is related to the number of stimulating infections given before treatment. No effect is evident after one infection or five infections, but the immunity is inhibited significantly after two and four infections. Assuming a quantitative basis of immunity, these results suggest that failure to interfere after one and five infections is due to the two extremes of immunity existing under these conditions. After one infection, as shown above, the immunity is feeble and cannot be demonstrated if the challenging infection is excessive compared with the stimulating infection

N

(Rappaport and Wells, 1951). This may be the explanation, since these doses were 900 and 300, respectively. In any case, with a feeble acquired immunity in the untreated controls, it would be difficult to demonstrate an altered acquired immunity in treated animals, since the difference can only be a minor one. Moreover, the natural immunity is not affected by prolonged alcohol treatment (Larsh and Kent, 1949), so this is not involved. After five infections, as shown above, the immunity is very potent. Thus, the failure to demonstrate a significant inhibition by these measurements might be expected if quantitative factors govern the immune responses, since striking interference could operate without being manifested in this way.

The interference of alcohol with the development of acquired immunity has not been explained, but such prolonged treatment interferes drastically with the nutrition of the mice, as evidenced by a great reduction in feed intake, loss of weight, and so forth. Hypovitaminosis, an indirect effect of alcoholism, may be involved as proved in alcoholic mice infected with *Hymenolepis* (Larsh, 1947). The interference with the maintenance of previously-established immunity may have a similar basis.

4. VITAMIN-A DEFICIENCY. Alcohol is known to drain vitamin A from its stores in the liver and other tissues, and a deficiency in this particular vitamin is known to reduce immunity of rats to *T. spiralis* (McCoy, 1934). These facts suggested an explanation for the alcoholic interference with immunity in mice, but prolonged feeding of a vitamin-A deficient diet to old mice failed to alter the immunity in this host (Larsh and Gilchrist, 1950). This is one of many examples of a difference in host response to a particular treatment, emphasizing the wisdom of avoiding sweeping conclusions in regard to the effect of a specific treatment.

5. CONCURRENT INFECTION. Old mice immunized against *T. spiralis* and given an oral dose of 800 filariform larvae of the dog hookworm, *Ancylostoma caninum*, 2 days before a challenging infection with 400 *T. spiralis* larvae exhibit a significantly increased degree of immunity against *T. spiralis* (Cox, 1952a, b). The *A. caninum* treatment has about the same effect as three stimulating infections with *T. spiralis*, measured by numbers of adult *T. spiralis* recovered after a challenging infection. A similar effect can be shown by giving the *A. caninum* larvae 10 days prior to the challenging infection with *T. spiralis*, but the action at this time is significantly less than that produced by hookworm larvae given 8 days later.

Old mice given a single stimulating infection with 200 *T. spiralis* larvae, followed 21 days later by 800 *A. caninum* larvae by mouth, resist a challenging infection with 400 *T. spiralis* larvae given 24 h after the hookworm larvae (Goulson, 1957, 1958). A significant reduction in adult

T. spiralis in the entire small intestine is noted by 5 days. Moreover, it is of interest in respect to the location of areas of greatest worm elimination that a significant reduction occurs by the 3rd day in the anterior half of the small intestine, and within this region the anterior quarter-section is most active in worm elimination.

The possibility that these effects of concurrent infection are due to cross immunity between the two parasites has been ruled out (Cox, 1952 a,b). On the other hand, there is good evidence that the apparent increased immunity to *T. spiralis* is due to the intestinal inflammation that results from the *A. caninum* infection. This response is evident by neutrophilic infiltration by 24 h, reaches a zenith by 48 h, and diminishes gradually until its virtual disappearance about 120 h after infection (Kerr, 1936). It seems probable that this non-specific inflammation has an indirect effect by creating an unfavorable environment for *T. spiralis*. Support for this is the striking effect against *T. spiralis* during the acute phase (24 h–48 h) and a significantly reduced effect during the chronic and reparative stages (10 days). Also in support of this view is the fact that the effects against *T. spiralis* of a non-specific inflammation caused by an entirely different agent, *Salmonella typhimurium*, are similar (Brewer, 1955).

6. ADRENALECTOMY. Old immunized mice adrenalectomized 4 days prior to a challenging infection with 100 larvae exhibit an increased acquired immunity to *T. spiralis*, based on adult-worm counts 7 days later (Baughn, 1952a, b). The effects of the operation and of the synthetic adrenal hormone (desoxycorticosterone acetate) administered to maintain the animals are not factors in the altered immune response. The three stimulating infections (100 larvae each at 3-week intervals) given to immunize the animals caused an average reduction of about 34 worms, and adrenalectomy alone accounted for about the same degree of reduction. The non-immunized, untreated controls showed a low precipitin titer (1:2), and all immunized groups, regardless of treatment, had about the same titer (1:32). The latter shows that adrenalectomy did not affect the preformed antibody titers. Removal of the adrenals produces a wide range of physiological effects that may influence directly or indirectly the immune reactions of the host and/or the maintenance of the parasite. However, the elimination of the adrenal cortex and thereby the release of the stress steroids (cortisone, etc.) probably is of the greatest importance. This probability will be pursued further after consideration of cortisone's effects on this immunity.

7. CORTISONE. Cortisone acetate given daily in a dose of 0.5 mg after mice receive a LD_{50} dose (30 days) of larvae produces a 99% mortality. In other words, cortisone combined with the LD_{50} dose has the effect of a LD_{99} dose, since it increases the mortality by more than 45% within

30 days (Stoner and Godwin, 1953). During the 3rd week, a lymphopenia and neutrophilia occur as well as a significant drop in circulating eosinophils. Antibiotics (1500 units crystalline penicillin-G and 1250 μg dihydrostreptomycin sulphate) fail to decrease the mortality when given separately or in combination with cortisone from the time of infection. Almost 90% of mice immunized with one stimulating infection survive a LD_{100} (30 days) challenging dose of larvae, whereas only 14.5% of those immunized and given daily cortisone treatment survive (Stoner and Godwin, 1954). With a smaller challenging dose (about a LD_{74} dose), 90% of the immunized, non-treated mice survive compared with 50% for the immunized-cortisone group. Antibiotics fail to alter the survival rate in either group, suggesting that deaths are not due to spontaneous bacterial infections from the intestinal tract.

Old mice immunized with three stimulating infections (200 larvae each at 3-week intervals) and given daily cortisone injections (0.25 mg to 2.0 mg in different groups), from 3 days prior to the challenging infection to necropsy, fail to exhibit acquired immunity. In fact, as late as 14 days after the challenging infection they harbor significantly more worms than the non-immunized controls given only the challenging infection (Coker, 1954, 1956a). Prompt and maximal reduction in spleen size occurs in the cortisone-treated mice, which results in spleen sizes that average 3.1 mm shorter in length and 1.0 mm shorter in width than in untreated mice. Moreover, cortisone reduces the numbers of circulating lymphocytes and eosinophils. A striking reversal in the lymphocyte/ neutrophil ratio is seen at both 7 and 14 days postinfection. In the small intestine of immunized mice treated with cortisone (0.05 mg daily), the cellular response is prevented almost completely (Coker, 1954, 1956b). This drastic effect of cortisone is shown best by comparing sections from cortisone-treated mice with comparable sections from untreated im- munized mice after the challenging infection. The non-treated mice show the typical zenith of the acute response at 4 days postinfection (Figs. 16–17), while in the cortisone-treated there are practically no cells other than the native supporting stroma of fibroblasts, other connective tissue, and extensions of the muscularis mucosa (Figs. 18–19). At later periods, the non-treated mice show a diminishing subacute response for many days before the inflammation runs its course, but the cortisone-treated show no change for at least 9 days postinfection. Even at these late periods, well developed female worms are observed with numerous larvae *in utero*. In the treated mice, intestinal eosinophils, normally frequent to abundant, practically disappear. The invasion of neutrophils, the prominent cell during the acute cellular response, fails to occur, since only a few widely scattered cells are observed. Finally, the native cell population in the lamina propria and submucosa is reduced greatly.

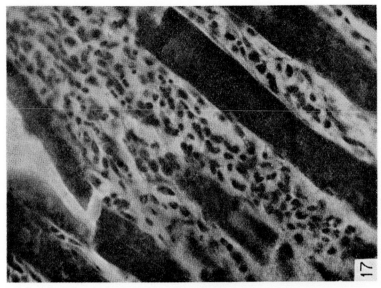

Fig. 17. Immunized old mouse 4 days after challenging infection; cross section, × 884. No worm is shown. Most of the cells are neutrophils, which is characteristic at this period. From Coker (1954); by permission of the Graduate School.

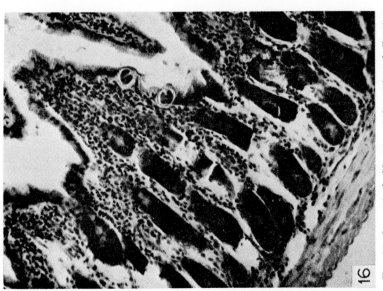

Fig. 16. Immunized old mouse 4 days after challenging infection; cross section, × 143 This represents the peak of the acute cellular reaction in immune mice and contrasts strongly with the condition of the cortisone-treated immunized mice as shown in Fig. 18. From Coker (1956b); by permission of the Publisher, *J. inf. Dis.*

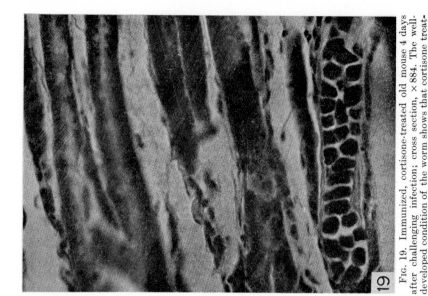

Fig. 19. Immunized, cortisone-treated old mouse 4 days after challenging infection; cross section, × 884. The well-developed condition of the worm shows that cortisone treatment has had no demonstrable effect. From Coker (1954); by permission of the Graduate School.

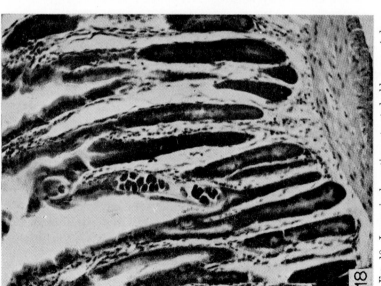

Fig. 18. Immunized, cortisone-treated old mouse 4 days after challenging infection; cross section, × 143. Worm is shown in sagittal section to left of center. Note near absence of inflammatory cells. From Coker (1954); by permission of the Graduate School.

Lacteals tend to occupy proportionately more space in the lamina propria, and villi tend to be long and thin and filled with blood.

There would seem to be a close relationship between the findings after adrenalectomy (Baughn, 1952a, b) and cortisone administration (Coker, 1954, 1956b). At the one extreme lies an association of a decrease in cortisone (implied in adrenalectomy), an increase over normal in lymphoid reserves (Santisteban, 1951), and an increased acquired immunity to $T. spiralis$. At the other extreme lies another association of an excess of cortisone, a decrease in lymphoid reserves, and a decreased acquired immunity. Within this framework the protective antibodies probably operate, since both treatments failed to affect the preformed antibody titers. The mode of action of cortisone in a given situation is difficult to ascertain. Some feel that the underlying mechanism is through blockade of the reticulo-endothelial system, thus preventing cellular defences from coming into play (Thomas, 1953). Others feel cortisone increases the structural integrity of cells (Ritterson, 1959b). Finally, Wells (1962) mentions the fact that it is known to impair mast cell functions.

8. WHOLE-BODY IRRADIATION. The LD_{50} for young mice (28 days old) exposed to γ-radiation (^{60}Co) is about 750 rep (roentgen-equivalent-physical; Stoner and Hale, 1952). All immunized mice (one stimulating infection with 100 larvae) exposed to 600 rep and challenged with 1500 larvae die within 30 days, whereas 74% of those not exposed to the irradiation survive. Very few irradiation controls die within this period. All non-immunized, untreated mice die, showing that the challenging dose within this time period represents a LD_{100}. The immunized mice, treated and untreated, have about the same precipitin titers, proving that irradiation does not affect these preformed antibody titers. After a 680 rep exposure, the total white cell count falls from about 12 000 to 2000 mm 3 within 24 h and fails to rise above 2100 by 14 days.

Mature mice infected with 200 larvae 24 h after being exposed to whole-body irradiation (50, 250, 450, or 650 r) show no interference with the development of acquired immunity, as measured by the number of adult worms present 14 days postinfection (Yarinsky, 1961, 1962). The irradiation in this case was delivered by a Picker 220 kV (deep therapy) X-ray unit. At 20 days, there is a significant interference with the maintenance of immunity, related in degree to the increasing doses of irradiation. Likewise, in strongly immunized old mice irradiated 24 h before receiving a 200-dose challenging infection, there is no demonstrable interference with the maintenance of immunity, as measured 7 days postinfection (8 days postirradiation). However, by 14 days postinfection (15 days postirradiation) those given the high doses of irradiation (450 or 650 r) have no greater degree of immunity than the non-immunized, untreated controls given only the challenging infection.

Old mice strongly immunized by four stimulating infections and given a challenging infection 4 days after being irradiated (450 r) show a complete loss of acquired immunity, as measured by the number of adult worms present at 7 days postinfection (11 days postirradiation). Their immunity is no greater than that of the non-immunized, untreated controls given only the challenging infection (Yarinsky, 1961, 1962). The time period between irradiation and infection, therefore, seems to be an important factor in determining whether interference occurs.

Similar results are obtained when the host irradiation (450 r) is administered 8 days before the challenging infection and counts made 7 days postinfection (15 days postirradiation). These irradiated mice show an 80–90% reduction in circulating white blood cells during the period when significant numbers of adult worms are known to be eliminated from strongly immunized mice (5–7 days postchallenge; Larsh et al., 1952). This severe leukopenia, due mainly to lymphopenia, is noted 1 day postirradiation and continues for about 21 days before recovery, and there is relatively little increase in the numbers of neutrophils to compensate for this great loss (Yarinsky, 1961, 1962). On the other hand, the untreated immunized mice show a leukocytosis (absolute increase in neutrophils) and a reversal of the lymphocyte/neutrophil ratio between 3–9 days postinfection, which includes the period of significant worm elimination. It would seem more than coincidental that the neutrophils are increased, since this is the dominant cell in the acute inflammatory reaction in the small intestine. Most important, as shown by Larsh et al. (1962), the intestinal inflammatory response at 7 days postinfection is characteristic, if less intense, for immunized mice at this time (Fig. 20). On the other hand, that for the irradiated mice is, at best, minimal in degree (Fig. 21). The reaction in the former is in the subacute or chronic phase characterized by a mixture of infiltrating mononuclear cells (plasma cells, lymphocytes, and macrophages). By this time postinfection, the zenith of the severe acute phase has passed (Figs. 12–13) and the reaction is diminishing in intensity. The reaction in the irradiated mice, however, is characteristic of that seen prior to the development of the acute phase, as in non-immunized mice given a single infection. In fact, the inflammatory reaction of the irradiated mice (Fig. 21) is even less than that of such non-immunized mice at about this period postinfection (Fig. 5). In this phase of inflammation, few polymorphonuclear cells are seen, the sparse cellular infiltrate being composed almost entirely of plasma cells and lymphocytes.

When host irradiation (450 r) is administered 12 days prior to the challenging infection, the numbers of worms recovered 7 days postinfection (19 days postirradiation) suggest that recovery from the irradiation interference is underway (Yarinsky, 1961, 1962). These mice

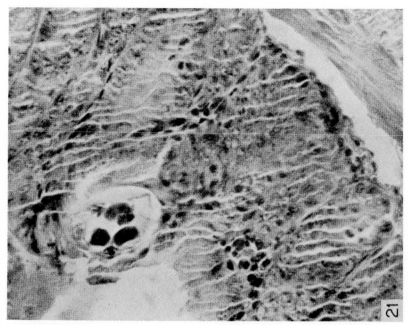

FIG. 21. Immunized, irradiated old mouse 7 days after challenging infection (15 days postirradiation). × 450. This reaction is very minimal and characteristic of that seen prior to the development of the acute phase. Almost all of the sparse infiltrating cells are lymphocytes and plasma cells. There is no indication of lymphoid proliferation. From Larsh *et al.*, 1962; permission of the Editor, *Amer. J. trop. Med. Hyg.*

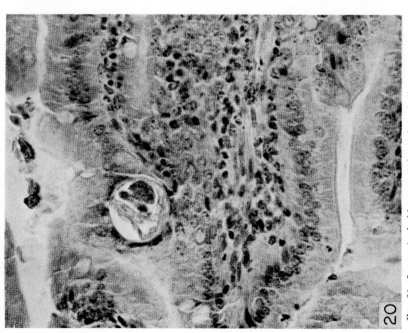

FIG. 20. Immunized old mouse 7 days after challenging infection. × 450. The reaction is in the subacute stage, characterized by infiltrating mononuclear cells, especially lymphocytes and plasma cells. From Larsh *et al.*, 1962; permission of the Editor, *Amer. J. trop. Med. Hyg.*

have significantly fewer worms than the untreated, non-immunized mice, but significantly more worms than the untreated, immunized mice. Evidence of recovery is also seen in the histological sections from the small intestine, since these mice show a subacute inflammatory reaction (Fig. 22), which is similar to, but less intense than, that of the untreated immunized mice (Fig. 20). Moreover, considerable infiltrates of lymphoid tissue are noted in the deeper mucosa of these irradiated mice (Fig. 22).

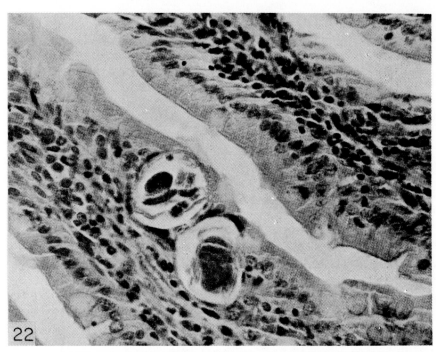

Fig. 22. Immunized, irradiated old mouse 7 days after challenging infection (19 days postirradiation). × 450. Similar, but milder, reaction to that shown in Fig. 20. Also note infiltrates of lymphoid tissue not seen in Fig. 21. From Larsh et al., 1962; permission of the Editor, Amer. J. trop. Med. Hyg.

Such compensatory lymphoid proliferation is characteristic during a certain recovery period after exposure to sublethal irradiation. It is, therefore, noteworthy that it was not evident in those irradiated 8 days prior to the challenging infection (Fig. 21).

Hemagglutinating antibody titers were recorded in these studies, but they did not reflect the immune status of the host as revealed by adult-worm recoveries, suggesting this test did not measure antibodies associated with protection. In any case, in all immunized mice peak titers were produced prior to the challenging infection, and there was no demonstrable inhibitory effect against these preformed antibodies after host irradiation (Yarinsky, 1961). This conforms to the findings for precipitins by Stoner and Hale (1952).

In these studies, a significant reduction in feed intake and striking weight losses occurred at specified periods postinfection in all mice showing a normal immune response to either an initial infection or a challenging infection given after immunity had been produced. These patterns were the same as those described above as being characteristically associated in time with the intestinal inflammatory response.

By considering the temporal relationships of the irradiation interference with immunity, the feed consumption and the body weight data, the blood picture, the histopathological findings, and the serological responses, a working hypothesis comes to mind to explain the mechanism of the irradiation interference. The irradiation effect appears to be an indirect one brought about by damage to the hematopoietic system, which is thereby unable to supply the large numbers of cellular elements needed to initiate and/or maintain an effective inflammatory response in the area of worm elimination. Without an effective response, worms remain despite unaltered preformed antibody titers. Indirect evidence of the irradiation damage to the lymphoid-macrophage system is reflected by strikingly reduced spleen sizes of immunized mice 7 days after a challenging infection (8 days postirradiation). That this organ serves conveniently as a biological dosimeter of irradiation, as noted by many other workers, was confirmed in that the reductions increased in proportion to increasing doses of irradiation (Yarinsky, 1961). The degree of acquired immunity in the host at the time of irradiation is a factor involved in interference, since this determines the timing and severity of the inflammatory response. Finally, the phase of the response, acute or subacute, affected appears to depend on the temporal relationship of irradiation and the challenging infection.

Until more information is available, another possibility to explain the irradiation interference must be considered. On the basis of other studies, it seems reasonable to assume that the accelerated intestinal inflammatory response in immunized mice is due to the high concentrations of antibodies present at reinfection. Although X-radiation does not alter the rate of preformed antibody destruction, there is a great variation between species in the turnover rate of serum globulins (Talmage, 1955). In the mouse, the half-disappearance time of antibody is 1–2 days. Therefore, the rate of antibody metabolism is very high compared, for example, with that in man where the estimated half-disappearance time is 14–21 days. By the time of recovery from a single mid-lethal radiation exposure the mouse would have a drastic drop in preformed antibody. Such a severe early loss, provided it triggers the inflammatory response and production of further quantities is prevented, could explain the various irradiation interferences demonstrated. Thus, in the case of re-infections given 4 and 8 days postirradiation, there would have been time for striking antibody reduction, whereas in the case of reinfection one day postirradiation, insufficient time would have elapsed to prevent the initiation of an effective inflammatory response and loss of worms by 7 days postinfection. Finally, in the case of reinfection 12 days post-irradiation, partial recovery, evidenced by the tissue studies and worm counts, could have taken place to permit the expression of an inter-mediate degree of immunity when measured at 7 days postinfection (19 days postirradiation). This probability is strengthened further by the fact that the total white cell counts began to increase about 17 days postirradiation, or 2 days prior to necropsy of these mice (Yarinsky, 1961). However, the major difficulty in applying this hypothesis lies in the fact that no significant change for long periods after reinfection has been noted in preformed antibody titers of irradiated mice (Yarinsky, 1961; Stoner and Hale, 1952). Another difficulty is the absence of in-formation on the effect, if any, that irradiation has in interfering with the formation of "new" antibody (i.e., that produced in response to the challenging infection given after irradiation). In general, the ability to form new antibody after X-radiation may or may not be impaired, depending on a variety of circumstances. There was no significant change for long periods in the hemagglutinating titers after the various challeng-ing infections, but the same was true for the non-irradiated, immunized mice (Yarinsky, 1961). Therefore, this needs further study. In referring back to pre-formed antibody, it should be noted that there is a difference between antibody types, e.g., hemolysin and precipitin, in the same host species (in this case the rabbit) as to rate of disappearance (Talmage, 1955). This may suggest that an antibody other than those charted in the irradiated mice of the two studies (hemagglutinating and precipitating) may serve to trigger the inflammatory response. In any case, it is clear that further work is needed in attempts to discover the true mechanism whereby host irradiation interferes with this strong immunity produced prior to exposure.

   f. The mechanism(s) of acquired immunity. Although important details are lacking, there is now sufficient information to form the basis of a working hypothesis to explain the major aspects of the mechanism of this immunity in the mouse host.

   There have been several indirect observations in mice to suggest that this immunity is general in nature, as that expected after any degree of antigenic stimulation. Three of the important observations are as follows. In the first place, there is an inverse relationship between pre-cipitin titers (serum antibodies and coproantibodies against adult-worm antigens) and numbers of adult worms, which is progressively pronounced as the number of stimulating infections is increased (Hendricks, 1950, 1951, 1952; Ivey, 1956). Secondly, the anti-adult precipitin titers produced by phases 1 and 2 are about the same as those produced by phases 1, 2, and 3, showing that antigenic substances from the intestinal phases give rise to high levels of circulating antibodies (Hendricks, 1951, 1952). Finally, a feeble immunity follows the subcutaneous introduction of ES antigens from either phase 1 or phase 2 (Campbell, 1954, 1955; Chipman, 1956, 1957), showing that antigenic stimulation via the intestinal tract is not required to produce a demonstrable immune response. However, these observations alone, including those in more recent years, could not rule out the possibility of a strong local intestinal immunity brought about after infection by the retention in the local tissues of most of the functional antigens before they reach the general circulation (Chandler, 1939 a, b). It was necessary, therefore, to design experiments to test directly the general (Taliaferro, 1940) and local (Chandler, 1939 a, b) hypotheses as to the nature of this immunity (Larsh, 1953b). *T. spiralis* adults establish and persist in about the same numbers after an oral or intracecal inoculation of larvae. Moreover, after the latter relatively few worms migrate into the small intestine and none is found in the anterior half. In old mice this region of the small intestine is the only area where the defensive mechanisms operate within specified periods (Larsh et al., 1952). Therefore, the fact that one or two stimulating infections given intracecally produce the same degree of acquired immunity as the same infections given by mouth rules out the operation of local immunity. Those immunized intracecally had no chance to be stimulated in the area of worm elimination, and yet after an oral challenging infection they exhibited the same degree of acquired immunity, based on adult-worm counts, as those immunized by mouth. It is apparent, therefore, that antigenic stimulation by all three phases of the parasite, regardless of the location of phases 1 and 2, produces a general immunity manifested later against the intestinal phases in the anterior half of the small intestine.

It is now clear that all phases of the parasite are not necessary to produce this generalized immunity. Phase 1 alone (Campbell, 1954, 1955; Kim, 1956, 1957; Larsh et al., 1959; Ewert and Olson, 1960), and phase 2 alone (Chipman, 1956, 1957) contain a functional antigen. There is evidence of much stronger immunity produced by phases 1 and 2 combined (Hendricks, 1951, 1952; Kim, 1956, 1957), suggesting a common functional antigen in these phases. There is little evidence to indicate that phase 3 plays an important role in the total immunity, despite the fact that it would be expected to contain some of the same common antigens. The determination of the relative role of the separate phases, however, awaits direct comparisons.

Before leaving this topic, it is tempting to speculate on the probable role of phase 3 in maintaining detectable levels of antibody in the host for long periods (6 months in rats, detected by a larval microflocculation test; Markell and Lewis, 1957). Since the half-disappearance time of antibody in mice is 1–2 days (Talmage, 1955), it would seem that only phase 3 could be responsible for such a long-continued antibody production. The fact that larvae encysted for long periods (180 days or more) exchange metabolites with the host (Stoner and-Hankes, 1955; Hankes and Stoner, 1958), certainly adds support to this speculation.

Accepting the general nature of this immunity does not explain the mechanisms involved. An important role of precipitating antibodies is generally accepted. They can be demonstrated *in vitro* around certain body openings of both phase 1 and phase 2 worms incubated in antiserum (Oliver-Gonzalez, 1940, 1941; Chute, 1956; Jackson, 1959), and protein precipitates have been observed deep in the mucosa of immune mice after a challenging infection (Larsh and Race, 1954). However, such precipitates have not been observed within the digestive tract of worms (Larsh and Race, 1954; Jackson, 1959). The evidence would seem to indicate that the most important antibodies are those formed against the physiological end products (digestive secretions and excretions) of, especially, phases 1 and 2. These are the "primary effective antigens" in rabbits infected orally, and their source appears to be the cells of the digestive tract of the worms, as revealed by extensive fluorescent antibody studies (Jackson, 1959). It is, therefore, likely that at reinfection specific antibodies against these substances come into play immediately, precipitating these antigens in areas of high concentration, especially at the oral opening. When of sufficient concentration, they probably can drastically inhibit normal development, presumably by interfering with all metabolic activities, as suggested by marked stunting (Rappaport and Wells, 1951; Campbell, 1954, 1955; Kim, 1956, 1957). Moreover, the reproductive potential of females is altered significantly, as demonstrated by reduced numbers of muscle larvae (Rappaport and Wells, 1951; Campbell, 1954, 1955; Chipman, 1956, 1957; Kim, 1956, 1957). This effect is due, in all probability, to the action against the "secondary effective antigens", probably secretions from the reproductive organs, which in females are excreted at the vulval orifice (Jackson, 1959). It is not possible to rule out actions against phase 3 that may contribute to the reduction in numbers of muscle larvae, since these larvae have been shown to be stunted in passively immunized rats given rabbit antiserum (Chute, 1956). This is interesting in view of the fact that in potent rabbit antiserum no precipitates can be seen on larvae recently emerged from adult females (Jackson, 1959). In any case, female worms removed from immunized hosts are not only stunted but show relatively few embryos

(Rappaport and Wells, 1951), and such effects are evident in the tissue sections of strongly immunized hosts (Larsh and Race, 1954). It is likely that these various effects result from the depression of all metabolic activities.

In addition to the primary and secondary effective antigens, there are, potentially, numerous other antigenic sites in the worms, such as those in other internal organs shown by staining with certain samples of fluorescent antisera from rabbits (Jackson, 1959). By use of gel diffusion techniques, it is observed that larval extracts and homologous rabbit antiserum prepared by injection of the extract give ten precipitating bands (Wodehouse, 1956). Also, by immuno-electrophoresis, eleven distinct antigens can be identified in buffered saline extracts of larvae (Tanner and Gregory, 1961). By physical and chemical procedures, others have isolated seven antigenic larval fractions and have evidence that antibodies in rabbits develop at different times for different fractions (Labzoffsky et al., 1959). The metabolic products collected after incubation of larvae in vitro contain at least three antigenic components (Oliver-Gonzalez and Levine, 1962). It is worth noting that all antigens are not entirely protein in composition. One (ethanol soluble) is a glycoprotein containing 75% protein and 15% carbohydrate, the polysaccharide being composed entirely of glucose units (Sleeman, 1961). Finally, it is known that certain antigen complexes (somatic and metabolic) produce mast cell sensitivity with release of granules upon re-exposure (Briggs, 1961). This suggests a similar relationship of mast cells, histamine, and eosinophils shown recently in *Nippostrongylus brasiliensis* infections (Wells, 1962). At any rate, these examples illustrate the complexity of the problem ahead in determining the relative role of the functional antigens in the 3 phases.

The question is not whether specific antibodies play an important role, since this is an accepted premise of a generalized immunity and has been proved beyond challenge. Rather, the question is whether such protective effects *per se* can bring about the expulsion of worms, or, as predicted from related immunity studies, whether cellular factors, probably triggered by an antigen-antibody reaction(s), offer assistance in this phenomenon. This answer likewise would appear to be without challenge. Despite great mechanical damage of the intestinal mucosa of old mice, the worms in non-immunized hosts appear to be entirely unhampered in their activities early in infection. After about 4 days, a mild inflammatory response is evident and thereafter the activities of the worms appear to be somewhat restrained (Larsh and Race, 1954). It is likely that this restraint is mediated by the direct action of specific antibodies, since these can be demonstrated in low titer in the feces 2 days postinfection (Ivey, 1956) and in the circulation a few days later (Baughn, 1952 a,b). As time

passes, the inflammation becomes acute and reaches a zenith about 8 days
after infection. It is of especial interest that the peak production of
copro-antibodies also occurs on this day (Ivey, 1956). A few days later
(11–14 days postinfection) when the inflammation is in a subacute phase
and diminishing, a significant loss of worms occurs from, and only from,
the anterior half of the small intestine (Larsh et al., 1952). It appears,
therefore, that when the combined direct effect(s) of antibodies and the
indirect effect(s) of the cellular inflammation reach a certain intensity
large numbers of worms are driven out. The evidence indicates that many
of these are not killed, since they live for a period in lower levels of the
intestine. This suggests a general lowering of all metabolic processes by
antibody action, which is aggravated by the creation of an unfavorable
environment produced by changes that accompany or follow the tissue
inflammation. The cellular effects are not direct, as against certain other
parasites, since the reaction is about the same throughout large areas of
the mucosa and submucosa as it is in areas adjacent to worms. Moreover,
even a non-specific inflammation, if intense, has a similar effect, and can
drive out significant numbers of worms even when specific immunity to
T. spiralis is feeble (Cox, 1952 a, b; Brewer, 1955; Goulson, 1957, 1958).
In any case, the specific inflammatory response is much more rapid and
severe in previously immunized mice, suggesting strongly that it is triggered by a specific antibody-antigen reaction. Apart from its instan-
taneous onset and more rapid and severe course, the response is the same
as that noted in the presence of a feeble immunity, and the same associated
factors (weight loss, etc.) are present. Finally, the evidence suggests that
the effects of the acute inflammatory response in both non-immunized
and immunized mice are responsible for the initial, significant loss of
worms, whereas the less severe subacute response causes the later worm
eliminations. In any case, the effect probably is a function of time,
rather than type of response, since worms are not driven out until the
tissue has been inflamed for a number of days.

Thus far, there is only indirect, if strongly supporting, evidence that
the specific inflammatory response is triggered by an antibody-antigen
reaction. In addition to the evidence already presented, mention should
be made of the interesting and important observations in rabbits
(Aikawa et al., 1951). Maximum physiological alterations (edema, increase
in interstitial fluid space, etc.) occur just prior to the detection of
circulating precipitins. The various changes observed indicate severe
injury and a resultant increased permeability of the vascular tree. Increased capillary permeability is an important feature of inflammation,
so these observations, especially in view of the time factors, would appear
to be more than coincidental in relating such changes to an antibody-
antigen reaction. In this connection, it is also worth noting that vascular

changes highly suggestive of inflammation are noted in hamsters early in infection (Humes and Akers, 1952).

The degree of the characteristic inflammatory response appears to be related to the degree of acquired immunity, as would be expected if it plays an important role in eliminating worms. The response is strongest in mice given repeated stimulating infections with non-irradiated larvae, *i.e.*, phases 1–3 (Larsh and Race, 1954; Figs. 11–14), intermediate in degree in those stimulated with irradiated (3500 r) larvae, *i.e.*, phases 1 and 2 (Larsh *et al.*, 1962; Fig. 20), and least in those stimulated with irradiated (7000 r) larvae, *i.e.*, phase 1 (Larsh *et al.*, 1959; Fig. 15). This may suggest the presence of a common functional antigen in all phases, but a definite conclusion will not be possible until direct comparisons of the three separate phases and/or their functional antigenic components are made. On the other hand, the degree of immunity produced by phase 1 alone, especially in view of its brief duration, may suggest a qualitative difference or, at least, a proportionately greater concentration of a common functional antigen.

It seems evident from the information at hand that acquired immunity in the mouse host is dependent on the direct effects of specific antibodies and an indirect effect of cellular factors. The question then arises as to the relative role of each in the actual elimination of adult worms, since this criterion is the one most often employed to measure a high level of immunity. Inasmuch as the cellular response appears to be triggered by a humoral response, to study this a means had to be found whereby one response could be inhibited, or prevented, and the other not affected to a demonstrable degree. Cortisone, by its striking anti-inflammatory effects, proved to be a useful tool in these determinations. By selecting mice after they had been strongly immunized by repeated stimulating infections ruled out any effect cortisone might have had on the development of acquired immunity. Despite the striking immunity of these mice and the apparent high titers of specific antibodies, daily injections of cortisone rendered them essentially non-immune, since they failed to eliminate adult worms for long periods after a challenging infection (Coker, 1954, 1956 a, b). This effect was, as expected from other work, not due to interference with the preformed antibody, but to strong interference with the cellular factors associated with the intestinal inflammation (Figs. 18–19). Therefore, it is obvious that the direct effects of antibodies against the worms, important as they are in the total immunity of the host, are ineffective by themselves, at least when the worm burden is at a certain level, in bringing about a significant loss of worms. It follows then that this role is performed by the indirect cellular factors, which, as suggested above, probably are triggered by an antigen-antibody reaction and are only as effective as the total inciting antibody production will allow. It

o

is not clear how the cellular response operates against the worms to bring
about their expulsion. The infiltrating cells do not seek out and encapsu-
late the worms as demonstrated in other cases. The answer may be
related to the fact that various types of cells in an inflammatory exudate
have capabilities in addition to those of encapsulation and phagocytosis
(Taliaferro, 1949). For example, lymphocytes, neutrophils and macrophages can secrete ferments, which may have an adverse effect upon an
invading organism. Perhaps more pertinent is the recent evidence that
mast cells, by disruption and release of granules, probably release histamine (Wells, 1962). Furthermore, this cell has been shown to be injured
and disrupted by various *T. spiralis* antigens (Briggs, 1961). Eosinophils,
on the other hand, are believed to absorb and thus neutralize protein
disintegration products (Downey, 1938), and they appear to be antagon-
ists to histamine (Wells, 1962). It may be, therefore, that products from
certain of the cells in the anterior half of the small intestine create an
unfavorable environment for *T. spiralis*. The fact that many worms re-
attach in lower levels of the intestine would seem to support this suggestion.

It is interesting that continuous cortisone treatment, while suppressing
almost completely the normal striking cellular infiltration in the musculature (Figs. 23–24; compare with Figs. 1–2), does not result in an increase
of larvae (Coker, 1956c). Discontinuing treatment after 13 days postinfection allows the development of a striking general myositis as
measured at 21 and 30 days, but no reduction in numbers of larvae is
noted. Therefore, if the characteristic inflammatory response in the
musculature is related to immune action against larvae, it requires
longer than 30 days to produce effects as measured in this way.

Whole-body irradiation provided another tool for measuring this indirect effect on adult worm elimination. Again, by using strongly immunized mice to prevent effects on the development of immunity,
whole-body irradiation (450 r) of mice, as expected from other work, did
not appear to affect the preformed antibodies. However, depending on
the time interval between irradiation and the challenging infection, it
interfered with the intestinal inflammatory response and prevented the
usual elimination of worms. The effects produced by irradiation given 8
days before the infection (Fig. 21) were similar to those produced by
cortisone (Figs. 18–19), while those produced by irradiation 12 days
prior to infection (Fig. 22) were intermediate both as to worm numbers
and inflammation. The latter suggests a recovery response within this
period.

With present knowledge, it seems entirely likely that most, if not all,
factors that modify a strongly established acquired immunity do
so by interfering with the characteristic inflammatory response, as

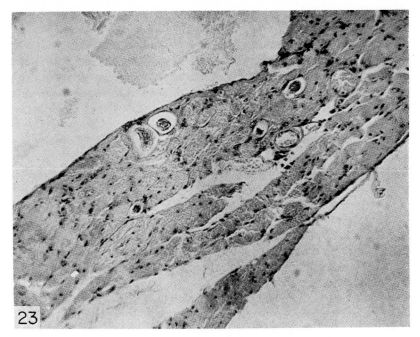

FIG. 23. Note the striking suppression of cellular infiltration in an old mouse at 21 days after infection when cortisone was given continuously. Photograph taken by use of a compound microscope (10× ocular and objective). From Coker (1956c); permission of the Editor, *J Parasit.*

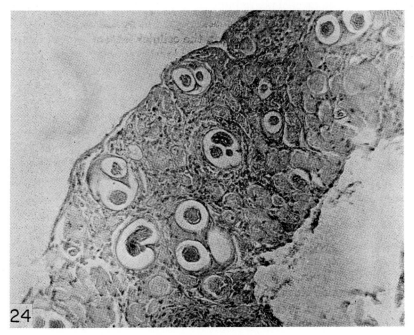

FIG. 24. Note the near total absence of cellular infiltration in an old mouse at 30 days after infection when cortisone was given continuously. Photograph taken by use of a compound microscope (10× ocular and objective). From Coker (1956c); permission of the Editor, *J. Parasit.*

demonstrated for cortisone and whole-body irradiation. Thus, in the case of socio-psychological stress (Davis and Read, 1958), one can visualize adrenal hypertrophy and increased secretion of cortical steroids, which in turn inhibit the inflammation and allow larger numbers of adult worms to persist. Adrenalectomy (Baughn, 1952a, b), on the other hand, would be expected to have the opposite effect by eliminating the source of this inhibitory mechanism. We cannot at present rule out interference with preformed antibody, despite the evidence for this after various treatments (adrenalectomy, cortisone, and whole-body irradiation), since antibodies other than those charted in these studies may be (after combining with specific antigen) responsible for triggering the inflammatory response.

Treatment administered during the development of immunity presents an entirely different situation. In this case, any factor that inhibits antibody production could be contributory to, or actually responsible for, a weakened response.

The evidence is now clear enough to suggest that this immunity is due to the primary (first to come into play) action of specific antibodies with secondary (later) cellular co-operation, as suggested some years ago to explain the immunity demonstrated against *Nippostrongylus muris* in rats (Taliaferro and Sarles, 1939). It would appear, moreover, that so far as action against the adult worms is concerned the antibody effects are direct, the cellular effects are indirect. Finally, both effects are required to drive out adult worms at the specified periods postinfection, but in the actual process of worm elimination the cellular factors are responsible. These, no doubt, operate at an effective level only after being triggered by a specific antigen-antibody reaction. Whether the same or different antibodies are involved in the primary and secondary actions is not known. Further studies are needed to clarify this and other details. If different antibodies are involved, it may explain the apparent inconsistency between a strong immunity as based on worm elimination and the relatively feeble protective action of certain circulating antibodies in high titer. This fact above all else led to the formation of the local immunity hypothesis, and although most workers now accept the general nature of the immunity this inconsistency remains and should be elucidated.

III. SUMMARY AND FORECAST

Many advances have been made in the past decade or so in our understanding of *T. spiralis* and the infection it produces in various experimental animals. New information has been contributed on certain morphological details, especially by electron microscopy, life cycle details vitally important in constructing proper experimental designs, and on the chemical composition and activities of the parasite. Perhaps the greatest advance, because of its many implications, is the one demonstrating that larvae encysted for long periods are actively exchanging metabolites with the host. Also, considerable new information has been presented concerning host responses to the parasite at specified periods during infection. Certain anatomical and/or physiological alterations have been noted in the excretory, endocrine, cardiovascular, muscular, and gastro-intestinal systems, and a large volume of new data has been added to our previous stores on acquired immunity.

The most encouraging feature of the work of this period, because of the great influence it will have on future progress in this field, is the great adaptability demonstrated by experimental parasitologists. When the problem demands it, he has shown no hesitation in drawing upon many other areas of biology. This, above all else, has accounted for the great advances of this period, since it is obvious that many of the contributions could not have been made without the use of modern tools of biochemistry, pathology, physiology, immunology, pharmacology, biophysics, biostatistics, and others.

Despite the recent advances, many gaps remain in our knowledge of the complex host-parasite relationships in experimental trichiniasis, and in many areas we have only scratched the tough surface of the great stores of future knowledge. Therefore, one may forecast with confidence that during the next decade or so interest in this field will remain high and the volume and depth of work will provide ample justification for another review. It may be of interest to forecast a few of the problems that may be considered.

Because of the great complexities encountered during infections with all three phases of the parasite (pre-adults, adults, muscle larvae), it may be expected that future investigators, taking advantage of present or future methods for separating the various phases, will study the parasite and host after infection with a single phase. This approach, used so effectively in present immunity studies, may prove the only means whereby we can relate definitely to parasite phases the many direct and indirect host responses in various parts of the body. In this connection, the phase thus far neglected (phase 3, muscle larvae) will receive full attention. With present evidence, showing an active exchange of metabolites with the host for many months and a reduction in work ability, more attention will be given to the likelihood that this phase accounts for various long-term effects in the host, making necessary the recognition and extensive study of a true "chronic" stage of the disease. It is already known that tryptophan metabolism is altered significantly. The precise role of the eosinophil, especially in view of the new information on its alkaline phosphatase content when engaged in certain activities, will be given further consideration. In all probability, attempts will be made to relate with confidence the various serum changes to specific pathological and/or physiological alterations in the body. Whether or not this is possible, predictable levels of certain substances in addition to antibodies may find application in laboratory diagnosis. A beginning has been made recently by determining the levels of histamine, aldolase, and trans-aminases (GO-T and GP-T) in human cases. Studies will be made in attempts to determine the mechanisms of the changes noted in various body systems, and, no doubt, interest in all aspects of immunity will continue until the true mechanisms of these complex host responses are elucidated. Further attempts will be made to induce immunological tolerance in experimental hosts, which will be aided, as will serological diagnosis and other areas, by the availability of pure antigens from one or more phases of the parasite. In fact, the availability of synthetic antigens is a distinct possibility. Finally, it is inevitable that more basic research will be carried out to give a better understanding of the hypersensitive phenomena, which are so obvious in this disease. This is long overdue and will be welcomed by many health authorities (Andrews, 1962). The immediate future, therefore, promises to be an exciting period for those attracted by the challenges of these and many other problems in experimental trichiniasis.

One who has reviewed the past and forecast the future of experimental trichiniasis cannot escape the thought that *T. spiralis*, despite its importance in relation to human health, has received more than its share of attention by parasitologists. There can be only one explanation—the facility of handling it under laboratory conditions, and, especially, the challenging problems encountered in the host due to its completely parasitic existence in intestinal and extra-intestinal sites. Much of the knowledge gained from studies of this unique parasite and the disease it produces can be of value in understanding parasitism in its broadest scope. Surely Dr. Leuckart and Dr. Virchow, and many later investigators, would be pleased that their favorite model of parasitism has served so well for so long to advance scientific knowledge.

References

Aikawa, J. K., Harrell, G. T., Jr. and Miller, T. B. (1951). *J. clin. Invest.* **30**, 575–81.
Andrews, J. M. (1962). *J. Parasit.* **48**, 3–12.
Baughn, C. O., Jr. (1952a). (Doctoral Dissertation), pp. 66. Department of Parasitology, University of North Carolina, Chapel Hill, N.C., U.S.A.
Baughn, C. O., Jr. (1952b). *J. Elisha Mitchell sci. Soc.* **68**, No. 2, 207–21.
Beckett, E. B. (1961). *Biochem. J.* **78**, No. 2, 17–18.
Beckett, E. B. and Boothroyd, B. (1961). *Ann. trop. Med. Parasit.* **55**, No. 1, 116–24.
Beresantev, Yu. A. (1962). *Wiad. Parazytol.* **8**, No. 1, 56–61.
Bernard, G. R. (1959). *Amer. Midl. Nat.* **62** (2), 396–401.

Bernard, G. R. (1961a). *J. inf. Dis.* **108**, 1–11.

Bernard, G. R. (1961b). *Amer. Zool.* **1**, No. 3, 166.

Bernard, G. R. (1961c). *J. Parasit.* **47**, No. 5, 721–6.

Bernard, G. R. and Sudak, F. N. (1960). *Amer. Heart J.* **60**, No. 1, 88–93.

Boyd, E. M. and Huston, E. J. (1954). *J. Parasit.* **40**, No. 6, 686–90.

Boyd, E. M. and Petersen, J. H. (1954). *Anat. Rec.* **120**, No. 3, 227.

Bozicevich, J. and Detre, L. (1940). *Publ. Hlth. Rep., Wash.* **55**, No. 16, 683–92.

Brand, T. von, Weinstein, P. P. and Wright, W. H. (1954). *Amer. J. Hyg.* **59**, No. 1, 26–31.

Brewer, O. M. (1955). *J. Elisha Mitchell sci. Soc.* **71**, 170–1.

Briggs, N. T. (1961). *J. Parasit.* **47**, No. 4, Section 2, 17.

Bullock, W. L. (1951). *J. Parasit.* **37** (5), Section 2, 20.

Bullock, W. L. (1953). *Exp. Parasit.* **2** (2), 150–62.

Campbell, C. H. (1954). (Doctoral Dissertation) pp. 110. Department of Parasitology, University of North Carolina, Chapel Hill, N.C., U.S.A.

Campbell, C. H. (1955). *J. Parasit.* **41**, No. 5, 483–91.

Chandler, A. C. (1939a). *Vol. Jub. Pro. Prof. Sadao Yoshida, Osaka, Japan*, **2**, 343–64.

Chandler, A. C. (1939b). *Amer. J. trop. Med.* **19**, 309–17.

Chipman, P. B. (1956). (Master's Thesis) pp. 74. Department of Parasitology, University of North Carolina, Chapel Hill, N.C., U.S.A.

Chipman, P. B. (1957). *J. Parasit.* **43**, No. 6, 593–8.

Chute, R. M. (1956). *Proc. helm. Soc. Wash.* **23**, No. 1, 49–58.

Chute, R. M. (1961). *J. Parasit.* **47**, No. 1, 25–9.

Coker, C. M. (1954). (Doctoral Dissertation) pp. 99. Department of Parasitology, University of North Carolina, Chapel Hill, N.C., U.S.A.

Coker, C. M. (1955). *J. Parasit.* **41**, No. 5, 498–504.

Coker, C. M. (1956a). *J. inf. Dis.* **98**, 39–44.

Coker, C. M. (1956b). *J. inf. Dis.* **98**, 187–97.

Coker, C. M. (1956c). *J. Parasit.* **42**, No. 5, 479–84.

Cox, H. W. (1952a). (Doctoral Dissertation) pp. 74. Department of Parasitology, University of North Carolina, Chapel Hill, N.C., U.S.A.

Cox, H. W. (1952b). *J. Elisha Mitchell sci. Soc.* **68**, No. 2, 222–35.

Culbertson, J. T. (1942). *J. Parasit.* **28**, 197–202.

Davis, D. E. and Read, C. P. (1958). *Proc. Soc. exp. Biol., N.Y.* 99, 269–72.

Downey, H. (1938). "Handbook of Hematology", Vol. I, 698 pp. P. B. Hoeber, Inc., New York.

Edney, J. M., Arbogast, F. and Stepp, J. (1953). *J. Tenn. Acad. Sci.* **28**, 62–68.

Ewert, A. and Olson, L. J. (1960). *J. Parasit.* **46**, No. 6, 849–54.

Fischthal, J. H. (1943). *J. Parasit.* **29**, 123–6.

Forrester, A. T. T., Nelson, G. S. and Sander, G. (1961). *Trans. R. Soc. trop. Med. Hyg.* **55**, No. 6, 503–13.

Goodchild, C. G. (1957). *J. Parasit.* **43**, 294–303.

Goodchild, C. G. and Frankenberg, D. (1960). *Ass. southeastern Biol. Bul.* **7** (2), 28.

Gould, S. E. (1945). "Trichinosis", 356 pp. Charles C. Thomas, Springfield, Illinois.

Gould, S. E., Van Dyke, J. G. and Gomberg, H. J. (1953). *Amer. J. Path.* **29**, 323–37.

Gould, S. E., Gomberg, H. J., Bethell, F. H., Villella, J. B. and Hertz, C. S. (1955). *Amer. J. Path.* **31**, No. 5, 933–63.

Gould, S. E., Gomberg, H. J., Villella, J. B. and Hertz, C. S. (1957). *Amer. J. Path.* **33**, No. 1, 79–105.

Goulson, H. T. (1957). (Doctoral Dissertation) pp. 117. Department of Parasitology, University of North Carolina, Chapel Hill, N.C., U.S.A.

Goulson, H. T. (1958). *J. Elisha Mitchell sci. Soc.* **74**, No. 1, 14–23.

Gursch, O. F. (1949). *J. Parasit.* **35**, 19–26.

Hankes, L. V. and Stoner, R. D. (1958). *Exp. Parasit.* **7**, 92–98.

Hartung, W. and Becht, H. (1960). *Strahlentherapie* **112**, No. 4, 613–20.

Hendricks, J. R. (1950). *J. Immunol.* **64**, No. 3, 173–7.

Hendricks, J. R. (1951). (Doctoral Dissertation) pp. 66. Department of Parasitology, University of North Carolina, Chapel Hill, N.C., U.S.A.

Hendricks, J. R. (1952). *J. Elisha Mitchell sci. Soc.* **68**, No. 1, 12–26.

Humes, A. G. and Akers, R. P. (1952). *Anat. Rec.* **114**, No. 1, 103–13.

Ivey, M. H. (1956). (Doctoral Dissertation) pp. 88. Department of Parasitology, University of North Carolina, Chapel Hill, N.C., U.S.A.

Jackson, G. J. (1959). *J. inf. Dis.* **105**, 97–117.

Kagan, I. G. (1960). *J. inf. Dis.* **107**, 65–93.

Kagan, I. G. and Bargai, U. (1956). *J. Parasit.* **42**, No. 3, 237–45.

Kagan, I. G. and Goodchild, C. G. (1961). *J. Parasit.* **47**, No. 3, 373–7.

Kerr, K. B. (1936). *Amer. J. Hyg.* **24**, 381–406.

Kilham, L. and Olivier, L. (1961). *Amer. J. trop. Med. Hyg.* **10**, No. 6, 879–84.

Kim, C. W. (1956). (Doctoral Dissertation) pp. 103. Department of Parasitology, University of North Carolina, Chapel Hill, N.C., U.S.A.

Kim, C. W. (1957). *J. Elisha Mitchell, sci. Soc.* **73**. No. 2, 308–17.

Kim, C. W. (1961). *Amer. J. trop. Med. Hyg.* **10** (5), 742–7.

Kucharczyk, W., Limański, M., Skorczyński, M. and Szaflarski, J. (1960). *Wiad. Parazytol.* **6**, No. 4, 329–30.

Labzoffsky, N. A., Kuitunen, E., Morrissey, L. P. and Hamvas, J. J. (1959). *Canad. J. Microbiol.* **5**, 395–403.

Larsh, J. E., Jr. (1947). *J. Parasit.* **33**, 339–44.

Larsh, J. E., Jr. (1953a). *Thapar Commemoration Vol.*, 159–72.

Larsh, J. E., Jr. (1953b). *J. inf. Dis.* **93**, 282–93.

Larsh, J. E., Jr. and Fletcher, O. K., Jr. (1948). *J. Elisha Mitchell sci. Soc.* **64**, No. 2, 196–203.

Larsh, J. E., Jr. and Gilchrist, H. B. (1950). *J. Elisha Mitchell sci. Soc.* **66**, No. 1, 76–83.

Larsh, J. E., Jr. and Goulson, H. T. (1962). (unpublished data).

Larsh, J. E., Jr. and Hendricks, J. R. (1949). *J. Parasit.* **35**, No. 1, 101–6.

Larsh, J. E., Jr. and Kent, D. E. (1949). *J. Parasit.* **35**, No. 1, 45–53.

Larsh, J. E., Jr. and Nichols, J. (1949). *Proc. Soc. exp., Biol., N.Y.* **71**, 652–4.

Larsh, J. E., Jr. and Race, G. J. (1954). *J. inf. Dis.* **94**, 262–72.

Larsh, J. E., Jr., Gilchrist, H. B. and Greenberg, B. G. (1952). *J. Elisha Mitchell sci. Soc.* **68**, No. 1, 1–11.

Larsh, J. E., Jr., Race, G. J. and Jeffries, W. B. (1956). *J. inf. Dis.* **99**, 63–71.

Larsh, J. E., Jr., Race, G. J. and Goulson, H. T. (1959). *J. inf. Dis.* **104**, 156–63.

Larsh, J. E., Jr., Race, G. J. and Yarinsky, A. (1962). *Amer. J. trop. Med. Hyg.* (in press).

Lewert, R. M. and Lee, C. L. (1954). *J. inf. Dis.* **95**, No. 1, 13–51.

Lord, R. A. (1958). *Amer. J. trop. Med. Hyg.* **7**, 611–7.

Louch, C. D. (1962). *J. Parasit.* **48**, No. 1, 24–6.

McCoy, O. R. (1934). *Amer. J. Hyg.* **20**, 169–80.

Maeir, D. M., Zaiman, H. and Howard, R. G. (1962). *Exp. Parasit.* **12**, No. 2, 114–7.

Markell, E. K. (1958). *J. inf. Dis.* **102**, 158–61.

Markell, E. K. and Lewis, W. P. (1957). *Amer. J. trop. Med. Hyg.* **6**, 553–61.

Moskwa, W., Stefan, W. and Urszula, B. (1958). *Wiad. Parazytol.* **4** (5/6), 373–5.

Oliver-Gonzalez, J. (1940). *J. inf. Dis.* **67**, 292–300.
Oliver-Gonzalez, J. (1941). *J. inf. Dis.* **69**, 254–70.
Oliver-Gonzalez, J. and Levine, D. M. (1962). *Amer. J. trop. Med. Hyg.* **11**, No. 2, 241–4.
Phillipson, R. F. and Kershaw, W. E. (1961). *Ann. trop. Med. Parasit.* **55**, No. 2, 231–4.
Pollay, M., Wein, B. and Hartmann, H. A. (1954). *Proc. Soc. exp. Biol., N.Y.* **86**, 577–80.
Rappaport, I. (1943a). *Amer. J. trop. Med.* **23**, 343–50.
Rappaport, I. (1943b). *Amer. J. trop. Med.* **23**, 351–62.
Rappaport, I. and Wells, H. S. (1951). *J. inf. Dis.* **88**, 248–53.
Ritterson, A. L. (1957). *J. Parasit.* **43**, No. 5, 542–7.
Ritterson, A. L. (1959a). *J. Parasit.* **45**, No. 4, Sec. 2, 36.
Ritterson, A. L. (1959b). *J. inf. Dis.* **105**, 253–66.
Ritterson, A. L. (1960). *J. Parasit.* **46**, No. 5, Sec. 2, 22.
Ritterson, A. L. and Mauer, S. I. (1957). *Science* **126**, No. 3286, 1293–4.
Robinson, E. J., Jr. (1961). *J. Parasit.* **47**, No. 4. Sec. 2, 16–17.
Rogers, W. P. (1941). *J. Helminth.* **19**, 87–104.
Ross, W. M. (1952). *Canad. J. Med. Sci.* **30**, 534–42.
Sadun, E. H. (1960). *Wiad. Parazytol.* **6**, No. 4, 344–5.
Sadun, E. H. and Norman, L. (1956). *J. Parasit.* **42**, No. 6, 608–12.
Santisteban, G. A. (1951). (Thesis) University of Utah, Salt Lake City, Utah, U.S.A.
Schwartz, B. (1960). *Proc. helm. Soc. Wash.* **27**, No. 3, 261–8.
Semrad, J. E. and Coors, M. J. (1951). *Trans. Ill. Acad. Sci.* **44**, 253–8.
Seniów, A. (1960). *Wiad. Parazytol.* **6**, No. 4, 331–4.
Shikhobalova, N. P. (1952). *Trud. Gel. Lab. Akad. Nauk. SSSR* **6**, 60–71. (Abstracted in *Helminth. Abstr.* **21**, 319).
Shikhobalova, N. P. (1953). *Izd. Akad. Nauk, SSSR*, 761–9. (Abstracted in *Helminth. Abstr.* **22**, 400).
Sleeman, H. K. (1961). *Amer. J. trop. Med. Hyg.* **10**, No. 6, 834–8.
Stoner, R. D. and Godwin, J. T. (1953). *Amer. J. Path.* **29**, 943–50.
Stoner, R. D. and Godwin, J. T. (1954). *Amer. J. Path.* **30**, 913–8.
Stoner, R. D. and Hale, W. M. (1952). *Proc. Soc. exp. Biol., N.Y.* **80**, 510–2.
Stoner, R. D. and Hankes, L. V. (1955). *Exp. Parasit.* **4**, 435–44.
Taliaferro, W. H. (1940). *Physiol. Rev.* **20**, 469–92.
Taliaferro, W. H. (1949). *Annu. Rev. Microbiol.* 1949, 159–94.
Taliaferro, W. H. and Sarles, M. P. (1939). *J. inf. Dis.* **64**, 157–92.
Talmage, D. W. (1955). *Annu. Rev. Microbiol.* **9**, 335–46.
Tanner, C. E. and Gregory, J. (1961). *Canad. J. Microbiol.* **7**, No. 4, 473–81.
Themann, H. (1960). *Wiad. Parazytol.* **6**, No. 4, 352–4.
Thomas, L. (1953). *Ann. N.Y. Acad. Sci.* **56**, 799–814.
Villella, J. B. (1958). *J. Parasit.* **44**, No. 4, Sec. 2, 41.
Villella, J. B., Gomberg, H. J. and Gould, S. E. (1961). *Science* **134**, 1073–5.
Weimer, H. E., Markell, E. K. and Nishihara, H. (1958). *Exp. Parasit.* **7**, 468–76.
Wells, P. D. (1962). *Exp. Parasit.* **12**, No. 2, 82–101.
Wodehouse, R. P. (1956). *Ann. Allergy* **14**, 121–138.
Wu, L. Y. (1955). *Canad. J. Zool.* **33** (6), 440–6.
Wu, L. Y. and Kingscote, A. A. (1957). *Canad. J. Zool.* **35**, 207–11.
Yarinsky, A. (1961). (Doctoral Dissertation) pp. 141. Department of Parasitology, University of North Carolina, Chapel Hill, N.C., U.S.A.
Yarinsky, A. (1962). *J. Elisha Mithcell sci. Soc.* **78**, No. 1, 29–43.

Zaiman, H. (1953). *Amer. J. Hyg.* **57**, 297–305.

Zaiman, H. and Rubel, J. (1953). *Amer. J. Hyg.* **57**, 311–5.

Zaiman, H. and Stoney, J. M. (1954). *Amer. J. Hyg.* **59**, No. 1, 52–9.

Zaiman, H. and Safholm, R. D. (1955). *Amer. J. Hyg.* **61**, No. 1, 1–4.

Zaiman, H., Omi, G. and Gapinski, L. (1953). *Amer. J. Hyg.* **57**, 306–10.

Zaiman, H., Wilson, J. D., Rubel, J. and Stoney, J. M. (1954). *Amer. J. Hyg.* **59**, No. 1, 39–51.

Zaiman, H., Stoney, J. M., Rubel, J. and Headley, N. C. (1955a). *Amer. J. Hyg.* **61**, 5–14.

Zaiman, H., Stoney, J. M. and Headley, N. C. (1955b). *Amer. J. Hyg.* **61**, 15–23.

Zaiman, H., Maeir, D. M. and Howard, R. G. (1961). *Amer. J. Path.* **38**, No. 5, 553–9.

Zapart, W. (1960). *Wiad. Parazytol.* **6**, No. 4, 351–2.

Zarzycki, J. (1960). *Wiad. Parazytol.* **6**, No. 4, 355–6.

Larvae and Larval Development of Monogeneans

J. LLEWELLYN

Department of Zoology and Comparative Physiology,
The University, Birmingham, England

I. Introduction 287
II. Morphology of Monogenean Larvae 288
  A. General Features 288
  B. External Ciliation 290
  C. The Haptor 293
  D. The Alimentary Canal 303
  E. The Osmo-regulatory System 305
  F. Glands 307
  G. Nervous System and Sense Organs......................................308
III. Post-Oncomiracidial Development...309
IV. The Development of the Haptor of the Adult in Polyopisthocotylineans 312
V. Discussion 315
VI. Summary 322
  References 323

I. INTRODUCTION

For about a hundred years, since the recognition by van Beneden of a group of parasitic platyhelminths generally referred to as monogenetic trematodes, the members of this group have been classified according to almost exclusively adult characteristics. In 1957 however, Bychowsky and Llewellyn, independently, made use of larval characters for this purpose. The two studies were based upon samples of monogenean larvae of largely different composition, and neither was able to include the descriptions of numerous larvae published since 1955 by Euzet and his associates at Sète. Until 1957 the larvae of less than thirty monogeneans were known, but since then the number has been raised to more than 100, mainly as a result of studies by Bychowsky, Euzet, and Llewellyn. However, more important than the number of species of larvae known is the expanded taxonomic range they represent.

Bychowsky (1957), in his book on the classification and phylogeny of monogeneans, recognized twenty-eight families and stated that larvae belonging to representatives of less than half of these families were known. However, larvae belonging to nine of those families whose larvae were not known to Bychowsky have now been reported. Euzet (1955) had described four of them (Monocotylidae, Amphibdellatidae, Hexostomatidae, and Hexabothriidae), Llewellyn (1957a) described another four of them (Acanthocotylidae, Anthocotylidae, Plectanocotylidae, and Gastrocotylidae, together with the Hexabothriidae already described by

287

Euzet), and Manter (1955) referred briefly to a larval form belonging to a ninth family, the Chimaericolidae.

There remain now seven families of monogeneans whose larvae are still not known: Protogyrodactylidae, Dionchidae, Loimoidae, Bothitrematidae, Protomicrocotylidae, Microbothriidae, and the new family Anchorophoridae ("Discocotylinea") (Bychowsky and Nagibina, 1958). Of these, only the Microbothriidae has been reported in British waters, and I have made numerous attempts, all of them unsuccessful, to rear larvae of *Leptocotyle minor* and *Pseudocotyle squatinae*. Other workers have also reported difficulties in obtaining monogenean larvae from eggs: Euzet (1955) with *Hexabothrium appendiculatum* (syn. *H. canicula*); Bychowsky (1957) with *Diclybothrium armatum*; Ramalingam (1961a) with *Lithidiocotyle secunda*; and Euzet and Trilles (1961) with *Cyclocotyla bellones*. There is thus a clear need for some experimental work to be done on the factors which influence the embryonic development and hatching of monogeneans. Euzet and Raibaut (1960) have given some evidence for a "hatching factor" derived from the potential host in *Squalonchocotyle torpedinis*, and Llewellyn (1962a) has indicated that it is possible that a diapause may occur during the development of *Gastrocotyle trachuri*.

Baer and Euzet (1961) have concluded that, while in their opinion the definitive systematics of monogeneans should be based on the larval haptor, such a scheme is not yet practicable because of the small number of larvae (at most a tenth of the number of known species) yet known to us. However, larvae representative of about three-quarters of the families of monogeneans are now known, and there are grounds for believing that those not yet known will be found not to differ substantially from those of species thought to be their close relatives when assessed in terms of adult characters, and so it is considered opportune to review here the present state of our knowledge about larval monogeneans, and to consider what contribution such knowledge may make to a study of the phylogeny of monogeneans. In implementing this task an attempt has been made to avoid using proper names that might have definite taxonomic status; in all cases the obvious interpretation is the one which is intended, but it is necessary to add that the terms "monopisthocotylineans" and "polyopisthocotylineans" have been used throughout in the traditional sense (see Dawes, 1946; Sproston, 1946) and not in the much more restricted way used by Bychowsky (1957).

II. MORPHOLOGY OF MONOGENEAN LARVAE

A. GENERAL FEATURES

A few monogeneans are viviparous and the newly-born young resemble the parents (Gyrodactylidae), but most are oviparous, and the newly-hatched young is a larva which has been called an oncomiracidium (Llewellyn, 1957a). Ovo-viviparity has been described in *Polystomoidella oblonga* by Oglesby (1961) and in *Callorhynchicola multitesticulatus* by Manter (1955).

An oncomiracidium is essentially a *hooked* larva, and the structure of *Gastrocotyle trachuri* as an example of such a larva is illustrated in Fig. 1.

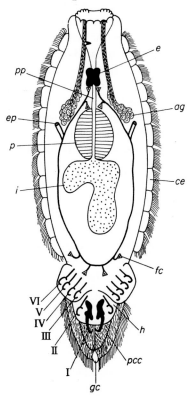

FIG. 1. A typical oncomiracidium of a monogenean: *Gastrocotyle trachuri* from the gills of *Trachurus trachurus*. For variations in oncomiracidia, see text. (Original.) *ag*, anterior gland; *ce*, ciliated epidermis; *e*, eye; *ep*, excretory pore; *fc*, flame cell; *gc*, glandular secretion; *h*, haptor; *i*, intestine; *p*, pharynx; *pcc*, posterior ciliated cone; *pp*, prepharynx; I – VI, marginal hooks.

Oncomiracidia vary in length between about 0.1 mm and 0.3 mm and, at least in artificial cultures, have a life-span of no longer than 24 h. During this time, according to Bychowsky, there are two phases of activity: first, a free-swimming phase in search of a host, and secondly a "creeping" or "gliding" phase the locomotion of which over the surface of its host resembles that of a turbellarian. In the first phase locomotion is purely by means of epidermal cilia, but in the second muscular movements take place, and may include leech-like progression utilizing the haptor and its sclerites together with the anterior (presumably "sticky") glands.

B. EXTERNAL CILIATION

Most oncomiracidia are at least partly covered externally with cilia, but some are said to be without cilia: *Sphyranura oligorchis* described by Alvey (1936), though Bychowsky has challenged the accuracy of this observation; *Squalonchocotyle torpedinis* described by Euzet and Raibaut (1960); and *Acanthocotyle "lobianchi"* described by Llewellyn (1957a). (When observations were made on this last-named species only two oncomiracidia were obtained from several dozen eggs, and in the light of subsequent experience it seems possible that cilia may normally be present; the oncomiracidium should be re-examined.) In *Polystomoidella oblonga* described by Oglesby (1961) and *Callorhynchicola multitesticulatus* recorded by Manter (1955) there are no external cilia, but these two species are ovoviviparous, and the embryos escape from the egg-capsules into the uterus. It is not known how non-ciliated oncomiracidia may find a new host and it is perhaps possible that there may be two kinds of oncomiracidia produced, a non-ciliated one for re-infecting the same host specimen and a free-swimming ciliated one for seeking out a new host specimen. In *Squalonchocotyle torpedinis* the host *Torpedo marmorata* is viviparous, but since the eggs of the parasite apparently leave the host, the infection of a new generation of hosts by the direct transfer of the oncomiracidium from the mother-host seems unlikely. However, *T. marmorata* spends a good deal of its time on the sea-bottom, as do the various species of *Raia* which act as hosts to *Acanthocotyle*, and so it could be that the absence of cilia in the larvae of these parasites is associated with a relatively sedentary habit, the larvae not actively swimming in search of a host but waiting on the sea bottom to receive a host coming to rest. *Udonella caligorum* hatches from the egg as a miniature of the adult, and cilia are not present.

The ciliated epidermal cells of most oncomiracidia are distributed in three zones, an anterior, a middle, and a posterior, and it is possible that in some of those larvae in which a more continuous distribution has been shown (e.g. *Diplectanum aequans* by Llewellyn, 1957a, Figs. 1a, b), a more rigorous re-examination will show that the cilia are in fact zoned. The posterior zone is frequently to be seen as a cone projecting posteriorly to the haptor and has been described as a "posterior ciliated cone" (Llewellyn, 1957a). It consists entirely of epidermal cells surrounding an axial efferent duct from glands in the body proper, so that when the ciliated epidermis of the oncomiracidium is cast off, the whole ciliated cone is lost (Fig. 2).

Details of the pattern of ciliation are known for about eleven monogeneans and fortunately these cover a fairly representative taxonomic range, though less is known about marine species than about freshwater species. This lack of balance is due, at least in part, to technical difficulties in investigating ciliated epidermal cells. While corresponding cells ("epidermal plates") may be distinguished in living specimens of the miracidia of digeneans (Nasir, 1960 and personal communication), they are made much more prominent by treatment with silver nitrate, e.g. as described by Lynch (1933). This treatment, however, is unsuccessful

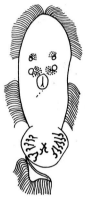

Fig. 2. Oncomiracidium of *Lamellodiscus fraternus* casting off the posterior ciliated cone. (Adapted after Bychowsky, 1957.)

when applied to oncomiracidia living in sea water because of the dense precipitate which is formed. The rinsing of marine oncomiracidia in fresh water before treatment with silver nitrate usually brings about the precocious shedding of the epidermal cells, as indeed so often happens under cover-glass pressure when oncomiracidia are mounted in sea water. Attempts to investigate the ciliation pattern of living marine oncomiracidia are now being made with electronic-flash photomicrography and by means of serial sections at 4μ of double-embedded newly-hatched larvae (see Fig. 11B).

The pattern of ciliated epidermal cells in *Polystoma integerrimum* has been described minutely by Bychowsky (1957), and Figs. 3A and 3B in this review are based on his diagrams. In the anterior zone there is a single apical cell and, separated from it and lying at the level of the anterior end of the pharynx, is a horseshoe-shaped band of twenty-four cells with the open end directed dorsally; in this continuous band, eighteen of the cells are situated ventrally, with a dorso-lateral group of three cells on each side. The middle zone is again horseshoe-shaped, but, in contrast to the anterior zone, the open end is directed ventrally; there are eighteen cells altogether in this zone. The posterior zone of ciliated cells consists of a horseshoe of twelve cells covering the dorsal surface of the haptoral region of the body proper; the ventral surface of the haptor itself is devoid of cilia.

A very similar pattern of ciliation to that of *Polystoma integerrimum* occurs in the polystomatid *Diplorchis ranae* as described by Ozaki (1936), and here again there are three horseshoe-shaped zones with the open end of the anterior one directed dorsally and those of the middle and posterior ones ventrally. The main difference between the ciliated epidermis of *D. ranae* and that of *P. integerrimum* is in the total number of cells: in

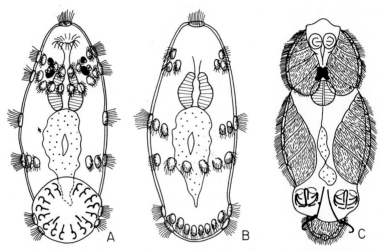

FIG. 3. Patterns of locomotory cilia in monogeneans. A. and B. *Polystoma integerrimum*. A. ventral view; B. dorsal view (Adapted after Bychowsky, 1957); *C. Diplozoon paradoxum* (Adapted after Bovet, 1959).

D. ranae there are two extra cells in each of the anterior (total twenty-seven) and posterior (total fourteen) zones.

In *Tetraonchus monenteron* as described by Gussev (in Bychowsky, 1957 translated by Hargis and Oustinoff, 1961), in contrast to the two polystomatids described above, the anterior zone is mainly a dorsal and lateral covering of about thirty-two cells, leaving the ventral surface in this region of the body devoid of cilia. The middle zone consists of a pair of ventro-lateral tracts of about fifteen cells each, leaving the median ventral and dorsal regions free of cilia. The posterior zone is made up of about seventeen ciliated cells.

Again according to Gussev, in the dactylogyrid *Bychowskyella pseudobagri* there are fewer cells in each of the three zones than in the corresponding zones of *T. monenteron*: in the anterior zone there are eighteen, in the middle twelve or fourteen, and in the posterior about twelve.

In *Entobdella soleae* there are about twenty cells in the anterior zone, sixteen in the middle, and nine in the posterior (Kearn, in press.)

The only polyopisthocotylinean in which the epidermis has been investigated by a silver nitrate technique appears to be *Discocotyle sagittata*, studied by Dr. I. L. Owen (personal communication). Here the anterior and middle zones are restricted to strips of single cells lying longitudinally along the lateral borders of the body, the anterior strips consisting of five cells on each side of the body, and the middle ones of six cells on each side. The posterior zone contains six cells. In another fresh water discocotylid *Diplozoon paradoxum* (see Fig. 3C) the anterior zone resembles that of *D. sagittata* in having five cells on each side of the body, but the middle zone is different in that there are only five cells in place of six on each side; the number of cells in the posterior zone could not be distinguished (Bovet, 1959). In the marine species *Mazocraes alosae* illustrated by Bychowsky (1957, Fig. 222) there are apparently only four cells on each side in the anterior zone, and six cells on each side in the middle zone.

Some detail is known of the ciliated epidermis in the oncomiracidia of three other marine polyopisthocotylineans: *Diclidophora denticulata* described by Frankland (1955), *Vallisia striata* described by Euzet and Raibaut (1961), and *Cyclocotyla belones* described by Euzet and Trilles (1961). In none of the three parasites was any distinction made between anterior and middle zones, but the total number of cells in the combined zones was recorded as eleven on each side, i.e. the same as in *Discocotyle sagittata*.

In the above sample of eleven monogeneans then there seems to be some association between the pattern of ciliation and phylogenetic development. Whereas the ciliated epidermal cells of the anterior and middle zones of monopisthocotylineans and polystomatids are arranged in bands set at right angles to the longitudinal axis of the body, those of diclidophorideans are restricted to laterally situated longitudinal strips. Furthermore, the total number of ciliated epidermal cells in the monopisthocotyleans and polystomatids was always forty-five or more, but in the diclidophorideans it was never more than thirty.

C. THE HAPTOR

At its posterior end the oncomiracidium invariably bears an adhesive organ or haptor in the form of a ventrally-directed disc or cup. The haptor is cup-like in *Hexabothrium appendiculatum* but shallow and disc-like with lateral expansions or "wings" in *Diclidophora denticulata*. In some species the haptor may appear to be terminal (e.g. *Entobdella soleae*) and in others subterminal (e.g. *Gastrocotyle trachuri*); however, the apparent difference is quite superficial, and is due to the presence in some of the

P

posteriorly-projecting deciduous ciliated cone (see Fig. 2), so that after the epidermis has been shed the haptor in any case becomes terminal.

Except in the Udonellidae (which Bychowsky does not in any case regard as monogeneans) and the Microbothriidae the haptor is always provided with skeletal structures in the form of hooks, and sometimes of bars as well, which have often been referred to as "cuticularizations". This term, however, implies an origin from the cuticle, and it will be shown elsewhere that many of the skeletal structures of monogeneans have an origin in tissues which are more deeply seated than the cuticle. Thus the term "cuticularization" is often inaccurate and may be misleading, and so the term "sclerite" will be used here for all the hardened skeletal structures of monogeneans, including all the haptoral hooks, bars and plates of the larva and the adult, together with the armament of the distal parts of the genitalia in some adults.

1. *Marginal Hooks*

The haptoral sclerites of the oncomiracidium are of several different kinds, but present invariably are *marginal hooks* whose shape is remarkably constant throughout monogeneans (Fig. 4) and, indeed, in

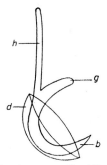

Fig. 4. A typical marginal hook of an oncomiracidium. (Original.) *b*, blade; *d*, domus; *g*, guard; *h*, handle.

larval gyrocotylideans, amphilinideans, and cestodes. Each marginal hook has a proximal straight *handle* and a distal curved *blade* which ends in a sharp point; the proximal part of the curved blade typically projects beyond its junction with the handle to form a so-called *guard*. Often the proximal part of the blade of the hook lies in the hollow of a dome-shaped sclerite which Halkin (1901) termed "ogives" in *Polystoma integerrimum;* similar structures were reported by Gallien (1934) in *Diclidophora luscae* and by Llewellyn (1957a, Figs. 7 and 9) in *Rajonchocotyle emarginata* and in *Entobdella soleae.* I am now convinced that Halkin, Gallien and I all observed a dome-shaped sclerite in optical section and gained the false impression of a pair of curved arches (hence Halkin's term "ogives"). Moreover, though I reported earlier (Llewellyn, 1957a) that in spite of a careful search I could not find "ogives" in any diclidophorideans, I have since seen them in several species belonging to this group. Euzet (1957a) has referred to marginal hooks provided with an accessory sclerite as "crochets à conducteur" but a term for the accessory structure itself would be convenient, and so *domus* (Latin, a house; plural *domus*) is proposed. The marginal hooks have been seen to move in the plane in which the ventrally (or medially) curved blade lies so that the point strikes savagely in an arc (= "gaffs"), but the muscles which move the hooks have not been described.

In most polyopisthocotylineans some of the marginal hooks become differentiated from the others by becoming larger and by becoming changed in shape. The relationship between such differentiated and unmodified hooks may be illustrated by reference to two polystomatids. In the well-known *Polystoma integerrimum* the marginal hooks are usually illustrated as being all of the same shape and size (though even here the posteriormost marginal hooks are in fact larger than the others) but in *Diplorchis ranae* as described by Ozaki (1936) the hooks of the posteriormost pair are much larger than the remainder (Figs. 5E, F). In many other polyopisthocotylineans, and especially in the diclidophorideans, the posterior marginal hooks (= "posterior hooks" of Frankland, 1955 and Llewellyn, 1957a) are of considerably more modified shape than in *Diplorchis ranae* (see Figs. 6A-H). The guard is usually absent and often the junction between the handle and the blade is flexible (Figs. 6A, C) so that the hook resembles somewhat a flail and for this reason has been termed a "crochet en fléau" by Euzet (1957a).

(It must be pointed out that Euzet and Raibaut (1960, Fig. 6), in their schematized diagrams of the development of the haptor of polyopisthocotylineans, have consistently misrepresented the relative positions of the posterior hooks and the postero-lateral hooks in *Diclidophora* and in *Microcotyle*. As may be seen from Frankland's diagram (1955, Fig. 6) of *Diclidophora denticulata* and Euzet's own diagrams (1958, Figs. 1-6) of *Microcotyle chrysophryii* and *M. sargi*, it is the *posterior* hooks, and not the postero-laterals, which are larger than the laterals.)

A further difference between the posteriormost marginal hooks and the other marginal hooks of polyopisthocotylineans is that a domus is absent from the posterior hooks but present in the other hooks in all but the polystomatids where it accompanies all sixteen marginal hooks. In some monogeneans some of the marginal hooks become modified in shape during post-oncomiracidial development, e.g. the posterior hooks in *Plectanocotyle gurnardi* and *Anthocotyle merluccii* (see Figs. 7A-D), and some of the anterior hooks of *Bychowskyella pseudobagri* (see Bychowsky,

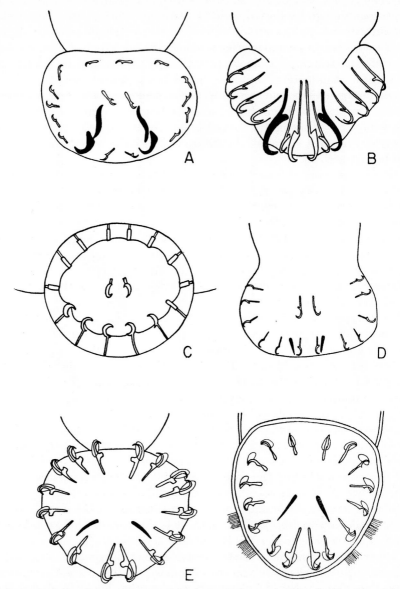

FIG. 5. Variations in the structure of the haptors of oncomiracidia. A. *Nitzschia sturionis*
(Adapted after Bychowsky, 1957); B. *Microcotyle labracis* (Original); C. *Acanthocotyle sp.*
(Original); D. *Dactylogyrus sp.* (Adapted after Malmberg, 1956); E. *Polystoma integerrimum*
(Original); F. *Diplorchis ranae* (Adapted after Ozaki, 1936).

1957, Figs. 175 and 176). In most monopisthocotylineans the posterior-most marginal hooks do not become modified in shape, and they retain the domus.

The number of marginal hooks present is an important taxonomic criterion, and in monogeneans varies between ten, e.g. in *Hexabothrium*

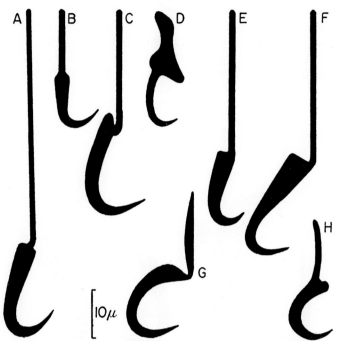

FIG. 6. The posteriormost marginal hooks (= hooks I) of representatives of eight of the nine families of diclidophorideans. (The oncomiracidium of a protomicrocotylid has not been described.) A. Discocotylidae: *Discocotyle sagittata:* B. Plectanocotylidae: *Plectanocotyle gurnardi:* C. Anthocotylidae: *Anthocotyle merluccii:* D. Gastrocotylidae: *Gastrocotyle trachuri:* E. Hexostomatidae: *Hexostoma thynnii:* F. Microcotylidae: *Microcotyle labracis:* G. Diclido-phoridae: *Diclidophora merlangi:* H. Mazocraeidae: *Kuhnia* (= *Octostoma*) *scombri*. (E. after Euzet, 1955; A. and H., original; others after Llewellyn, 1957a.) (All to same scale.)

appendiculatum, and sixteen, e.g. in *Polystoma integerrimum*. (In gyro-cotylideans and in amphilinideans there are ten hooks and in cestodes six.)

The marginal hooks may be arranged equidistantly around the haptor, e.g. in *Polystoma integerrimum* (see Fig. 5E), but more usually there is a relatively large interval between the two most anteriorly placed hooks so that the symmetry becomes bilateral, e.g. in *Microcotyle labracis* (Fig. 5B). It is convenient to be able to refer to particular marginal hooks, and for this purpose they may be numbered in anterior-posterior or posterior-anterior succession. Bychowsky has used the two systems, e.g. in *Dogielius forceps* (see Bychowsky, 1957, translated by Hargis and

P*

Oustinoff, 1961) he referred to the more posterior marginal hooks as the
sixth and seventh, but in a general discussion (Hargis and Oustinoff,
1961, p. 103) said that it was more precise to regard the posteriormost
marginal hooks as the first pair. In preparing the present review the
numbering of the marginal hooks in posterior-anterior succession has
been found to be preferable, and so the hooks of the posteriormost pair
will be called hooks I and the others consecutively anteriorly on each
side as hooks II to VIII respectively. Thus, in Frankland's (1955) scheme
for referring to the larval hooks of *Diclidophora denticulata*, since followed
by Llewellyn (1957a, 1959) and Euzet and Raibaut (1960) for other

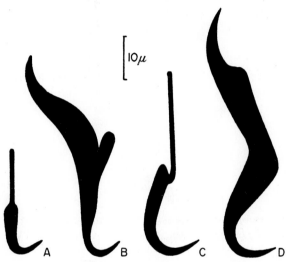

FIG. 7. Post-oncomiracidial growth of the posteriormost marginal hooks (hooks I) of some
monogeneans. A, B. *Plectanocotyle gurnardi*. A. oncomiracidium; B. adult. C, D. *Anthocotyle
merluccii*. C. oncomiracidium: D. adult. (All to same scale.) (Original.)

diclidophorideans, the "posterior" hooks become I, the "postero-
laterals" II, and the "laterals" III, IV, V and VI respectively in posterior-
anterior succession.

The basic complement of sixteen hooks is present in gyrodactylids,
polystomatids, sphyranurids, chimaericolids, tetraonchids, entobdellids
and acanthocotylids, but whereas in the first four of these groups all the
hooks remain marginal, in the last three groups two hooks resembling
exactly the marginal hooks are situated in the middle of the haptor (Figs.
5A, C). It is very probable that these centrally situated hooks are in fact
marginal hooks which have migrated to a superficial position, but the
reason for the migration is not obvious. Since the bilateral symmetry
about an anterior-posterior axis is preserved, it may be assumed that the
hooks which have migrated are those of either the anteriormost pair

(VIII) or the posteriormost pair (I). In the absence of direct embryological evidence concerning the identity of these medianly-placed marginal hooks, another factor may be considered, namely, the relationship of these hooks to the median hooks proper (see p. 300) that constitute an important part of the adhesive apparatus of either the post-oncomiracidium or the adult. In polyopisthocotylineans, e.g. the polystomatids, and in monocotylids, loimoids, and dionchids, these median hooks of the adult develop in the intervals between hooks II and III on each side of the haptor (e.g. in *Polystoma integerrimum* and *Calicotyle kroyeri*), so that there are *two* pairs of marginal hooks (I and II) on the posterior border of the haptor between the median hooks (Fig. 5E). On the other hand in the capsalids and dactylogyrids there is only *one* pair of hooks on the posterior border of the haptor of the adult between the radii in which the median hooks lie (Fig. 5A). However, one of the pairs of marginal hooks in a representative of the capsalids, *Entobdella soleae*, has been shown by Kearn (1963 a, c) to become centrally placed and to undergo modification during embryonic development so as to become accessory structures ("the third, anteriormost, pair of median hooks" of Bychowsky) in the adhesive apparatus of the adult. A similar process takes place in *Nitzschia sturionis* where in the oncomiracidium, according to Bychowsky (1957, Figs. 193, 4 and 5), the (median) hooks of "the third pair, located almost in the centre of the disc . . . resemble closely the marginal hooks in structure", but they too grow and change their shape during post-oncomiracidial development. Thus if the migratory marginal hooks of the capsalids are regarded as hooks I, the median hooks of the adult lie in the intervals between hooks II and III, just as they do in monocotylids and polystomatids. Conversely, if the centrally-placed marginal hooks of capsalids are regarded as hooks VIII, then the median hooks of the adult would lie in the intervals between hooks I and II, i.e. they would differ in their site of origin from those of monocotylids and polystomatids. However, there seems to be no reason at all for regarding the median hooks in the different groups as other than homologous structures, and so the migratory centrally-placed marginal hooks will be regarded as hooks I.

The complete set of marginal hooks present in the larva at the time of hatching may persist throughout adult life, e.g. *Entobdella soleae* and *Amphibdelloides maccallumi*, or the complete set may disappear, e.g. *Calicotyle kroyeri* and *Diclidophora merlangi*, or again only some of the oncomiracidial marginal hooks may persist, the others being replaced each by a specialized adhesive organ peculiar to the adult, e.g. *Gastrocotyle trachuri* and *Polystoma integerrimum*. In *Entobdella soleae* and *E. diadema* the oncomiracidial marginal hooks do not merely survive in the adult, but they almost certainly remain functional, each hook in the adult retaining a nervous supply (Llewellyn and Euzet, unpublished). In some diclidophorideans the (modified) hooks I survive in the adult, and when they do so they are usually accompanied by hooks II and a pair of median post-oncomiracidial hooks (see p. 315), e.g. in *Gastrocotyle trachuri* and *Plectanocotyle gurnardi*.

As well as the ontogenetic losses of hooks referred to above, there has been a tendency throughout monogeneans for some groups to have lost, during phylogenetic development, some of the anteriorly-placed marginal hooks. Thus in dactylogyrids (see Fig. 5D) and monocotylids hooks VIII have been lost, leaving only fourteen marginal hooks in the oncomiracidium. In diclidophorideans (see Fig. 5B) and diclybothriids hooks VIII and VII have disappeared, leaving only twelve marginal hooks. In the hexabothriids, in addition to the loss of anterior hooks VIII and VII, the posterior hooks I are also missing.

2. *Median Hooks* (*Hamuli*)

In some oncomiracidia there are present the primordia of medianly-situated hooks; their occurrence is widespread through the various groups of monogeneans, and occasionally they may have reached a relatively advanced stage of development. The site taken up by these hooks on the haptor, between marginal hooks II and III, has been discussed above (p. 299). Corresponding hooks are present also in the oncomiracidia of some polyopisthocotylineans, e.g. *Microcotyle labracis* (see Fig. 5B). Because such hooks are present in only some oncomiracidia at the time of hatching but in some others make their appearance and also reach their definitive size very early in post-oncomiracidial development, e.g. in *Gastrocotyle trachuri*, these hooks have been referred to previously as "post-oncomiracidial hooks" (Llewellyn, 1959). Euzet and Raibaut (1960), however, have used the term *hamulus* for such a hook in *Squalonchocotyle torpedinis* in recognition of Dollfus' earlier reference by this name to these hooks in adult hexabothriids. It is proposed here that "hamulus" now be generally adopted for the median hooks which either undergo embryonic development between marginal hooks II and III (e.g. *Polystoma integerrimum*, see Fig. 5E and the "tigelle" of *Microcotyle sargi*, see Euzet, 1957b), or develop there in the post-oncomiracidium (e.g. *Gastrocotyle trachuri*, see Llewellyn, 1959). The variety of hamuli in monogeneans is illustrated in Fig. 8. Their shape and size may be of taxonomic importance, e.g. in amphibdellids—see Llewellyn (1960).

In most monogeneans apart from polyopisthocotylineans and monocotylids the hamuli constitute the principal part of the adhesive apparatus of the adult parasite, but in the two exceptional groups cited, the hamuli play their most important role after the oncomiracidial marginal hooks have completed theirs, and before the acquisition of the definitive

Fig. 8. Various forms of hamuli (= post-oncomiracidial median hooks) in monogeneans. A, B. *Entobdella soleae:* C, D. *Amphibdella flavolineata:* E. *Gyrodactylus longiradix:* F. *Dactylogyrus peltatus:* G. *Dactylogyrus robustus:* H. *Rajonohocotyle emarginata:* I. *Kuhnia scombri:* J. *Hexostoma thynnii:* K. *Anthocotyle merluccii:* L. *Gastrocotyle trachuri:* M. *Plectanocotyle gurnardi:* N. *Axine belones:* O. *Diclybothrium armatum.* (C, D, after Llewellyn, (1957a; E, after Malmberg, 1956; F, G, after Gussev, 1955; O, after Bychowsky and Gussev, 1950; others, original. All to the same scale).

adhesive organs of the adult. Exceptionally, as in the polyopisthocotylinean mazocraeids (e.g. *Kuhnia scombri*), the hamuli continue to grow after the formation of the adult adhesive organs or clamps (see Llewellyn, 1957c). Hamuli are present in most polyopisthocotylineans but they are absent, probably having been secondarily lost, in the discocotylids and the diclidophorids. In discocotylids the absence of hamuli may be correlated with the precocious embryonic appearance of some of the adult clamps (see Bovet, 1959), and in diclidophorids the absence of hamuli is probably associated with the special adhesive attitude adopted by the adults (see Llewellyn, 1956).

Commonly the number of hamuli may be increased from one pair to two pairs, the members of the second pair developing close to the members of the first pair; they thus bear the same kind of spatial relationship to marginal hooks II and III as do the first pair of hamuli, e.g. *Amphibdella flavolineata* (see Llewellyn, 1960).

3. *Accessory Sclerites*

In some monogeneans the hamuli are accompanied by accessory sclerites in the form of transverse bars or plates (Fig. 9). Their function has not been investigated in many monogeneans, but in *Amphibdelloides maccallumi* they serve for the attachment of some of the muscles and

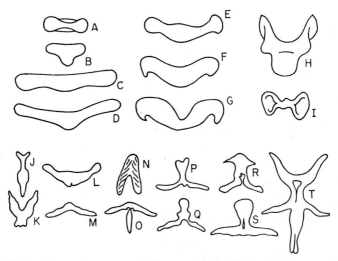

FIG. 9. Various forms of accessory sclerites associated with the hamuli of monogeneans. A. *Dactylogyrus anchoratus:* B. *simplicimalleata:* C. *D. drjagni:* D. *D. longicopula:* E. *D. cryptomeres:* F. *D. wunderi:* G. *D. kulwieci:* H. *Gyrodactylus arcuatus:* I. *Tetraonchus monenteron:* J. *Dactylogyrus simplicimalleata:* K. *D. bicornis:* L. *D. cryptomeres:* M. *D. alatus:* N. *D. facetus:* O. *D. parabramis:* P. *D. zandti:* Q. *D. difformis:* R. *D. minor:* S. *D. linstowi:* T. *D. affinis.* (All after Bychowski (1957). Both B and J are apparently of *D. simplicimalleata,* and E and L are of *D. cryptomeras.*) The figures are not all drawn to the same scale.

fibres which are involved in the operation of the hamuli (Llewellyn, 1960). Sometimes primordia of these accessory pieces are present on the oncomiracidium, e.g. in *Ancyrocephalus cruciatus* (see Bychowsky, 1957, Fig. 153), but usually they appear during post-oncomiracidial development. Bychowsky and his associates have found that there is a certain degree of variation in the times of appearance of the hamuli and the accessory pieces with respect to each other, and that this variation may have taxonomic significance.

As stated earlier (p. 299) accessory pieces become incorporated into the adhesive apparatus of entobdellids, where they form the anteriormost of the three pairs of median hooks (see Kearn, 1963 a,c), but here the accessory structures are derived from modified oncomiracidial marginal hooks, and are not *de novo* structures as are the bars in *Amphibdelloides maccallumi* and *Diplectanum aequans*.

D. THE ALIMENTARY CANAL

A gut is present in all of the oncomiracidia that have been described so far, and in this character then the larvae of monogeneans resemble those of aspidobothreans and differ from those of digeneans, gyrocotylideans, amphilinideans, and cestodes.

The form of the alimentary canal in the newly-hatched oncomiracidium already foreshadows the particular form of that of the group to which the corresponding adult belongs. Thus in monopisthocotylineans, e.g. *Entobdella soleae*, the mouth opens ventrally at some distance from the anterior end of the body and leads almost directly into a pharynx (Fig. 10A) whereas in polyopisthocotylineans, e.g. *Plectanocotyle gurnardi*, the mouth opens sub-terminally at the anterior end of the body and a

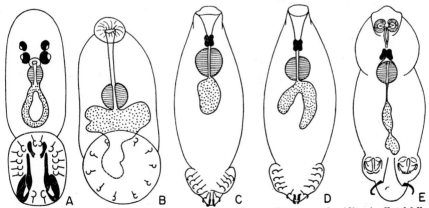

FIG. 10. Variations in the form of the alimentary canal in oncomiracidia. A. *Entobdella soleae* (Original); B. *Squalonchocotyle torpedinis* (Adapted after Euzet & Raibaut, 1960); C. *Plectanocotyle gurnardi* (Original); D. *Gastrocotyle trachuri* (Original); E. *Diplozoon paradoxum* (After Bovet, 1959.)

long prepharynx communicates with the pharynx (Fig. 10C). Within the polyopisthocotylineans, an oral sucker corresponding to that of adult hexabothriids, e.g. *Squalonchocotyle torpedinis* and polystomatids is present in the respective oncomiracidia (Fig. 10B), but the paired buccal suckers of adult diclidophorideans are only rarely represented in the oncomiracidium, e.g. in *Diplozoon paradoxum* (Fig. 10E).

There is considerable variation in the state of development of the intestine at the time of hatching of the oncomiracidium. In *Plectanocotyle gurnardi* the intestine is a simple sac (Fig. 10C) but in *Gastrocotyle trachuri* often the sac has already begun to give rise to the two main intestinal limbs characteristic of the adult (Fig. 10D). In the oncomiracidium of *Entobdella soleae* the two intestinal limbs have already become confluent posteriorly to form the ring-shaped gut typical of the adult (Fig. 10A).

With regard to the histology of the intestine Bovet (1959) has stated that in the oncomiracidium of *Diplozoon paradoxum*, as in other diclidophorideans, the intestine appears to be lined by a syncytial epithelium. However, I have been able to trace only one other reference to the structure of the larval gut, namely that by Halkin (1901) to *Polystoma integerrimum*, and this author illustrated the gut as being bounded by discrete spherical cells, not all of which were contiguous with each other. I have not seen sections of newly-hatched oncomiracidia of *P. integerrimum*, but in sections of larvae attached to the gills of tadpoles that had been exposed to infection only a few days previously, the intestine was seen to be bounded by a limiting membrane devoid of cells or of nuclei (Fig. 11A). The structure of the intestinal lining of the oncomiracidium of *Diclidophora luscae*, as seen in sections (Fig. 11B), resembles that of *Polystoma integerrimum*, and Bovet's reference to diclidophorideans having a syncytial intestinal lining appears to be without foundation.

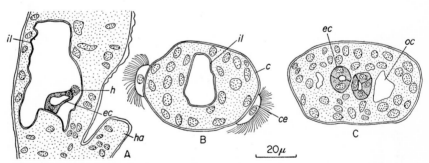

Fig. 11. The structure of the intestine of oncomiracidia. A. *Polystoma integerrimum* (Longitudinal section of post-oncomiracidium two or three days after invasion of tadpole gills); B. *Diclidophora luscae* (Transverse section); C. *Entobdella soleae* (Transverse section); (All figures original. All to same scale).

c, cuticle; *ce*, ciliated epidermal cell; *ec*, epithelial cell of intestine; *h*, haematin granules; *ha*, haptor; *il*, intestinal lining; *oc*, osmo-regulatory canal.

In sections of the newly-hatched oncomiracidium of *Entobdella soleae* prepared by Mr. G. C. Kearn I have seen the intestinal lining to consist of a continuous layer of epithelial cells (Fig. 11C). Thus, while the extent of this evidence is recognized to be limited, nevertheless the inference is that the gut wall of larval monopisthocotylineans already resembles that of adults in consisting of a continuous cellular epithelium, and similarly the limiting gut membrane in larval polyopisthocotylineans foreshadows that of the adult in being non-cellular, though it has not yet acquired the discontinuous lining of phagocytic cells typical of the adult (see Llewellyn, 1954).

In the newly-hatched oncomiracidia of most monogeneans the gut may be seen, especially when using phase-contrast microscopy, to contain highly refractive droplets that become blackened with osmium tetroxide, and the inference is that they are lipoid food reserves brought over from the parent.

E. THE OSMO-REGULATORY SYSTEM

In common with other platyhelminths, larval monogeneans have a system of flame cells and efferent ducts. Usually the collecting ducts are lined with cilia which promote currents in the direction of the paired excretory pores that open dorso-laterally at about the level of the pharynx. A terminal excretory bladder may sometimes be seen, e.g. in *Entobdella soleae*, but its size varies, presumably with the volume of its contents. Occasionally no bladder is evident in specimens belonging to species known to have a bladder.

The complete osmo-regulatory system has been described in only very few oncomiracidia, and these are illustrated in Fig. 12.

In addition to these osmo-regulatory systems illustrated, something is known of some others. Bovet (1959) and Halkin (1901) have illustrated the collecting ducts of *Diplozoon paradoxum* and *Polystoma integerrimum* respectively, and I have observed five pairs of flame cells in *Microcotyle labracis*, but was unable to trace the course of the collecting ducts. The osmo-regulatory system of a very early post-oncomiracidium of a species of *Dactylogyrus* has been illustrated by Malmberg (1956), and is reproduced here as Fig. 12C.

While recognizing the scant nature of the information available, nevertheless some observations may be pertinent. The monopisthocotylineans *Bendenia melleni* with ten pairs of flame cells (Fig. 12A), and *Entobdella soleae* and *E. diadema* with nine pairs of flame cells (Fig. 12B), each has more flame cells than any of the four polyopisthocotylineans *Diclidophora denticulata* (4×2) (Fig. 12D), *Gastrocotyle trachuri* (4×2), *Pseudaxine trachuri* (4×2) (Fig. 12E) and *Vallisia striata* (3×2) (Fig. 12F). This might represent a basic phylogenetic difference, or might be indicative merely of a relatively earlier hatching in the polyopisthocotylineans. Some evidence in support of the latter view is forthcoming if the increased number of flame cells in the polyopisthocotylineans *Microcotyle labracis* (5 × 2) and *Diplozoon paradoxum* (7? × 2) is considered alongside the precocious appearance during embryonic development of the hamuli

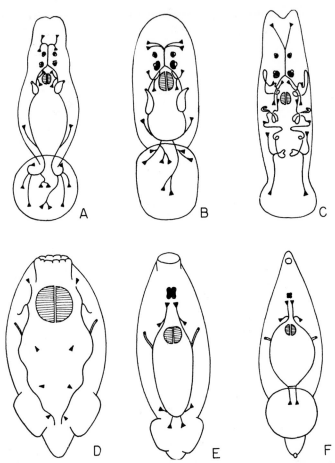

Fig. 12. The osmo-regulatory system of oncomiracidia. A. *Benedenia melleni* (After Jahn and Kuhn, 1932); B. *Entobdella diadema* (Drawn by Llewellyn and Euzet, previously unpublished); C. *Dactylogyrus* sp., early post-oncomiracidium (Adapted after Malmberg, 1956); D. *Diclidophora denticulata* (Adapted after Frankland, 1955); E. *Gastrocotyle trachuri* (Original); F. *Vallisia striata* (Adapted after Euzet and Raibaut, 1960).

in *M. labracis* and of the first pair of adult clamps in *Diplozoon paradoxum*. With regard to the arrangement of the collecting ducts, it is perhaps significant that in the three monopisthocotylineans illustrated (Figs. 12A, B, C) there is a common median longitudinal duct anterior to the pharynx, but that in the three polyopisthocotylineans (Figs. 12D, E, F) there is no corresponding duct.

The osmo-regulatory system may be of more use for the identification of species than as a guide to phylogenetic descent. The oncomiracidium of *Bendenia melleni* may be distinguished from those of *Entobdella soleae* and *E. diadema* by the presence in *B. melleni* of an extra pair of flame cells in the haptor. However, within the family Gastrocotylidae the distribution of the flame cells in *Gastrocotyle trachuri* (4 × 2) is indistinguishable from that in *Pseudaxine trachuri* (4 × 2) even though both are distinguishable from *Vallisia striata* (3 × 2) by the presence in each of them of an extra pair of flame cells in the posterior end of the body, anterior to the haptor. In these three larval gastrocotylids the similarity in shape of the posterior marginal hooks (Hook I) of the haptor (see Fig. 6D) is a better guide to the affinities of these monogeneans than the pattern of the osmo-regulatory system.

During post-oncomiracidial development the number of flame cells increases, but details of the elaboration of the system do not appear to have been worked out in any monogenean. One constant feature is known however. The excretory pores, which were situated at about the level of the pharynx in the oncomiracidium–i.e. they were placed approximately midway along the length of the body proper–retain their position relative to the pharynx, but, together with this organ, become relatively more anteriorly placed in the body of the adult because of differing growth rates along the length of the body, possibly to accommodate the developing genitalia. Accompanying the relative forward shift of the excretory pores, the main longitudinal duct on each side acquires a very long posterior loop and thus appears double. The whole process appears to be somewhat reminiscent of the development of the recurrent laryngeal nerve in mammals. But whatever the developmental details may be, the definitive site of the excretory pores appears to be a significant indicator of ancestry. In adult monogeneans the excretory pores become disposed as they are in *Gyrocotyle*, i.e. anteriorly placed, but in digeneans the excretory pores become successively more posteriorly placed in the various polyembryonically developing redia and cercaria larvae (see Baer and Joyeux, 1961, Fig. 497).

F. GLANDS

Little work has been done yet on the glands present in oncomiracidia, and probably the most detailed accounts are those of *Entobdella soleae* and *Capsala martinieri* given by Kearn (1963a and 1963b respectively). In *Entobdella soleae* there is on each side of the body a prominent group of five cells lying at the level of the pharynx, with long ducts opening on to the antero-lateral borders of the body. Similar gland cells have been illustrated for *Tristoma integrum* by Euzet and Quignard (1961, Fig. 2), the ducts of such glands have been illustrated for *Capsala martinieri* by Kearn, and similar glands and ducts have been seen in *Entobdella diadema* by Euzet and Llewellyn (unpublished). In *Entobdella soleae*, *E. diadema*, and *Tristoma integrum*, the ducts of these glands are joined near their openings by ducts from an anteriorly placed median gland, and in *E. soleae* there is present a second median gland, anterior to the median gland already referred to, and whose ducts take a distinctly different course from those of the more posterior median gland (see Kearn, 1963a).

In most of the diagrams of oncomiracidia that have been published, the cell bodies of "anterior glands" or of glands near to the mouth have been included, but often the course of the ducts has been omitted.

At the posterior end of diclidophorideans there is frequently to be seen a drop of glandular secretion at the apex of the ciliated cone (see pp. 290) but the gland itself has not yet been located.

Halkin (1901, Fig. 63) has illustrated in the larva of *Polystoma integerrimum* gland cells that open into the alimentary canal at the junction between the pharynx and the intestine; these glands are similarly placed and very similar in appearance to those shown in adult amphibdellids by Llewellyn (1960, Figs. 14, 15).

G. NERVOUS SYSTEM AND SENSE ORGANS

Only rarely has a brain been referred to in the larvae of monogeneans, but this organ has been reported in *Polystoma integerrimum* by Halkin (1901) and in *Diplozoon paradoxum* by Bovet (1959); I have seen the brain in sections of *Diclidophora luscae* and *Entobdella soleae* at about the level of the pharynx.

Two kinds of eyes occur in larval monogeneans: first, pigment cups with permanent crystalline lenses, the whole structure probably resembling that in juvenile specimens of *Polystoma integerrimum* described in detail by André (1910), and secondly pigment cups without permanent crystalline lenses but sometimes with prominent oil drops that probably function temporarily as lenses. The first type occurs in monopisthocotylineans and in some polyopisthocotylineans, but the second type is restricted to diclidophoridean polyopisthocotylineans. Eyes of the first kind always occur as two pairs, usually a larger more posterior pair directed antero-laterally, and a smaller more anterior pair directed postero-laterally. Eyes of the second kind occur most commonly in the form of a single pair of pigment cups with the concavities directed laterally, e.g. in *Plectanocotyle gurnardi*, but two pairs occur in *Hexostoma thynni* (see Euzet, 1955, Fig. 3) and in some microcotylids, e.g. *Axine belones* (see Euzet, 1955, Fig. 9 and Bychowsky, 1957, Fig. 257). Eyes are absent in *Grubea cochlear* of the family Mazocraeidae, though they are present in *Kuhnia* (=*Octostoma*) *scombri* of the same family (see Euzet, 1957a). Eyes are absent from all of the oncomiracidia described so far from the Diclidophoridae: *Diclidophora denticulata* (see Frankland, 1955); *D. merlangi* (see Llewellyn, 1957a); *D. luscae* (see Gallien, 1934); and *Cyclocotyla belones* (see Euzet and Trilles, 1961).

Oncomiracidial eyes of the first type (i.e. with permanent lenses) frequently persist in the adult in both monopisthocotylineans, e.g. *Entobdella soleae* (see Kearn, 1963a) and in polyopisthocotylineans e.g. *Diclybothrium armatum* (see Bychowsky, 1957), but eyes of the second type (i.e. without permanent lenses) have not been recorded as persisting in adult diclidophorideans.

In some oncomiracidia the eye pigment is somewhat diffuse, e.g. in *Axine belones* (see Euzet, 1955), and in *Capsala martinieri* there are very extensive areas of a pigment resembling that of the eye cups and arranged in a distinctive bilaterally symmetrical pattern (see Kearn, 1963b).

Nothing appears to be known of sense organs other than eyes in oncomiracidia, but it is possible that the three "ciliated tufts" present on the anterior borders of *Diplozoon paradoxum* described by Bovet (1959) and *Cyclocotyla belones* described by Euzet and Trilles (1961) may be sense organs. The cilia of these tufts are said to remain attached to the cells which bear them, and the cilia-bearing cells themselves remain attached to the larva, i.e. they are not deciduous as are the locomotory ciliated cells.

III. Post-Oncomiracidial Development

As with the study of oncomiracidia themselves, our knowledge of the post-oncomiracidial development of monogeneans has been increased considerably in the last 5 or 6 years. Until 1957 the post-oncomiracidial development of only about half-a-dozen monogeneans had been studied; these included *Polystoma integerrimum* by Zeller (1872b) and Gallien (1935), *Diplozoon paradoxum* by Zeller (1872a), *Benedenia melleni* by Jahn and Kuhn (1932), *Sphyranura oligorchis* by Alvey (1936), *Microcotyle spinicirrus* by Remley (1942), and *Diclidophora denticulata* by Frankland (1955). Since then Bychowsky (1957) has described the post-larval development of many monogeneans and especially that of dactylogyrideans, and the development of the following has also been studied: *Microcotyle chrysophryii* by Euzet (1958), *Gastrocotyle trachuri* and *Pseudaxine trachuri* by Llewellyn (1959), *Squalonchocotyle torpedinis* by Euzet and Raibaut (1960), and *Lithidiocotyle secunda* and *L. bivaginalis* by Ramalingam (1961a and b respectively). Thus a fairly representative spectrum of taxonomic examples has been studied, but there is one outstanding gap in our knowledge, namely, a study of the post-oncomiracidial development in a monocotylid, e.g. *Calicotyle kroyeri*. Bychowsky

(1957) has made important inferences concerning the larval development of members of this group, but they were based upon comparative studies of adults and not upon direct observations of their development.

The post-oncomiracidial development of monogeneans includes three main facets: growth, the development of the genitalia, and the development of the definitive adhesive apparatus; (some other features of post-oncomiracidial development have already been referred to, namely the development of the alimentary canal, p. 303 and the osmo-regulatory system, p. 305).

Little is known about the rate of growth of monogeneans, but Gallien (1935) has shown experimentally that *Polystoma integerrimum* normally takes 3 years to achieve sexual maturity (rapidly-developing neotenics are also present in the life cycle), and Bychowsky (1957) has shown that in *Dactylogyrus vastator* the corresponding period is only 6 days. Llewellyn (1962a), from a study of the population dynamics of *Gastrocotyle trachuri* and *Pseudaxine trachuri* has estimated that these monogeneans may become fully grown in 3 or 4 months. There is some evidence that some monogeneans do not stop growing when they have become sexually mature. Sproston (1945) has shown that in *Kuhnia* (=*Octostoma*) *scombri* the testes and ovary have begun activity by the time the parasite has reached a length of 3.5 mm but that growth may continue to a length of over 6 mm. Similarly *Gastrocotyle trachuri* becomes sexually mature at a length of about 2.0 mm but continues growth to a length of about 3.0 mm (see Llewellyn, 1959), and *Entobdella soleae* matures at about 2.0 mm but continues to grow until it is about 5.0 mm long (see Kearn, 1963a).

In all monogeneans whose larval development has been studied protandry has been found to be the rule, e.g. in *Amphibdella flavolineata* (see Llewellyn, 1960), in *Entobdella soleae* (see Kearn, 1963a), in *Kuhnia* (=*Octostoma*) *scombri* (see Sproston, 1945), and in *Gastrocotyle trachuri* (see Llewellyn, 1959). A survey of the development of different kinds of genitalia in monogeneans would not be profitable at present since no proper comparative study has been made yet of the genitalia in adults.

While the fate of the oncomiracidial haptor and the development of the definitive haptor are of course important adaptive features in the life cycle of every individual monogenean, nervertheless it seems likely that a study of these features may yield the most important clues to the relationship of monogeneans with each other. The oncomiracidial haptor may suffer one of three kinds of fate.

1. It may not undergo any further development at all, and though it may persist, it does not grow and remains unaltered morphologically; it becomes replaced functionally by a completely new structure, the *pseudohaptor*, developed anterior to the larval haptor, e.g. in *Acantho-*

cotyle. (Somewhat similar pseudohaptors are also developed in diplecta-nids, see below.)

2. The larval haptor may grow and preserve its same general discoidal shape but acquire one or two pairs of hamuli, sometimes accompanied by accessory sclerites.

In the adults of dactylogyrids and gyrodactylids there is one pair of hamuli, nearly always accompanied by accessory plates of varying degrees of complexity; in diplectanids there are two pairs of hamuli, accompanied in *Diplectanum aequans* by three accessory bars and also by two squamodiscs (pseudohaptors) and a well developed gland (Paling, unpublished): in the tetraonchids and amphibdellids there are two pairs of hamuli and one accessory bar; in the entobdellids (not including capsalines) there are two pairs of hamuli and one pair of accessory sclerites which are not homologous with the accessory bars of dactylo-gyrids but which are derivatives of oncomiracidial marginal hooks; and in monocotylids there is only one pair of hamuli, unaccompanied by any accessory structures so that the haptor bears some resemblance to that of the polyopisthocotylineans to be described below.

Often the hamuli in the adult lie near the lateral margins of the haptor, and in acquiring this position they leave marginal hooks I and II relatively widely separated from each other in the median posterior region of the haptor, but marginal hooks III to VII inclusive form characteristically compact groups of five hooks, one group on each side of the haptor, e.g. in *Diplectanum similis* (see Bychowsky, 1957, Fig. 14) and many of the dactylogyrids illustrated by Gussev (1955). In amphib-dellids, where the oncomiracidium has sixteen hooks, there are groups not of five marginal hooks on each of the lateral borders of the haptor of the adult, but of six. However, one hook in each group of six does not form part of the otherwise linear series, but was described as a "submarginal" hook by Llewellyn (1960); it is likely that this hook is the persistent hook VIII. In *Amphibdella flavolineata* the papillae bearing the marginal hooks I and II grow enormously during post-oncomiracidial development and contribute very substantially to the specialized adhesive apparatus of the adult (Llewellyn, 1960).

3. The larval haptor may grow and acquire a number of adhesive organs of a completely new kind, e.g. unarmed suckers (*Calicotyle kroyeri*, *Polystoma integerrimum*), clamps (*Plectanocotyle gurnardi*, *Discocotyle sagittata*), clamp-suckers (*Diclidophora* spp.), or clamps which have reverted secondarily to being suckers (*Cyclocotyla belones*). The clamp-like structures may be supported by complex arrangements of sclerites, e.g. in diclidophorideans, or by a single hook, e.g. in hexabothriids.

In the polyopisthocotylineans there is abundant evidence that the adult adhesive organs replace oncomiracidial marginal hooks *in a definite pattern of correspondence* (see below), but information about the precise *developmental* relationship between the oncomiracidial marginal hooks and the adult suckers in monocotylids is lacking.

IV. The Development of the Haptor of the Adult in Polyopisthocotylineans

As stated above, in polyopisthocotylineans at least some of the on-comiracidial marginal hooks are replaced in the adult by a new kind of adhesive organ. The replacement may take place directly at the site of the corresponding oncomiracidial hooks, e.g. in *Polystoma integerrimum* (see Gallien, 1935), *Hexabothrium appendiculata* and *Rajonchocotyle emarginata* (both described by Coupland, 1960), or medially with respect to the corresponding marginal hooks, e.g. in *Gastrocotyle trachuri* and *Plectanocotyle gurnardi* (Llewellyn, unpublished) and in *Pricea* spp. and *Lithidiocotyle secunda* (see Ramalingam, 1960b). Bychowsky and Gussev (1950) and Bychowsky (1957) believe that the marginal hooks themselves metamorphose to form a sclerite of the adult adhesive organs, but offer no supporting evidence. In fact this is not so, at any rate in *Hexabothrium appendiculatum* and *Rajonchocotyle emarginata* where Miss Coupland (1960) has observed the oncomiracidial hooks and the primordia of the corresponding adult hooks to be co-existent and to be quite distinct from each other. Similarly, in *Gastrocotyle*, *Plectanocotyle*, *Pricea* and *Lithidiocotyle*, the developing adult clamp and its sclerites are quite removed from the corresponding oncomiracidial marginal hooks.

Hooks I and II are never replaced by new adhesive organs in the adult, and the replacement of hooks III to VI inclusive always takes place in posterior-anterior succession.

The relationship between the oncomiracidial hooks and the adhesive organs of the adult in the various groups of polyopisthocotylineans is outlined below, and is illustrated very diagrammatically in Fig. 15.

1. *Polystomatids*

The oncomiracidium has the full complement of sixteen marginal hooks together with the primordia of the hamuli. Hooks III, IV and V are replaced by unarmed suckers, and the other marginal hooks usually persist in the adult, together with the hamuli; e.g. *Polystoma integerri-mum* (see Gallien, 1935).

2. *Sphyranurids*

Here development proceeds as in the polystomatids excepting that it is only hooks III which are replaced by unarmed suckers, the other fourteen hooks persisting, e.g. *Sphyranura osleri* as described by Alvey (1936).

3. *Hexabothriids*

The oncomiracidium has only ten marginal hooks and no hamuli, hooks I, VII, and VIII being missing. A hamulus appears during post-oncomiracidial development, and hook III is replaced by the relatively small unarmed sucker which, together with the hamulus and the occasionally persistent hook II, is found at the distal (posterior) tip of the "caudal appendage" of the adult. Oncomiracidial hooks IV, V, and VI are replaced by relatively large suckers each armed with a single protrusible hook, e.g. *Squalonchocotyle torpedinis* described by Euzet and Raibaut (1960), and *Hexabothrium appendiculatum* described by Coupland (1960).

4. *Chimaericolids*

Our knowledge of the oncomiracidium is based solely on larvae observed in the uterus of the ovo-viviparous *Callorhynchicola multitesticulatus* by Manter (1955) and on observations on oncomiracidia which I have dissected from the uterus of a specimen of the same species mounted for several years in Canada Balsam and very kindly presented to me by Dr. Manter.

As much of the structure as could be determined from these fixed, stained preparations is indicated in Fig. 13. The body is narrower

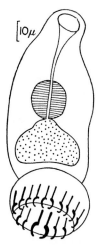

FIG. 13. Oncomiracidium of *Callorhynchicola multitesticulatus*. (Original.)

anteriorly so that "shoulders" are present, and locomotory cilia are absent. The mouth is sub-terminal, the pharynx is spherical and centrally placed in the body proper, and there is a simple sacciform or slightly bi-lobed gut. The haptor is somewhat bell-like, thus resembling that of *Hexabothrium appendiculatum*, and in its concavity there are sixteen inwardly-directed hooks. Of these fourteen are of the typical structure, and are provided each with a domus (see Fig. 4); they are about 16 μ long. The two remaining hooks are situated posteriorly (hooks I) and are of the same general shape but are somewhat stouter and measure about 22 μ long. The slender handles of the hooks make measuring rather difficult, and a more reliable indication of the difference in size is given by the relative lengths of the blade portion of the hook, which is about 6 μ in the smaller hooks and about 10 μ in the larger hooks. There are no hamuli.

In adult chimaericolids there are four pairs of sucker-clamps supported by sclerites, and they appear to correspond with the replacements of hooks III, IV, V and VI in diclidophorideans, but insufficient is known of any persistent oncomiracidial hooks. Brinkmann (1952a, p. 98) failed to find any hooks in *Chimaericola leptogaster* and I could find none in a sample of five specimens of the same species; but Ruszkowski is reported to have observed two pairs of dissimilar hooks in this parasite and Bychowsky (1957, Figs. 53 and 293) illustrates what appear to be one pair of hooks I and one pair of persistent marginals (hooks II?). Manter (1955) found one pair of hooks in *Callorhynchicola multitesticulatus*, but Brinkmann (1952b, p. 16) could find no hooks in *C. branchialis*.

5. *Diclidophorideans*

The oncomiracidium has twelve marginal hooks: hook I is always differentiated from the others to a greater (e.g. *Gastrocotyle trachuri*, Fig. 6D) or lesser (e.g. *Kuhnia scombri*, Fig. 6H) degree, and VII and VIII are missing. Hamuli are occasionally present at hatching (e.g. *Microcotyle labracis*, Fig. 5B), but in any case a pair of these hooks usually develops soon afterwards except in the Diclidophoridae. Hooks III, IV, V, and VI on each side are normally replaced by clamps or suckers provided with sclerites, but in some asymmetrical monogeneans, e.g. Gastrocotylidae the replacement takes place on one side only of the haptor, marginal hooks III to VI inclusive of the other side simply disappearing (see Llewellyn, 1959). That this kind of unilateral development is a secondary phenomenon has been demonstrated by Ramalingam (1961c) in *Monaxine bivaginalis*, where four clamps are formed on each side at first, but later all the clamps of one side are lost. The relationship between the asymmetrical development and the environment of the parasite has been explained by Llewellyn (1956, 1957b, and 1962b).

In some diclidophorideans (microcotylids, gastrocotylids, the discocotylid ("diplozooid") *Diplotrema barbi* Tripathi, 1957 and a new diclidophorid referred to by Bychowsky, 1957 p. 468), following the replacement of oncomiracidial marginal hooks III, IV, V and VI by clamps, further clamps are produced anteriorly in continued posterior-anterior succession, so that the total number of clamps may eventually amount to dozens, scores, or even hundreds. Much more rarely, e.g. in *Plectanocotyle gurnardi*, only hooks III, IV, and V are replaced by clamps; hook VI disappears without replacement (Llewellyn, unpublished) but in *Octolabea turchinii*, ascribed to the same family Plectanocotylidae by Euzet and Trilles (1960), the usual four pairs of clamps are present.

Oncomiracidial marginal hooks I and II often persist in the adult, (hook I sometimes being modified, see Fig. 7), and then, together with the hamuli, they are usually borne on a "terminal lappet", or "anchor-bearing lappet" or "languette", e.g. in *Plectanocotyle gurnardi*, *Gastrocotyle trachuri*, and *Anthocotyle merluccii*, but there are no persistent hooks or a terminal lappet in the Diclidophoridae, probably because in the adult this part of the body is applied to a different kind of host surface from that utilized by the oncomiracidium (see Llewellyn, 1956, p. 123).

6. *Diclybothriids*

There are twelve marginal hooks and a pair of hamuli present in the oncomiracidium. Hook I grows in length by a factor of about $10 \times$ during post-oncomiracidial development and persists in the adult as the "first pair of middle hooks" (Bychowsky, 1957, translated by Hargis and Oustinoff 1961, p. 211). Hook II may persist unaltered or be lost; hook III is replaced in the adult by a relatively small adhesive organ armed with a single hook which is one of members of the "third pair of hooks of the narrowed part of the disc". Hooks IV, V and VI are replaced by relatively large adult adhesive organs, all of the same pattern as those which replace hook III, but larger. The hamuli undergo very considerable post-oncomiracidial development (see Fig. 8) and eventually become very similar in size and appearance to the hooks of the adhesive organs which replace hooks IV, V and VI, but, at least functionally if not morphologically (see Bychowsky and Gussev, 1950, Fig. 2A) the orientation is reversed. The hamuli are the "second pair of middle hooks" of the oncomiracidium described by Bychowsky (1957, translated by Hargis and Oustinoff 1961, p. 211), i.e. the second pair of middle hooks of the narrow part of the disc of the adult.

V. Discussion

On the basis of the foregoing observations on the comparative morphology of the oncomiracidia and post-oncomiracidial developmental stages of monogeneans, an attempt will now be made to trace the possible lines of evolution within the group.

The ancestral monogenean, arising from a free-living, bottom-dwelling, ciliated platyhelminth, took to creeping over and feeding upon the skin of the ancestors of modern vertebrates when these animals came to rest on the bottom. Then, becoming increasingly dependent upon browsing upon host tissues, there was developed an attachment organ in the form of a muscular pad which permitted the parasite to maintain itself on the host when the latter swam away. This muscular pad was developed at the posterior end of the body, leaving the mouth region free for feeding. Eventually the attachment pad of this ancestral monogenean acquired hooks, and though our knowledge of the embryonic development of the hooks of modern monogeneans is practically nil, it seems possible that phylogenetically the hooks could have developed as sclerotizations of the distal regions of octo-diametrically disposed fibres of the muscular disc, thus giving rise to a monogenean with a sixteen-hooked radially symmetrical haptor at the posterior end of the body. The adoption of the habit of feeding on skin tissues meant that practically unlimited food supplies were available on a single host specimen, and the ciliary covering was retained only for the initial finding of a host.

Now committed to parasitism, the "protomonogeneans" became increasingly more specialized. Either because the hosts became faster swimmers, or because unlimited feeding contributed to bigger parasites, or both, the problem of attachment became more difficult. One way of meeting the situation was the adoption of a specialized attachment *attitude* in which the haptor was habitually disposed in an upstream position, leaving the anterior feeding end of the parasite to drift downstream. As the problem became more acute, the survivors were those parasites which developed further adhesive apparatus in the form of an extra pair of relatively large hooks, the hamuli, to act as anchors. Greater lateral stability resulted from the development of these large hooks, not at the posterior tip of the body, but nearer to the lateral margins of the haptor, between the second and third marginal hooks from the posterior end on each side. The localization of these supplementary hooks or hamuli at the posterior end of the haptor was accompanied in some monogeneans by the loss of some of the anteriorly-placed primary hooks, namely the eighth pair from the posterior end (as in modern monocotylids and dactylogyrids) and sometimes the seventh pair as well (as in present-day diclidophorideans, hexabothriids, and diclybothriids). At the same time the first (i.e. the posteriormost) pair of marginal hooks often became involved in changes. In some monogeneans these hooks became specialized as in the oncomiracidia of most present-day polyopisthocotylineans (excepting the hexabothriids where, and so far inexplicably, they have been lost altogether), and in others they migrated to a central position on the haptor as in modern amphibdellids, dactylogyrids, and entobdellids; lastly, in yet others such as modern monocotylids, they simply remained unaltered in shape or position.

Subsequently there followed experiments in improving the efficiency of the adult haptor. These sometimes took the form of increasing the size of the hamuli as in present-day dactylogyrids, or of doubling the hamuli as in modern amphibdellids and entobdellids. In both cases accessory skeletal bars were usually developed for the attachment of some of the muscles working the hamuli, these bars sometimes being completely new structures as in dactylogyrids and amphibdellids, or sometimes the centrally-placed first pair of marginal hooks was utilized, as in entobdellids. This elaboration of the hamulus apparatus was usually accompanied by the abandonment of the marginal hooks. An alternative to developing further the hamuli was to supplement the work of those marginal hooks lying anterior to the hamuli; this was done by ancestral monocotylids, capsalines, and polyopisthocotylineans, by the development near to or around these hooks, of muscular depressions that eventually became organized into suckers.

The above speculations about the lines of evolutionary development in monogeneans are consistent with the scheme illustrated in Fig. 14, but it is emphasized that this scheme is, by intent, based almost entirely upon the development of the haptor and does not include such adult features as the genitalia or any of the more general biological characters such as host specificity and micro-habitat. However, since Bychowsky's (1957) classification is also based upon mainly larval characters, the chief features of the two schemes will be compared.

1. Bychowsky suggests a primary division into the "Polyonchoinea" with twelve to sixteen marginal hooks and the "Oligonchoinea" with ten hooks. It is curious that such great importance should be attached to the number of hooks (the number is used as the basis for the names proposed for the groups) when Bychowsky did in fact realize that the "first pair of median hooks" in polyonchoineans were really marginal hooks, bringing the total number of marginal hooks in this group to twelve. The present review suggests that the variation in the actual number of larval hooks is not fundamentally important, there being a tendency in three of the seven major groups for the anteriormost marginal hooks to have been lost as the more posterior ("upstream") parts of the haptor became more specialized. Of more importance is whether the hooks are replaced by new, essentially adult adhesive organs, or whether, instead, the hamulus apparatus is elaborated.

2. The "Gyrodactylidea" in Bychowsky's classification appears to be a quite unnatural group, including as it does the gyrodactylids (which retain and utilize marginal hooks along with hamuli and accessory sclerites in the adult) and the polystomatids (which replace some of the marginal hooks with suckers, and use the hamuli mainly during a post-oncomiracidial and pre-adult phase). Moreover there is no justification for separating polystomatids from polyopisthocotylineans (i.e. those monogeneans recognized by Odhner, Fuhrmann etc. as such), either on

Q

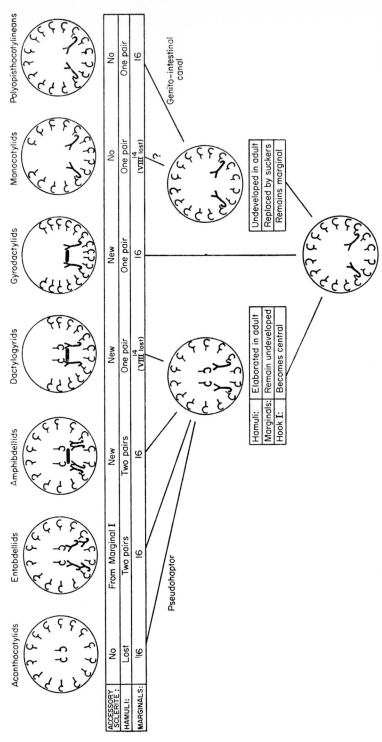

Fig. 14. Possible lines of development of the haptor in monogeneans. The further development of the haptor in polyopisthocotylineans is illustrated in Fig. 15.

developmental characters or on adult characters such as the genito-intestinal canal and the form of the gut epithelium.

3. Under the term "Dactylogyridea" Bychowsky includes what the present review shows to be a very heterogeneous assembly of mono-geneans, including such diverse types as dactylogyrids, acanthocotylids, monocotylids, and capsalids, the last of these groups itself including both capsalines and entobdellids. There does not appear to be here any one character, or even combination of characters, that could be called "dactylogyridean".

4. Of the seven major groups included in Fig. 14, most is probably known about the polyopisthocotylineans, and the possible evolution of the modern representatives of this group is discussed below.

The ancestral polyopisthocotylineans, equipped with suckers that at first were supplements to, and later replacements for, some of the marginal hooks lying immediately anterior to the hamuli, now invaded the gill chambers of their hosts and fed almost exclusively on blood. It has been suggested previously that this habit may have promoted a greater degree of host specificity and also made necessary a connection between the gut and the female genitalia to facilitate the passage of symbiotic bacteria (Llewellyn, 1957a). Be that as it may, present-day polyopisthocotylineans, all having a genito-intestinal canal and all feeding on blood, exhibit a very high degree of specificity towards certain host groups, the only exceptions being some very rare records of hexabothriids on holocephalans, the usual hosts being elasmobranchs. There is no reason for supposing other than that the polyopisthocotylineans have displayed this strict host specificity throughout their history, and so it may be assumed that the different parasite lines have been separated from each other as long as have those of the corresponding hosts, i.e. since Devonian times.

The segregation of polyopisthocotylineans on different host groups is matched by corresponding differences in the oncomiracidial haptor and its post-oncomiracidial development (Fig. 15). However, while the arrangement of polyopisthocotylineans into groups according to the morphology of the larval haptor and its subsequent development is relatively easy, the problem of assessing the phylogenetic relationships between these groups is as difficult to solve as vertebrate palaeontologists have found the corresponding task in the hosts.

The chimaericolids, hexabothriids, diclybothriids, and diclidophori-deans, i.e. all those polyopisthocotylineans on "fish-like" hosts, replace marginal hooks III to VI inclusive with adhesive organs that are probably primarily adapted to grasping the free borders of gill lamellae, though very little is known yet about the functional morphology of the adhesive organs of adults of the first three groups, and several families of

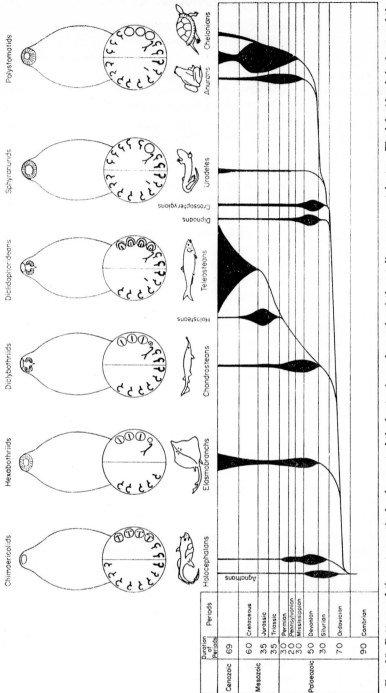

FIG. 15. Patterns of the ontogenetic development of the haptor in modern polyopisthocotylineans on vertebrates. The left side of the haptor of the parasites represents the oncomiracidial condition, the right side the adult. The representation of host ancestry is freely adapted after various diagrams by Colbert (1955), modified by a proposal by Westoll (1962) concerning Holocephalans.

diclidophorideans remain to be investigated. There is a particular need for a comparative study of the development of the sclerites in all of these groups.

The chimaericolids have retained all sixteen marginal hooks in the oncomiracidium, but the hexabothriids, diclybothriids, and diclidophorideans have lost the two anteriormost pairs (VIII and VII); in addition the hexabothriid oncomiracidium has lost hooks I, a condition which appears to be unique in monogeneans. While the chimaericolids and diclidophorideans nearly always develop equally all four pairs of adult adhesive organs at the sites of hooks III to VI (the diclidophoridean anthocotylids are an example of an exceptional group in the relatively enormous development of the clamps replacing hooks VI), in the hexabothriids and diclybothriids the adhesive organs replacing hooks III remain relatively small, and in the hexabothriids they have lost, or have never acquired, the supporting sclerite. A further peculiarity of hexabothriids is that during post-oncomiracidial development there is differential growth along the length of the haptor so that the unarmed suckers replacing hooks III become separated from the posteriormost pair of armed suckers (replacing hooks IV) by a long "caudal appendage" whose function is not known.

The chimaericolids appear not to develop a special feeding sucker, the hexabothriids develop a single oral sucker, and both the diclybothriids and the diclidophorideans develop a pair of buccal suckers.

The sphyranurids and polystomatids retain sixteen marginal hooks in the oncomiracidium and during post-oncomiracidial development replace some of them with unarmed suckers adapted for attachment to relatively flat surfaces. The sphyranurids develop suckers only at the sites of hooks III, but the polystomatids develop them also at the sites of hooks IV and V.

While there appear then to be no clearly distinguishable lines of evolution that can be easily recognized by studying the larvae and larval development of polyopisthocotylineans, when these features are considered along with host-specificity, some interesting inferences emerge. Thus, on the parasitological evidence, the hosts of polystomatids (with suckers developing at the sites of hooks III, IV, and V), namely anurans and chelonians, would be expected to have closer affinities with each other than either has with the hosts of sphyranurids (with suckers developing only at the sites of hooks III), namely, the urodeles. And indeed, during the past 30 years or so a substantial body of palaeontological evidence has been accumulated showing that this probably is so (Jarvik, 1960). Again the chimaericolids have sometimes been classified, on adult characters and on host specificity, as relatives of hexabothriids, the two respective host groups being considered to belong to the

Chondricthyes. However, in the present study it has been shown that the larva of the chimaericolid *Callorhynchicola multitesticulatus* retains the primitive character of being equipped with sixteen marginal hooks, and it is therefore especially interesting that Westoll (1962), having examined Orvig's material of *Ctenurella gladbachensis*, has stated that the study of this newly-found fossil adds very greatly to the probability that the Holocephali (the hosts of chimaericolids) are descended from the Ptychodontida, which are regarded as arthrodiran placoderms, a group generally accepted as being the earliest jawed vertebrates. If the chimaericolid-hexabothriid-diclybothriid-diclidophoridean association and the sphyranurid-polystomatid association are true phylogenetic groupings, and if these groupings accurately reflect host ancestry, it would suggest a more fundamental divergence between actinopterygians and crossopterygians than hitherto suspected by vertebrate palaeontologists.

From the helminthological point of view, the most interesting feature emerging from a comparison of the larval development of polyopisthocotylineans and host specificity (see Fig. 15) is the suggested transfer of the diclybothriids (parasitic on chondrostean actinopterygians) from their association with hexabothriids (parasitizing elasmobranchs) to a close relationship with diclidophorideans (parasitizing teleostean actinopterygians).

Finally, the contribution made by studying larval monogeneans to an assessment of the position of monogeneans themselves may be considered. Among the larvae of parasitic platyhelminths, the oncomiracidium clearly resembles more the decacanth (lycophore) larva of gyrocotylideans and amphilinideans and the coracidium or hexacanth larva of cestodes than it does the hookless larva of aspidogastreans and the hookless and haptorless miracidium of digeneans. On the evidence of larval characters then, Bychowsky's (1957) proposal, first published in 1937, to divorce monogeneans from digeneans and associate them with gyrocotylideans was well-founded.

VI. Summary

The past five years or so have seen a great increase in the number of monogeneans whose oncomiracidia and larval development are known, and a comparative study of these phases in the life histories has been made. The larval alimentary canal and nervous system merely foreshadow the adult condition, but the patterns of external ciliation and of the osmo-regulatory system may reflect phylogenetic development. However, it is a study of the development of the haptor which has yielded the most useful clues to the probable evolutionary trends in monogeneans.

An ancestral monogenean with a posterior haptor bearing sixteen equidistantly-spaced marginal hooks developed a supplementary adhesive apparatus consisting of a pair of median hooks or hamuli situated between the second and third marginal hooks from the posterior end on each side of the haptor. As these posteriorly-placed hamuli became established, some of the anteriorly-placed marginal hooks were lost.

Further development now took one of two main directions. The first was to elaborate the hamuli and abandon the marginal hooks, and the second was to replace some of the marginal hooks with new muscular adhesive organs that are essentially adult features, leaving the hamuli as largely post-oncomiracidial, pre-adult organs.

The elaboration of the hamulus apparatus took place either by doubling the number of hooks, or by incorporating accessory sclerites, or both. The accessory sclerites were sometimes new structures, or sometimes they were modified centrally-placed marginal hooks.

The replacement of marginal hooks by adult muscular organs took place in a variety of definite patterns, and if the parasites are arranged according to these patterns, there is a conspicuous correlation between these groupings and groups arranged according to hosts.

The monogenean oncomiracidium resembles more the decacanth lycophore of gyrocotylideans and amphilinideans and the coracidium or hexacanth of cestodes than it does the miracidia of digeneans or the larva of aspidobothrideans, and Bychowsky's removal of monogeneans from trematodes and their placing alongside gyrocotylideans is justified.

REFERENCES

Alvey, C. H. (1936). *Parasitology* **28**, 229–53. The morphology and development of the monogenetic trematode *Sphyranura oligorchis* (Alvey, 1933) and the description of *Sphyranura polyorchis* n.sp.

André, I. (1910). *Z. wiss. Zool.* **95**, 203–20. Die Augen von *Polystoma integerrimum* Froel.

Baer, J. G. and Euzet, L. (1961). *In* Grassé, P.-P.: *Traité de Zoologie*, **4**, Fasc. 1, 243–325. Paris: Masson. Classe des Monogènes.

Baer, J. G. and Joyeux, C. (1961). *In* Grassé, P.-P.: *Traité de Zoologie*, **4**, Fasc. 1, 561–692. Paris: Masson. Classe des Trématodes.

Bovet, J. (1959). *Bull. Soc. neuchâtel. Sci. nat.* **82**, 231–45. Observations sur l'oeuf et l'oncomiracidium de *Diplozoon paradoxum* von Nordmann, 1832.

Brinkmann, A. (1952a). *Univ. Bergen Arb. naturv. R.* **1**, 1–134. Fish trematodes from Norwegian Waters.

Brinkmann, A. (1952b). *Lunds Universitets Arsskrift*, N.F. Avd. 2, **47**, No. 11, 1–26. Some Chilean Monogenetic Trematodes.

Bychowsky, B. E. (1957). "Monogenetic Trematodes, their Classification and Phylogeny", 509 pp. Moscow: Leningrad, Academy of Sciences, U.S.S.R.

Bychowsky, B. E. and Gussev, A. V. (1950). *Parazitolog. sb. Zoolog. inst. AN SSSR* **12**, 275–98. Sem. Diclybothriidae (Monogenoidea) i ego polozhenie v sisteme.

Bychowsky, B. E. and Nagibina, L. F. (1958). *Acta Zoologica Sinica* **10**, 1–18. *Anchorophorus sinensis* Bychowsky et Nagibina gen. et sp. nov.

Coupland, A. C. (1960). "Studies on the monogenean gill parasites of elasmobranchs." Unpublished thesis in the Library of the University of Birmingham. 72 pp.

Colbert, E. H. (1955). "Evolution of the Vertebrates", 479 pp. New York: John Wiley.

Dawes, B. (1946). "The Trematoda." Cambridge University Press.

Euzet, L. (1955). *Bull. Soc. neuchâtel Sci. nat.* **78**, 71–9. Larves gyrodactyloides nageantes de quelques trématodes monogénétiques de poissons marins.

Euzet, L. (1957a). *Ann. Parasit. hum. comp.* **32**, 469–81. Recherches sur les Monogenoidea parasites de poissons marins.

Euzet, L. (1957b). *Bull. Soc. neuchâtel Sci. nat.* **80**, 187–94. Larves gyrodactyloides nageantes de quelques Microcotylidae (Trematoda-Monogenea).

Euzet, L. (1958). *Bull. Soc. neuchâtel Sci. nat.* **81**, 79–84. Sur le développement post-larvaire des Microcotylidae (Monogenoidea, Polyopisthocotylea).

Euzet, L. and Quignard, J. (1961). *Rapp. Comm. int. Mer Medit.* **16**, 321–3. Sur deux parasites de *Xiphias gladius* L.

Euzet, L. and Raibaut, A. (1960). *Bull. Soc. neuchâtel Sci. nat.* **83**, 101–8. Le développement postlarvaire de *Squalonchocotyle torpedinis* (Price, 1942) (Monogenea, Hexabothriidae).

Euzet, L. and Raibaut, A. (1961). *Rapp. Comm. int. Mer Médit.* **16**, 287–9. L'oncomiracidium de *Vallisia striata* Parona et Perugia 1890 (Monogenea, Polyopisthocotylea).

Euzet, L. and Trilles, J. (1960). *Ann. Parasit. hum. comp.* **35**, 504–8. *Octolabea turchinii* n.g., n.sp. (Plectanocotylidae) un monogène nouveau, parasite de *Peristhedion cataphractum* (L.).

Euzet, L. and Trilles, J. (1961). *Rev. suisse Zool.* **68**, 182–93. Sur l'anatomie et la biologie de *Cyclocotyla bellones* (Otto 1821) (Monogenea-Polyopisthocotylea).

Frankland, H. M. T. (1955). *Parasitology* **45**, 313–51. The life history and bionomics of *Diclidophora denticulata* (Trematoda: Monogenea).

Gallien, L. (1934). *Bull. Soc. zool. Fr.* **59**, 68–73. Sur la larve de *Dactylocotyle luscae* v. Ben. and Hesse, trématode monogénétique marin.

Gallien, L. (1935). *Trav. Sta. zool. Wimereux*, **12**, 1–182. Recherches expérimentales sur le dimorphisme évolutif et la biologie de *Polystomum integerrimum* Froel.

Gussev, A. V. (1955). *Trav. Inst. zool. Acad. Sci. U.R.S.S.* **19**, 171–398. Monogenetic trematodes of the fishes of the Amur River System.

Halkin, H. (1901). *Arch. Biol., Paris.* **18**, 291–363. Recherches sur la maturation, la fécondation et le développement du *Polystomum integerrimum*.

Hargis, W. J. and Oustinoff, P. C. (1961). "Monogenetic trematodes, their systematics and phylogeny." (English translation of Bychowsky, B. E., 1957.) Washington: American Institute of Biological Sciences, pp. xix 627.

Jahn, T. L. and Kuhn, L. R. (1932). *Biol. Bull., Wood's Hole* **62**, 89–111. The life history of *Epibdella melleni* MacCallum, 1927, a monogenetic trematode parasitic on marine fishes.

Jarvik, E. (1960). "Théories de l'evolution des Vertébrés", pp. 104. Paris: Masson.

Kearn, G. C. (1963a). *Parasitology* **53** (In press). The egg, oncomiracidium and larval development of *Entobdella soleae*, a monogenean skin parasite of the Common Sole.

Kearn, G. C. (1963b). *Parasitology* **53** (In press). The oncomiracidium of *Capsala martinieri*.

Kearn, G. C. (1963c). *Parasitology* **53** (In press). The attachment of the monogenean *Entobdella soleae* to the skin of the Common Sole.

Llewellyn, J. (1954). *Parasitology* **44**, 428–37. Observations on the food and gut pigment of the Polyopisthocotylea (Trematoda: Monogenea).

Llewellyn, J. (1956). *J. Mar. biol. Ass. U.K.* **35**, 113–27. The host-specificity, microecology, adhesive attitudes, and comparative morphology of some trematode gill parasites.

Llewellyn, J. (1957a). *J. Mar. biol. Ass. U.K.* **36**, 243–59. The larvae of some monogenetic trematode parasites of Plymouth fishes.

Llewellyn, J. (1957b). Host specificity in monogenetic trematodes. In: "First Symposium on Host Specificity among parasites of Vertebrates", 161–212. Neuchâtel.

Llewellyn, J. (1957c). *Parasitology* **47**, 30–9. The mechanism of the attachment of *Kuhnia scombri* (Kuhn, 1829) (Trematoda: Monogenea) to the gills of its host *Scomber scombrus* L., including a note on the taxonomy of the parasite.

Llewellyn, J. (1959). *J. Mar. biol. Ass. U.K.* **38**, 461–7. The larval development of two species of gastrocotylid trematode parasites from the gills of *Trachurus trachurus*.

Llewellyn, J. (1960). *J. Mar. biol. Ass. U.K.* **39**, 561–89. Amphibdellid (Monogenean) parasites of Electric Rays (Torpedinidae).

Llewellyn, J. (1962a). *J. Mar. biol. Ass. U.K.* **42**, 587–600. The life histories and population dynamics of monogenean gill parasites of *Trachurus trachurus* (L.).

Llewellyn, J. (1962b). The effects of the host and its habits on the morphology and life cycle of a monogenean parasite. In: *Symposium on helminths bound to aquatic conditions.* Prague: Parasitologicky Ustav Ceskoslovenske Akademie Ved. (In press).

Llewellyn, J. and Owen, I. L. (1960). *Parasitology* **50**, 51–9. The attachment of the monogenean *Discocotyle sagittata* Leuckart to the gills of *Salmo trutta* L.

Lynch, J. E. (1933). *Quart. J. micr. Sci.* **76**, 13–33. The miracidium of *Heronimus chelydrae* MacCallum.

Manter, H. W. (1955). In "Essays in the natural sciences in honor of Captain Allan Hancock", pp. 211–20. Los Angeles: University of Southern California Press. Two new monogenetic trematodes from elephant fishes (*Callorhynchus*) from South Africa and New Zealand.

Malmberg, G. (1956). *Skr. sverig. FiskFören*, Årsskrift 1956, 19–76. Om förekomsten av Gyrodactylus på Svenska Fiskar.

Nasir, P. (1960). *J. Parasit.* **46**, 833–47. Studies on the life history of *Echinostoma nudicaudatum* n. sp. (Echinostomatidae: Trematoda).

Oglesby, L. C. (1961). *J. Parasit.* **47**, 237–43. Ovoviviparity in the monogenetic trematode *Polystomoidella oblonga*.

Ozaki, Y. (1936). *J. Sci. Hiroshima Univ.* Ser. B. Div. I. Zool. **4**, 23–34. Studies on the frog trematode *Diplorchis ranae*. II. Morphology and behaviour of the swimming larva.

Ramalingam, K. (1960). *Proc. nat. Inst. Sci. India* **26**, B, 352–8. Comparative and functional morphology in monogenean haptor as revealed in the most advanced types.

Ramalingam, K. (1961a). *J. Madras Univ.*, B., **31**, 161. A redescription of *Lithidiocotyle secunda* Tripathi Monogenea and its bionomics.

Ramalingam, K. (1961b). *J. Madras Univ.* B. **31**, 175–81. On a new species of the genus *Lithidiocotyle* (Monogenea: Gastrocotylidae), its juvenile and immature forms from the gills of *Scomberomorus guttatus*.

Ramalingam, K. (1961c). *Ann. Mag. nat. Hist.*, Ser. 13 **3**, 699–704. Morphological descriptions of juvenile and immature *Monaxine* Unnithan (1957) (Monogenea) and their significance.

Remley, L. W. (1942). *Trans. Amer. micr. Soc.* **61**, 141–55. Morphology and life history studies of *Microcotyle spinicirrus* MacCallum, 1918, a monogenetic trematode parasitic on the gills of *Aplodinotus grunniens*.

Sproston, N. G. (1945). *Parasitology* **36**, 176–90. The genus *Kuhnia* n.g. (Trematoda: Monogenea). An examination of the value of some specific characters, including factors of relative growth.

Sproston, N. G. (1946). *Trans. zool. Soc. Lond.* **25**, 185–600. A synopsis of the monogenetic trematodes.

Tripathi, Y. R. (1957). *Indian Journal of Helminthology* **9**, 1–149. Monogenetic trematodes from fishes of India.

Westoll, T. S. (1962). *Nature, Lond.* **194**, 949–52. Ptyctodontid fishes and the ancestry of the Holocephali.

Zeller, E. (1872a). *Z. wiss. Zool.* **22**, 168–80. Untersuchungen über die Entwicklung des *Diplozoon paradoxum*.

Zeller, E. (1872b). *Z. wiss. Zool.* **22**, 1–28. Untersuchungen über die Entwicklung und Bau des *Polystomum integerrimum* Rud.

Author Index

Numbers in italics indicate the page in the References on which a reference is listed

A

Abadie, S. H., 129, *174*
Ackert, J. E., 111, 154, *171, 172*
Aikawa, J. K., 225, 276, *282*
Akers, R. P., 215, 218, 277, *284*
Akiba, K., 59, *61*
Albis-Jimenez, F. S., 141, *175*
Al-Dabagh, M. A., 27, 47, 52, 53, *61*, 69, *104*
Alfert, M., 84, *104*
Alger, N., 153, *177*
Algire, G. H., 9, *61*, *63*
Alicata, J. E., 123, 139, *171*
Allan, D., 183, 194, *209*
Alvey, C. H., 290, 309, 312, *323*
Anderson, R. C., 58, *62*
André, I., 308, *323*
Andrews, J. M., 282, *282*
Anfinsen, C. B., 29, *61*
Antony, D. W., 57, *64*
Arbogast, F., 222, *283*
Archer, R. K., 194, *209*
Augustin, R., 101, *104*
Augustine, D. L., 135, 139, 154, *171, 172*

B

Bachman, C. W., 102, *104*
Baer, J. G., 288, 307, *323*
Baines, R. C., 142, *171*
Bair, T. D., 128, *171*
Baker, J. R., 16, 42, 45, 53, *61, 62*, 94, *105*
Ball, E. G., 29, *61*
Ball, G. H., 17, 21, *61, 64*
Bano, L., 11, 12, *61*
Barnett, H. C., 27, *61*
Bargai, U., 224, 236, *284*
Batista, S., 36, *63*

Baughn, C. O., Jr., 246, 263, 267, 275, 280, *282*
Baxter, J. T., 183, *209*
Beattie, J., 95, 96, *105*
Beaver, P. C., 139, 140, *171*
Becht, H., 232, 256, *284*
Becker, E. R., 21, 53, *61*, 69, 70, 73, 74, 83, 84, 86, 88, 102, *104, 106, 107*
Becker, R. B., 193, *209*
Beckett, E. B., 239, 242, *282*
Behrenz, W., *171*
Bell, E. J., 183, *210*
Bell, L. H., *64*
Bennett, G. F., 54, 55, 58, 59, *61, 62*
Bergeson, G. B., 144, *171*
Berberian, J. F., 140, *171*
Beresantev, Yu, A., 243, *282*
Bergman, B. H. H., 160, 161, *171*
Bernard, G. R., 216, 217, 218, 219, 246, *282, 283*
Bertram, D. S., 153, *171*
Berry, J., 206, *209*
Bethell, F. H., 221, 222, 231, 249, *283*
Birchfield, W., 141, *171*
Bird, A. F., 111, 116, 117, 137, 160, 161, 171, *171*
Bird, R. G., 16, 42, 45, *62*, 94, *105*
Bishop, A., *17*, 18, *61*
Bishop, D., 159, *171*
Blake, C. D., 157, 159, *172*
Blaschko, H., 91, *104*
Bliznick, A., 68, 73, 81, 83, *104, 105*
Böhm, O., 143, *171*
Boles, J. I., 70, 73, 74, *104*
Booth, V. H., 148, *176*
Boothroyd, B., 239, *282*
Bosker, J. E., 142, *171*
Bovet, J., 292, 293, 302, 303, 304, 305, 308, 309, *323*

327

Bovien, P., 119, 121, 133, 142, *171*
Boyd, E. M., 215, 216, 229, *283*
Bozicevich, J., 230, *283*
Brachet, J., 84, 90, *104*
Brackett, S., 68, 73, 81, 83, 84, *104*, *105*
Braden, A., 91, *105*
Bragden, D. E., 91, *105*
Brandley, C. A., 102, *105*
Bray, R. S., 36, *61*
Brewer, O. M., 263, 276, *283*
Briggs, N. T., 58, *61*, 231, 275, 278, *283*
Brinkmann, A., 314, *323*
Brodine, C. E., 53, *61*
Brown, F. T., 194, 195, *211*
Brown, H. W., 140, *172*
Brown, J. A., 76, 78, *106*
Buckley, J. J. C., 133, *172*
Bullock, W. L., 223, 226, 227, 234, *283*
Burns, W. C., 74, 96, *105*
Buxton, A., 103, *105*
Bychowsky, B. E., 287, 288, 291, 292,
    293, 296, 297, 299, 301, 302, 303,
    308, 309, 310, 311, 312, 314, 315,
    317, 322, *323*
Byrd, M. A., 57, 59, *61*

C

Cairns, E. J.. 142, *172*
Calam, C. T., 115, *172*
Campbell, C. H., 238, 258, 259, 273, 274,
    283
Campbell, D. H., 196, *209*
Campbell, J. A., 132, *176*
Camper, 179, *209*
Carter, R. D., *106*
Challey, J. R., 74, 96, *105*
Chandler, A. C., 273, *283*
Chao, J., 17, *61*
Chase, F. A., 165, *177*
Chaudhuri, R. N., 34, *62*
Cheissin, E. M., 69, 83, 84, 85, 86, 88, 90,
    105
Chipman, P. B., 258, 259, 273, 274, *283*
Chitwood, B. G., 111, 116, 121, *172*
Chitwood, M. B., 111, 116, 121, *172*
Christie, J. R., 143, 144, *172*
Chute, R. M., 216, 225, 230, 231, 236,
    258, 274, *283*
Clarke, D. H., 30, *61*

Clarkson, M. J., 76, 77, 78, 79, 80, 82, 96,
    105
Cleland, J. B., 117, *172*
Coker, C. M., 240, 241, 242, 246, 264, 265,
    266, 267, 277, 278, 279, *283*
Colbert, E. H., 320, *324*
Colglazier, M. L., 194, *209*
Collis-George, N., 157, 159, *172*
Coors, M. J., 229, 231, 236, 238, *285*
Cordi, J. M., 139, *172*
Cornwell, R. L., 193, 199, 200, 201, 206,
    207, 208, *209*, *210*
Corradetti, A., 22, 36, 47, *61*
Cort, W. W., 154, *172*
Costello, L. C., 126, 127, 129, *172*
Cotteleer, C., 186, *209*
Coulston, F., 12, *62*
Coupland, A. C., 312, 313, *324*
Cowan, A. B., 55, 56, *61*
Cox, H. W., 262, 263, 276, *283*
Cram, E. B., 153, *172*
Crewe, W., 155, *173*
Crofton, H. D., 132, 133, 134, 140, 165,
    172, *173*
Cuckler, A. C., 68, *105*
Culbertson, J. T., 245, *283*
Cunningham, P. C., 144, *172*
Cunningham, P. M., 181, *209*

D

DasGupta, B., 34, 35, 38, 53, *61*, *64*
Daubney, R., 188, *209*
Daulton, R. A. C., *172*
Davies, S. F. M., 74, 75, *105*
Davis, D. E., 260, 280, *283*
Dawes, B., 288, *324*
Dawson, B., 116, *172*
Demina, H. A., 36, *61*
Demina, N. A., 22, *61*
Dempsey, F. W., 91, *107*
de Oliveira Musacchio, M., 36, 37, 43, *63*
Dennis, W. R., 193, 195, 208, *211*
Den Ouden, H., 122, 143, *175*
Deschiens, R., 49, *62*
Detre, L., 230, *283*
Deutsch, K., 116, *171*
Devolt, H. M., 102, *107*
Dewey, D. W., 150, *172*
Dickinson, E. M., 68, 163, *105*

Dickinson, S., 162, *172*
Djafar, M. I., 193, 194, *209, 211*
Dobson, E. L., 76, *105*
Doncaster, C. C., 156, 159, *172, 177*
Douglas, J. R., 134, *176*
Douvres, F. W., 180, *209*
Downey, H., 278, *283*
Drinnon, V. P., 36, *62, 63*
Dropkin, V. H., 114, *172*
Drudge, J. H., 138, *172*
Dubin, I. N., 36, *62, 63*
Duggan, J. J., 143, *172*
Duke, B. O. L., 138, *172*
Duncan, D., 42, 44, 45, *62*
Durie, P. H., 133, *172*
Dutta, B. N., 34, 53, *62, 64*
Duwel, D., 194, *209*

E

Eades, J., 44, 45, *62*
Edgar, S. A., 70, 74, 86, *105*
Edney, J. M., 222, *283*
Eisma, M., 130, *172*
Ellenby, C., 112, 114, 115, 116, 144, *172*
Elliot, A., 126, *173*
Englebrecht, H.. 204, *209*
Enigk, D., 194, *209*
Enigk, K., 194, *209*
Enzie, F. D., 194, *209*
Etkin, W., 165, *173*
Euzeby, J., 204, *211*
Euzet, L., 287, 288, 290, 293, 295, 297, 298, 300, 303, 306, 308, 309, 313, 315, *323, 324*
Evans, A. S., 197, *211*
Ewert, A., 258, 259, 273, *283*

F

Fairbairn, D., 86, *107*, 111, 116, 124, 125, 126, 127, 128, 129, 130, 141, 146, 147, 152, 170, *173, 175*
Fallis, A. M., 53, 54, 55, 58, 59, *61, 62*
Farmer, J. M., 69, 70, *104*
Farr, M. M., 92, *105, 107*
Fassuliotis, G., 144, *173*
Fauré-Fremiet, E., 128, *173*
Federmann, M., 194, *209*
Feldmesser, J., 144, *173*
Fenwick, D. W., 114. 115, 144, 159, *173*, *177*

Ferguson, M. J., 27, *63*
Fernex, M., 52, *62*
Ferris, V. R., 116, *173*
Fischtal, J. H., 229, 231, *283*
Fish, F., 69, *105*
Fisher, E. W., 193, *209*
Fletcher, O. K., Jr., 261, *284*
Ford, A. C., 121, *174*
Forrester, A. T. T., 229, *283*
Fox, L. E., 198, 199, *212*
Frankenberg, D., 219, *283*
Frankland, H. M. T., 293, 295, 298, 306, 309, *324*
Frazer, L. A., 86, *105*
Freer, P. M., 153, *173*
Freyvogel, T., 4, *62*
Fritts, D. H., 138, *174*
Furman, D. P., 134, *173*

G

Gallien, L., 294, 309, 310, 312, *324*
Gapinski, L., 229, *286*
Garnham, P. C. C., 16, 36, 42, 45, *62*, 94, *105*
Gauthen, G. E., 181, 195, *211*
Geigy, R., 4, *62*
Geiman, Q. M., 29, *61*
Germans, W., 140, *173*
Ghosh, T. N., 25, 35, *62, 64*
Gilbert, A. B., 114, 115, *172*
Gilchrist, H. B., 237, 246, 251, 252, 268, 273, 276, *284*
Gill, B. S., 84, 88, 90, 91, *105, 106*
Gingrich, W. D., 48, *62*
Ginsburg, A. S., 84, *106*
Giovannola, A., 85, 126, 128, *105, 173*
Girth, H. B., 121, 153, *173*
Glaser, R. W., 121, 153, *173*
Glenn, S., 28, *62*
Glick, D., 91, *105*
Goble, F. C., 48, *62*
Godfrey, G. H., 162, *173*
Godwin, J. T., 264, *285*
Goldberg, A., 138, *173*
Goldberg, E., 129, *173*
Golden, A. M., 141, 143, *173*
Gomberg, H. J., 221, 222, 231, 232, 249, 255, 256, *283, 285*
Goodchild, C. G., 219, 222, 223, 236, *283*

Goodey, T., 154, 155, *173*
Goodman, M., 97, *105*
Gordon, R. M., 153, 155, *171*, *173*
Gould, S. E., 221, 222, 229, 231, 232, 249, 255, 256, *283*, *285*
Goulson, H. T., 237, 243, 246, 252, 256, 257, 262, 273, 276, 277, *283*, *284*
Greenberg, B. G., 237, 246, 251, 252, 268, 273, 276, *284*
Greenberg, J., 13, 14, 15, 34, *62*, *64*
Gregoire, C., 186, 195, *209*
Gregory, J., 275, *285*
Grevan, V., 74, *105*
Gripper, J. N., 194, *209*
Grollman, S., 126, 127, 129, *172*
Groves, T. W., 194, *209*
Gudzhabidze, S. I.. 140, *173*
Guilhon, J., 194, *209*
Gupta, S. P., 140, *173*
Gursch, O. F., 221, 222, 228, 237, 238, *284*
Gussev, A. V., 301, 311, 312, 315, *323*, *324*

H

Hagemeyer, J. W., 123, *173*
Hager, A., 102, *104*
Hale, W. M., 267, 271, 272, *285*
Hale, C., 90, *105*
Haley, A. J., 134, 155, *175*
Halkin, H., 294, 304, 305, 308, *324*
Hall, P. R., 102, *104*
Hamvas, J. J., 275, *284*
Hankes, L. V., 124, *173*, *176*, 224, 240, 241, 243, 274, *284*, *285*
Harding, D. E., 53, *62*
Hargis, W. J., 292, 297, 315, *324*
Harrell, G. T., Jr., 225, 276, *282*
Harris, J. E., 165, *173*
Hartmann, H. A., 225, 228, *285*
Hartung, W., 232, 256, *284*
Haskins, W. T., 129, *173*, *177*
Hastings, R. J., 142, *173*
Hawking, F., 153, 154, 155, *173*
Hawkins, P. A., 78, *105*
Headley, N. C., 229, *286*
Hechler, H. C., 114, *173*
Heisch, R. B., 16, *62*
Hendricks, J. R., 238, 249, 251, 252, 255, 258, 273, *284*

Herrick, C. A., 86, *105*
Hertz, C. S., 221, 222, 231, 232, 249, 255, 256, *283*
Hesling, J. J., 114, 143, 158, 159, *173*
Hewitt, R., 1, *62*
Hill, C. H., 141, *173*
Hirschmann, H., 116, *173*
Hodgetts, V. E., 150, *177*
Hollander, W. F.. 21, *61*
Hollis, J. P., *174*
Holst, A. P., 102, *107*
Hönig, G., 90, *106*, 111, 112, *175*
Horton-Smith, C., 69, 80, 88, 92, 93, 95, 96, 97, 98, 99, 100, 101, 102, 103, *105*, *106*
Howard, R. G., 223, 235, *284*, *286*
Hudson, J. R., 193, *209*
Huff, C. G., 6, 7, 9, 12, 19, 20, 21, 22, 25, 27, 36, 37, 38, 39, 40, 42, 44, 49, 55, 60, *62*, *63*
Huff, G. C., 128, *174*
Hughes, F. W., 4, *63*
Hull, R. W., 6, 50, *63*, *64*
Humes, A. G., 215, 218, 277, *284*
Huston, E. J., 215, 216, *283*
Hyman, L. H., 116, 120, *174*

I

Ingram, R. L., 49, *63*
Irreverre, F., 24, 25, *64*
Isa, J. M., 55, *64*
Itikawa, O., 84, 90, *106*
Ivanic, M., 55, *63*
Ivey, M. H., 246, 249, 251, 252, 258, 273, 275, 276, *284*

J

Jackson, G. J., 258, 274, 275, *284*
Jacobs, H. R., 27, *63*
Jacobs, L., 141, *174*
Jacobson, W., 91, *104*
Jahn, T. L., 306, 309, *324*
Janzen, G. J., 115, *174*
Jarrett, W. F. H., 180, 181, 183, 188, 189, 190, 193, 195, 196, 197, 198, 199, 200, 201, 202, 203, 205, 206, 207, 208, *209*, 210
Jarvik, E., 321, *324*
Jaskoski, B. J., 111, 126, 128, *174*
Jaumin, J., 186, *209*

Jeannin, A., 204, *211*
Jeffries, W. B., 238, 248, 249, 250, *284*
Jennings, F. W., 188, 189, 190, 195, 196,
   197, 198, 199, 200, 201, 202, 203,
   205, 206, 207, 208, *210*
Jensen, D. V., 6, 37, 38, 42, 44, *62, 63*
Jernberg, N. A., 32, *64*
Jeumaux, C., 170, *174*
Joest, E., 188, *210*
Johnson, G. E., 120, *174*
Johnson, R. W., 114, *172*
Johnson, W. T., 68, 70, 74, *106*
Johnston, T. H., 117, *172*
Jones, B. V., 180, 188, 198, 200, 203, 205,
   207, *210, 211*
Jones, C. A., 129, *174*
Jones, C. M., 59, *63*
Jones, E. E., 74, 81, *107*
Jones, F. G. W., 136, 137, 159, 161, 170,
   174
Jones, M. F., 141, *174*
Jordan, H. B., 5, *63*
Josephson, E. S., 34, *64*
Joyeux, C., 307, *323*
Joyner, L. P., 73, 75, *105, 106*
Julian, S. R., 42, 44, 45, *62*
Jumper, J. R., 49, *63*
Jungherr, E., 102, 103, *105, 106*

K

Kämpfe, L., 159, *174*
Kagan, I. G., 214, 223, 224, 236, *284*
Kartman, L., 153, 154, 155, *174*
Katahira, K., 120, 135, 150, *176*
Kates, K. C., 131, 138, *174*
Kasparek, T., 181, *210*
Kauffman, M., 48, *64*
Kearn, G. C., 293, 299, 303, 305, 307, 308,
   309, 310, *324*
Keilin, D., 142, *174*
Kendall, S. B., 92, *106*
Kent, D. E., 261, 262, *284*
Kerr, K. B., 196, 197, 263, *210, 284*
Kershaw, W. E., 239, *285*
Khabir, P. A., 33, *63*
Kikuth, W., 36, *62*
Kilham, L., 235, *284*
Kim, C. W., 238, 255, 256, 260, 273, 274,
   284

Kingscote, A. A., 221, 237, 256, *285*
Klingler, J., 137, 160, *174*
Kreuzer, L., 116, *174*
Kruize, J., 204, *212*
Krusberg, L. R., 163, *174*
Kucharczyk, W., 242, *284*
Kühn, H., 160, *174*
Kuhn, L. R., 306, 309, *324*
Kuitunen, E., 275, *284*
Kurnick, N. B., 103, *106*
Kurochkin, Y. V., 111, *174*

L

Labzoffsky, N. A., 275, *284*
Laffer, N. G., 102, *107*
Laird, R. L., 36, *62, 63*
Landers, E. J., 75, *106*
Lapage, G., 117, *174*
Larsen, M. E., 205, *210*
Larsh, J. E., Jr., 225, 237, 238, 240, 243,
   244, 245, 246, 247, 248, 249, 250, 251,
   252, 253, 254, 256, 257, 261, 262, 268,
   269, 270, 273, 274, 275, 276, 277, *284*
Latchford, W. B., 126, 127, *176*
Lavoipierre, M. M. J., 153, 155, *174*
Lawlor, H. J., 197, *210*
Lee, C. L., 227, 228, 234, *174, 284*
Lee, D. L., 117, *174*
Lee, H. J., 150, *172*
Lees, E., 118, *174*
Leland, Jr., S. E., 138, *172*
Levine, D. M., 258, 275, *285*
Levine, P. P., 68, 69, *106*
Lewert, R. M., *174*, 227, 228, 234, *284*
Lewis, G. D., 142, *174*
Lewis, W. P., 225, 233, 236, 274, *284*
Lillie, R. D., 84, 86, *106*
Limański, M., 242, *284*
Limber, D. P., 142, *174*
Linford, M. B., 114, 120, 157, 162, 163,
   170, *174, 175*
Lison, L., 90, *106*
Liu, Si-Kwang, 57, *63*
Llewellyn, J., 287, 288, 289, 290, 294,
   295, 297, 298, 300, 301, 302, 303, 305,
   308, 309, 310, 311, 314. 315, 319, *324,
   325*
Loeffler, C. A., 33, 53, *63*
Looss, A., 117, *174*

Long, P. L., 69, 70, 80, 84, 88, 92, 93, 95, 96, 97, 98, 99, 100, 101, 102, 103, *105, 106*
Lord, R. A., 225, *284*
Louch, C. D., 235, *284*
Lownsbery, B. F., 144, 160, 161, *174*
Lucker, J. T., 138, *173*, 180, 196, 205, *209, 210, 211, 212*
Lynch, J. E., 291, *325*

M

McConnachie, E. W., 18, *61*
McCoy, E. E., 121, 153, *173*
McCoy, O. R., 111, 126, 127, *174, 176*, 262, *284*
McCullough, F. S., 92, *106*
McFadzean, J. A., 197, *210*
McGhee, R. B., 7, 8, 10, 22, 23, 48, *63*
McGuire, W. C., 68, *106*
McIntyre, W. I. M., 180, 181, 183, 188, 190, 193, 195, 196, 197, 198, 199, 200, 201, 202, 203, 205, 206, 207, 208, *209, 210*
McKee, R. W., 29, *61*
MacKenzie, R. E., 186, *210*
McManus, J. F. S., 91, *105, 106*
Maeir, D. M., 223, 235, *284, 286*
Mai, W. F., 142, 143, *174*
Malanga, C. A., 68, *105*
Malewitz, T. D., 199, *212*
Malher, G., 204, *211*
Manter, H. W., 288, 289, 290, 313, 314, *325*
Manton, V. J. A., 190, *211*
Manwell, R. D., 4, 5, 6, 28, 29, 33, 36, 53, *62, 63, 64, 65*
Marchbank, D. F., 6, 19, 20, 21, 25, 49, *62*
Marguardt, W. C., 138, *174*
Markell, E. K., 224, 225, 233, 236, 237, 274, *284, 285*
Marousek, A. E., 53, *61*
Marston, H. R., 150, *172*
Martin, B., 201, *210*
Martin, G. C., 114, *172*
Mauer, S. I., 217, 246, *285*
Meklman, B., 125, 129, *172*
Merrill, J. H., 121, *174*
Meyer, H., 36, 37, 43, *63*
Michel, J. W., 184, *211*

Michel, J. F., 182, 183, 184, 185, 186, 187, 193, 194, 195, 199, 200, *209, 210, 211*
Micks, D. W., 27, 42, 44, 45, *62, 63*
Miller, H. M., 196, *210*
Miller, T. B., 225, 276, *282*
Minter, D. M., 16, *62*
Miretski, O. Y., 141, *174*
Miura, A., 120, 135, 150, *176*
Mizelle, J. D., 140, *171*
Mjassojedoff, S. W., 103, *106*
Mohammed, A. H. H., 53, *63*
Mohan, B. N., 13, *63*
Molinari, V., 28, *63*
Monné, L., 90, *106*, 111, 112, 116, *174, 175*
Mönnig, H. O., 134, 139, 140, 155, *175*
Moore, E. N., 76, 78, *106*
Morehouse, N. F., 68, 78, 94, *106*
Morrissey, L. P., 275, *284*
Moses, H. E., 102, *105*
Moskwa, W., 236, *284*
Most, H., 153, *177*
Moulder, J. W., 32, 47, *63*
Mudrow, L., 36, *63*
Mudrow-Reichenow, L., 36, *63*
Müller, G., 141, *175*
Mulligan, W., 188, 189, 190, 195, 196, 197, 198, 199, 200, 201, 202, 203, 205, 206, 207, 208, *210*
Muniz, J., 36, *63*

N

Nadel, E. M., 34, *64*
Nagibina, L. F., 288, *323*
Nakladova, V. B., 141, *175*
Nasir, P., 291, *325*
Neilen, D., *175*
Nekipelova, R. A., 134, *175*
Nelson, A. M. R., 180, 188, 198, 200, 203, 205, 207, *210, 211*
Nelson, G. S., 229, *283*
Neri, I., 22, *61*
Newberne, J. W., 56, *63*
Nichols, J., 225, 240, *284*
Nichols, 179, *210*
Nishihara, H., 224, 233, *285*
Nolf, L. O., 141, *175*
Newton, W., 142, *173*
Norman, L., 215, 216, *285*
Norton, S., 97, *105*

Nydegger, L., 29, *63*
Nye, P. A., 23, *63*

O

O'Donoghue, J. G., 194, *211*
Oglesby, L. C., 289, 290, *325*
Oldham, J. N., 119, 121, *175, 177*
Oliveira, J., 162, *173*
Oliver-Gonzalez, J., 225, 258, 274, 275, *285*
Olivier, L., 235, *284*
Ollerenshaw, C. B., 185, *210*
Olson, A., 204, *211*
Olson, L. J., 258, 259, 273, *283*
Omi, G., 229, *286*
Onions, T. G., 114, *175*
Oostenbrink, M., 143, *175*
Orken, L. E., Jr., 49, *63*
Ormsbee, R. A., 29, *61*
O'Sullivan, P. J., 133, *175*
Ott, W. H., 68, *105*
Otto, G. F., 139, *172*, 197, *211*
Ouchterlony, O., 97, *106*
Oustinoff, P. C., 292, 297, 315, *324*
Owen, I. L., 293, *325*
Ozaki, Y., 292, 295, 296, *325*

P

Parker, J. C., 134, 155, *175*
Parker, W. H., 194, 195, *211*
Parfitt, J. W., 183, 184, 186, *210*
Passano, L. M., 164, *175*
Passey, R. F., 125, 126, 127, 128, 129, 130, *175*
Pattillo, W. H., 21, *61*, 69, 70, 83, 84, 86, 88, *104, 106*
Paul, S., 204, *212*
Payne, F. K., 126, 133, 154, *172, 175*
Payne, G. C., 154, *172*
Peacock, F. C. 144, 159, 160, 161, 162, *175*
Peacock, R., 180, 188, 190, 198, 200, 203, 205, 207, *210, 211*
Pearse, E., 91, *106*
Pearson, J. C., 58, *62*
Peters, B. G., 121, *175*
Petersen, J. H., 229, *283*
Petit, J. P., 194, *209*
Phillipson, R. F., 239, *285*
Pick, F., 49, *62*

Pierce, A. E., 92, 93, 97, 98, 99, 100, 101, 102, 103, *105, 106*
Pierre, M., 204, *211*
Pipkin, A. C., 6, 9, 37, 38, 42, 44, *62, 63*
Podger, K., 198, *211*
Polizzi, Sciarrone, M., 5, *63*
Pollay, M., 225, 228, *285*
Poole, J. B., 138, *175*
Porter, D. A., 181, 183, 195, *211*
Porter, R. J., 36, *63*
Pouplard, L., 186, *209*
Poynter, D., 180, 187, 188, 190, 198, 200, 203, 206, 207, *211*
Prasad, D., 139, 140, *175*
Prehn, R. T., 9, *61*

Q

Quanjer, H. M., 161, *175*
Quignard, J., 308, *324*

R

Race, G. J., 238, 243, 244, 246, 247, 248, 249, 250, 252, 253, 254, 256, 257, 268, 269, 270, 273, 274, 275, 277, *284*
Raffaele, G., 10, 36, 50, *63, 64*
Raibaut, A., 288, 290. 293, 295, 298, 300, 303, 306, 309, 313, *324*
Rama Rao, R., 32, 52, *64*
Ramalingam, K., 288, 309, 312, 314, *325*
Ramaswamy, A. S., 50, *64*
Rappaport, I., 238, 249, 260, 262, 274, 275, *285*
Rase, F., 186, *209*
Raski, D. J., 111, 162, *175*
Raven, B., 130, *175*
Ray, H. N., 25, 34, 38, 53, *62, 64*, 84, 88, 90, 91, *105, 106*
Read, C. P., 260, 280, *283*
Rees, G. F., 133, 134, *175*
Reesal, M. R., 135, 139, *175*
Refuerzo, P. G., 141, *175*
Reid, E., 144, *173*
Reid, W. M., 75, *106*
Reinders, J. S., 204, *212*
Remley, L. W., 309, *325*
Rhoades, H. L., 114, 120, 157, 170, *175*
Richey, D. J., 56, 59, *63, 64*
Ridges, P. A., 101, *104*
Riek, R. F., 133, *175*

Ritterson, A. L., 216, 217, 219, 220, 221, 234, 246, 267, *285*
Roberts, F. H. S., 133, *175*
Roberts, H. E., 194, 195, *211*
Robinson, E. J., Jr., 261, *285*
Robinson, F. O., 6, *63*
Robinson, J., 180, 187, 188, 198, 200, 203, 207, *211*
Rogers, W. P., 112, 117, 121, 123, 126, 127, 128, 130, 133, 134, 135, 139, 146, 147, 148, 149, 150, 151, 152, 166, 170, 171, *171, 175, 176*, 243, *285*
Rohde, R. A., 160, *176*
Rootes, D. G., 84, 88, 103, *106*
Rose, J. H., 140, *176*, 182, 184, 185, 186, *210, 211*
Rose, M. E., 92, 93, 98, 100, 101, 103, *105, 106*
Roskin, G. I., 84, *106*
Ross, W. M., 258, *285*
Roughton, F. J. W., 148, *176*
Rowan, W. B., 115, *176*
Rubel, J., 229, *286*
Rubin, R., 138, *173*, 193, 194, 195, 196, 197, *211, 212*
Rudzinska, M. A., 30, 40, 41, *64*
Rust, J. W., 138, *172*
Ruysch, F., 179, *211*

S

Sadun, E. H., 214, 215, 216, *285*
Safholm, R. D., 229, *286*
Salle, A. J., 163, *176*
Sander, G., 229, *283*
Sandstedt, R., 161, *176*
Santisteban, G. A., 267, *285*
Sarauw, U., 49, *62*
Sarles, M. P., 196, *211*, 280, *285*
Sasa, M., 120, 135, 150, *176*
Sassuchin, D., 84, *105*
Savage, A., 55, *64*
Scarrza, M., 22, *61*
Schanzel, H., 140, *176*
Schinazi, L. A., 21, 51, *64*
Schofield, R. M., 68, *105*
Scholtyseck, E., 70, 73, 74, *106*
Schneider, R. L., *64*
Schuster, M. L., 161, *176*
Schuurmans Stekhaven, J. H., 130, *175*
Schwabe, C. W., 128, 129, *176*
Schwartz, B., 213, *285*

Scott, J. A., *176*
Seamster, A. P., 140, *176*
Seghetti, L., 138, *174*
Semrad, J. E., 229, 231, 236, 238, *285*
Sen, H. G., 34, 53, *64*
Senger, C. M., 138, *174*
Sen Gupta, P. C., 38, *64*
Seniów, A., 224, *285*
Senseman, V. F., 194, *211*
Shafer, T., 143, *173*
Shand, A., 183, *210*
Sharma, N. N., 75, *106*
Shepherd, A. M., 122, 143, *176*
Sharp, N. C. C., 188, 189, 190, 201, 202, 203, 207, 208, *210, 211*
Sherman, I. W., 50, *64*
Shikhobalova, N. P., 249, 259, *285*
Shirasaka, R., 120, 135, 150, *176*
Shiroishi, T., 6, 19, 20, 21, 25, 49, *62*
Siegel, B. M., 116, *173*
Silverman, P. H., 132; *176*, 180, 188, 198, 200, 203, 207, *211*
Simmonds, R. A., 117, *176*
Simpson, C. F., 57, *64*, 193, 199, 208, *211, 212*
Simpson, W. F., 124, 131, *172*
Singer, I., 31, 48, *62, 64*
Sirsi, M., 32, 52, *64*
Skorczyński, M., 242, *284*
Skovronski, R. V., 193, *211*
Sledge, E. B., 163, *176*
Sleeman, H. K., 275, *285*
Slidders, W., 103, *106*
Smith, P. E., 123, *176*
Smith, R. O. A., 25, *64*
Smyth, D., 90, *106*
Soares, R., 36, *63*
Soliman, K. N., 134, 140, *176*, 180, 183, *211*
Sommerville, R. I., 111, 118, 121, 123, 139, 146, 149, 150, 151, 170, *176*
Soulsby, E. J. L., 118, *176*
Spandorf, A. A., 4, 29, *63, 64*
Spedding, C. R., 184, *211*
Spedding, C. R. W., 185, *210*
Spiers, R. S., 194, *211*
Sprent, J. F. A., 134, 135, 139, *176*
Sproston, N. G., 288, 310, *326*
Stableforth, A. W., 183, *211*
Stahler, N., 24, 25, 26, *64*
Stannard, J. N., 126, 127, *176*

Stauber, L. A., 23, *64*
Stefan, W., 236, *284*
Steiner, G., 142, *176*
Stephenson, W., 121, *176*
Stepp, J., 222, *283*
Stevens, A. J., 113, 139, *176*
Stewart, D. F., 118, *176*
Stewart, M. A., 134, *176*
Stirewalt, M. A., 197, *211*
Stohler, H., *64*
Stoll, N. R., 123, 131, 153, *176*
Stone, W. M., 195, *211*
Stoner, R. D., 124, *173, 176*, 224, 240, 241, 243, 264, 267, 271, 272, 274, *284, 285*
Stoney, J. M., 229, *286*
Street, J., 42, *62*
Sudak, F. N., 218, *283*
Sussuchin, D., 84, *106*
Švarc, R., 152, *176, 177*
Swanson, L. E., 193, 194, 195, 198, 199, 208, *209, 211, 212*
Swartzwelder, J. C., 129, *174*
Swietlikowski, M., 183, *211*
Sylvén, B., 90, *106*
Szaflarski, J., 242, *284*

T

Taliaferro, L. G., 46, 47, *64*
Taliaferro, W. H., 46, 47, 48, 51, *63, 64,* 196, *211*, 273, 278, 280, *285*
Talmage, D. W., 271, 272, 274, *285*
Tanaka, H., 120, 135, 150, *176*
Tanner, C. E., 275, *285*
Tarshis, B. I., 133, *176*
Tarshis, I. B., 53, *64*
Tatum, A. L., 4, *63*
Taylor, A., 146, 147, 148, *176*
Taylor, A. E. R., *64*, 124, *176*
Taylor, D. J., 34, *64*
Taylor, D. P., 114, *176*
Taylor, E. L., 92, *106*, 182, 193, 194, 195, 206, *211*
Terrell, N. L., 103, *106*
Terry, R. J., 180, 187, 188, 190, 198, 200, 203, 206, 207, *211*
Terzian, L. A., 10, 11, 24, 25, 26, *64*
Tetley, J. H., 131, *176*
Theiler, H., 74, 81, *107*
Themann, H., 223, *285*

Thomas, B. A. C., 196, 199, 200, *210*
Thomas, H. A., 118, 160, 162, *176*
Thomas, L., 267, *285*
Thomas, R. J., 113, 139, *176*
Thorne, G., 143, 144, 157, 161, *176*
Tillotson, A. J., 194, 195, *211*
Todd, A. R., 115, *172*
Trace, J. C., 194, *212*
Tracey, M. V., 113, 163, *177*
Trager, W., 26, 30, 31, 32, 40, 41, *64*
Triffitt, M. J., 119, 123, 156, *177*
Trilles, J., 288, 293, 309, 315, *324*
Tripathi, Y. R., 314, *326*
Tsunoda, K., 84, 90, *106*
Turner, A. W., 150, *177*
Turner, J. H., 138, 139, *177*
Twohy, D. W., *177*
Tyzzer, E. E., 68, 69, 70, 73, 74, 76, 78, 81, 102, *106, 107*

U

Unsworth, K., 153, *171*
Urgrin, I. N., 193, *212*
Urquhart, G. M., 180, 181, 183, 188, 189, 190, 193, 195, 196, 197, 198, 199, 200, 201, 202, 205, 207, 208, *209, 210*
Ursula, B., 236, *284*

V

Vallely, T. F., 194, 195, *211*
van der Tuin, F., 115, *174*
van Doorninck, W. M., 74, *107*
van Duuren, A. J., 160, 161, *171*
van Dyke, J. G., 232, *283*
van Eck, G., 204, *212*
van Gundy, S. D., 113, 118, 141, 142, 160, *173*
van Weerdt, L. G., 113, *177*
Vasina, S. G., 36, *65*
Vassington, J. J., 102, *107*
Veglia, F., 122, 132, *177*
Vegors, H. M., 205, *210*
Verolini, F., 47, *61*
Viglierchio, D. R., 160, 161, *174*
Villella, J. B., 221, 222, 231, 232, 249, 255, 256, *283, 285*
Vinovev, V. G., *177*
von Brand, T., 91, *105*, 124, 125, 126, 128, 129, 131, *172*, 226, *283*

von Mechow, J., 143, *174*
von Rahm, U., 48, *64*

W

Wade, A. E., 193, 194, 195, 198, 199, 208, 211, *212*
Wald, G., 164, 165, *177*
Wallace, H. R., 131, 132, 133, 136, 137, 142, 158, 159, 160, 161, *173*, *177*
Walley, J. K., 194, *212*
Ward, R. A., 11, *64*
Ware, R. E., 56, *64*
Waring, W. S., 115, *172*
Waterman, T. H., 165, *177*
Weathersby, A. B., 9, 15, 16, 37, 38, 42, 44, 45, *62*, *63*, *64*, *65*
Weaver, J. M., 9, *61*
Weber, T. B., 193, 196, 197, 199, 200, *211*, *212*
Wehr, E. E., 92, *105*, *107*
Weil, P., 103, *107*
Weimer, H. E., 224, 233, *285*
Wein, B., 225, 228, *285*
Weinbach, E. C., 125, 129, *172*
Weinstein, P. P., 125, 129, 130, 131, *172*, *173*, *177*, 226, *283*
Weischer, B., 160, *177*
Weiss, M. L., 4, 36, *63*, *65*
Wells, H. S., 249, 260, 262, 274, 275, *285*
Wells, P. D., 267, 275, 278, *285*
Wertejuk, M., 138, *177*
Westoll, T. S., 320, 322, *326*
Wetzel, R., 183, 195, *212*
Wharton, R. H., 153, *177*
Whitlock, J. H., 146, 147, 148, *176*

Widdowson, E., 114, 115, 159, *173*, *177*
Wieser, W., 116, 159, *177*
Wigglesworth, V. B., 165, *177*
Wilson, J. D., 229, *286*
Wilson, J. H. G., 204, *212*
Wilson, P. A. G., 86, 113, 140, *107*, *177*
Wingstrand, K. G., 55, *65*
Winslow, R. D., 143, 144, 156, 170, *177*
Wislocki, G. B., 91, *107*
Wodehouse, R. P., 275, *285*
Wolcott, G. B., 12, *65*
Wood, D. M., 53, *62*
Woolfe, H. R., 97, *105*
Worms, M., 153, 154, 155, *173*
Wright, W. H., 226, *283*
Wu, L. Y., 221, 237, 239, 256, *285*
Wyant, Z. N., 138, *172*

Y

Yamamoto, H., 120, 135, 150, *176*
Yarinsky, A., 240, 243, 245, 252, 267, 268, 269, 270, 271, 272, 277, *284*, *285*,
Yoeli, M., 153, *177*
Young, F., 57, *64*

Z

Zaiman, H., 223, 229, 235, *284*, *286*
Zapart, W., 230, *286*
Zarzycki, J., 224, 239, 240, *286*
Zasukhin, D. N., 36, *65*
Zeller, E., 309, *326*
Zimmerman, W. J., 69, 70, *104*
Zmoray, I., 152, *176*, *177*
Zuckerman, A., 8, 9, 49, *65*

Subject Index[1]

A

A.C.T.H., 216
Acid,
  affect on susceptibility, 26
  amino acids in parasitemia, 51, 52, 242
  environment, 147, 148–150
  organic, used in cultures, 146
Acidosis, respiratory, 193
Adhesive organs, 301, 302
Adrenal,
  alterations in post-infection periods, 217
  cortical lipid, 246
  glandular effects, 34
  hormone, 263
  hypertrophy, 261–280
Adrenalectomy, 263, 267, 280
Agar-gel diffusion plates, 97
Age,
  and mortality rates, 5
  effect on *Eimeria* infection, 83
  influence on immunity, 24, 249
  of adult worms, 238, 251
  of cattle related to infection by lung-
    worm, 181
  of host, 214, 215, 238
  of infection in host, 97, 226
  of mice host, 238, 240, 243
  best for vaccination of calf, 205
Alcohol, effect on mice immunity, 261,
  262
Alimentary canal of oncomiracidia, 303
Altitude, effect on vertebrate host of
  malaria, 3, 4
Amino acids, 51, 52, 111, 224
Amino acids, labelled, 124, 240
Amino-peptidase, 243
Anaerobic conditions, and oxygen debt,
  128
Anaerobic conditions, experiments under,
  148
Anaemia in infected ducklings, 49, 56

Antibiotics, 10, 57, 190, 264
Antibody, 97–225, 233
  and radiation, 272
  auto, 49
  coproantibody, 246, 272
  complement-fixing, 197–200
  E.S., 273
  formation of, 194
  hemagglutinating, 236, 270
  produced by spleen, 45
  secondary, 274
  transfer of, 103
Antigen,
  E.S., 236, 273
  Eimeria, 97
  freeze-dried *Dictyocaulus*, 197
  secondary, 273–275
Arthropod,
  carrier, 119
  hosts, 153–155
  vector, 137
Asexual,
  cytological details of *Plasmodium*, 40,
    41
  generations of *Eimeria*, 73, 80, 92
  periodicity of in *Plasmodium*, 22
  stages associated with immune re-
    sponse, 92
  stages and lack of glycogen, 88
A.T.P., 29, 129

B

Bacteria,
  as secondary infection in lungworm
    disease, 180, 190–3
  effect on infection of nematodes, 161
  effects on malaria infection, 27
  symbiotic, 319
Bases,
  in diet affecting susceptibility, 26
  in solutions for feeding, 29

[1]As generic and specific names appear so frequently throughout the text it was
considered unnecessary to repeat them here (Ed.).

337

Beetle, dung-transporting larvae, 119
B.G.G., effects of injection of, 50
Bile duct as intestinal route of sporo-
    zoites and sporocysts, 76
Biochemistry of Malaria parasites, 32–35
Blood,
    changes due to infection, 218
    content of circulating larvae, 222–4,
        240
    content of in infected calves, 193
    flow of, 218
    of infected mice, 240
    migration of parasites in 75–76, 219
    physiology affecting susceptibility, 24
Blood meal,
    effect on ageing mosquitoes, 24
    effect on susceptibility of mosquitoes,
        24, 25
    result of on midgut of infected *Aedes*,
        16
Blood sucking arthropods, 137
Bronchitis, parasitic, 183, 186, 193

C

C^{14}, 124, 240–242
Carbon dioxide,
    as stimulus for infection, 146–7, 160,
        169
    content in plasm of infected calves, 193
    effect of concentration on movement,
        135
    end product of aerobic respiration of
        larvae, 129
Carbonic acid, influencing detachment
    of cuticle, 120
Carcinoma, 234
Cellular factors in immunity, 277
Chemotherapy of avian malaria, 23 *see
    also* Drugs
Chitin, 90, 112, 113, 150, 170, 171
Chromic phosphate, 76
Cilia,
    in collecting ducts, 305
    locomotory, 313
    patterns in monogeneans, 289, 290–2
    sensory tufts of, 309
    zones of, 209–4
Climatic conditions, effect of, 138, 144,
    181, 182, 184
Coccidia, 27, 69, 81–3
Collagen, 117, 219

Copro-antibodies, 246, 251, 272
Cortisone,
    dosages, 263
    effect on immunity, 220, 221, 233–6,
        264
    effect on tissues, 277
Cryptobiotis, 142
Culture,
    in vitro, 17–19, 24–30, 30, 31
    in modified Harvard media, 29
    of avian malaria parasites, 28
    of exo-erythrocytic stages of *Plasmo-
        dium*, 36, 37, 43
    tissue cultures, 36, 37, 43
Cuticle,
    lining of anus, 122
    of cysts, 116
    of nematodes, 110, 115, 117, 120, 153
    of larvae, 115–17, 119
Cyanacethydrazide, trials on infected
    animals, 194
Cytochemistry,
    of *Eimeria*, 84
    of gametogenesis in *Plasmodium*, 17
    of *Haemoproteus columbae*, 34
    of muscle larvae, 223
    of oocysts 5
    of *Plasmodium*, 41, 42
Cytochrome oxidase, 129
Cytoplasm
    importance in cell division of *Plasmo-
        dium*, 41, 42
    inheritable factors in, 14
    of *Eimeria*, 84
    proteins in, 85
    glycogen varying amounts in stages of
        Eimeria, 86
Cytology
    of Malaria parasite, 4, 12, 37, 38, 42–
        45
    of cytokinesis of schizonts, 41, 44
    of *Eimeria,* 83, 84

D

Dactylogyrid, 292
D.D.T., affect on mosquito, 13
Desiccation of larvae, 139–42
Diastase, 88
Diet, *see also* Feeding and Culture
    C^{14} labelled diets, 240, 241, 242
    oil-rich, 34, 219

Diethyl carbamazine, 195
DNA, 34, 83, 84, 239
Dormancy, 143, 144
Drugs,
  affect on respiration cycle, 31
  affect on sporagenous cycle, 11
  anti-coccidial, 91
  resistance to, 13, 14
  treatment of husk, 194, 195
  treatment of malaria, 8, 11, 13–15, 18, 20, 24, 31
Ducts of glands in oncomiracidia, 307, 308
Dung beetle and larvae transport, 119

E

Ecdysis, *see* Moulting
Eclepic acid, 115
Ecological factors effecting *D. viviparous*, 182, 186, 187
Ectoparasites on plants, 162
Egg of nematodes, 113, 123
Eggs, effect of soil, 141–3, 157–9
Eggs, effect of reducing agent, 147
Eimeria,
  antigen, 97
  asexual generations, 73, 80, 92
  cytology, 83, 84
  gametocytes, 73, 77, 78
  glycogen, 85–91
  immunity to, 102
  infection by, 68, 75, 76, 81
  infection of liver, 76
  inoculation of oocysts, 75, 81, 82
  inoculation of sporozoites, 75
  life cycle, 70–79
  mortality due to, 76, 78
  oocysts, 68–73, 76
  pathology, 68, 69, 76
  sexual reproduction, 80, 92
  sporozoites, 74
  staining, 84, 85
  tissue changes, 78
  villi glands, infection of, 76, 78
Electron Microscope (results obtained by),
  in Malaria, 40–42
  on encysted larvae, 239
  on host cells, 239
  on infected rat muscles, 223

Embryological development in monogeneans, 299–303
Environmental changes,
  affecting *D. viviparus*, 182
  and infective stage of nematodes, 164
  and life cycle, 167
Enzymes,
  and infection, 91
  coenzyme A, 29
  collagenase, 227
  cyst wall, action on, 219
  cytochrome oxidase, 129, 152, 155
  diastase, 88
  hyaluronidase, 88–91, 228
  penetration, 163, 227
  phosphatase, 91, 226, 227, 234
  released by larva, 115
  secreted by blood cells, 278
Eosinophil, 188, 194, 225, 226, 240, 275
Eosinophilia, 193–5
Erythroblasts, 49
Erythrocytes, 8, 9, 29, 33, 218, 225
ES antigens, 273
Evolution
  lines of, 321
  of monogeneans, 315
Excretion,
  of infected hamsters, 217
  organs of platyhelminths, 305
  pores, 307
Ex-erythocytic stages,
  culture of, 9, 36
  cytology, 43
  distribution of, 38, 39
Extra-cellular parasites, 30
Eye, in larval monogeneans, 308, 309

F

Faecal pellets, 132, 133
Faeces,
  and grazing cattle, 185
  as reservoir of infection, 185
  consistency of affecting larvae, 184
  Pilobus development on, 187
  spreading of infected faeces, 184
Farm experiments on vaccination, 201–6
Feeding,
  experiments on mosquitoes, 24–29
  methods for extracellular parasites, 30
  oil-rich diet to host, 34, 219
  survival without, 124

Feulgen staining, 84
Flame-cells, 305–7
Fluorescence,
  in antibodies, 274, 275
  in parasitised blood, 49
  tracer techniques, 102
Foetus of infected cow, 181
Fog Fever, 193
Folic acid, 27–31
Freund's complete adjuvant, 198

G

Galls, expulsion of larval mass from, 157
Gametocytes,
  cytochemistry of, 35, 42
  in *Eimeria*, 73, 78
Gametogenesis,
  in *Eimeria*, 77, 78
  in *Plasmodium*, 17, 33
Gel-diffusion, 275
Genetic factor in cytoplasm, 14
  in reproduction, 22, 23
Genetic studies of *Plasmodium*, 13
Gibberellic acid, 137
Gill chambers of host, 304, 319
Glands,
  larval penetration of, 228
  of immune chickens, 94
  of monogeneans, 290
  of villi infected by *Eimeria*, 76, 78
  oncomiracidia, 307, 308
  secretions in infected hamsters, 217
Globulin, 51, 100, 102, 197, 224, 233, 235, 236
γ–Globulin, 51, 100
Glucose,
  consumption in gametocytes, 53
  rate of consumption by red cells, 33
Glycogen,
  in *Eimeria*, 85–91
  in nematodes, 124–6
Glycolysis, 129
Glyco-Protein, 224, 226, 227, 228, 233, 234, 235, 275
Growth factors, 30, 31

H

Haemoproteus, 53, 54
Hamuli, 300, 301, 302, 306, 311, 313, 315, 317, 323
Haptor, 290, 292, 294, 296, 297, 300, 307, 310–13, 316, 317, 320, 322

Harvard Medium, 29
Heart,
  abnormalities due to infection, 218
  larvae in, 215, 223
Heat, effect on larval activity, 134, 135
Heredity,
  mutants, 14
  susceptibility of mosquitoes, 13–15
Hibernation of host, effect of, 216
Histamine, 275, 278, 281
Histopathology
  of avian malaria, 46
  of husk, 187
  of *Leucocytozoon*, 56
  of rat muscles, 226
Hooks, 294–300, 311–17, 321
  replaced by clamps, 321
Hormones,
  adrenal, 263
  in nematodes, 165, 166
Host,
  fish-like, 319
  influence of vertebrate, 261
  mammalian compared to avian, 34
  -parasitic relationship, 32, 118, 136, 157, 168, 169
  physiological state of, 17
  responses in, 57, 243
  secretions of, 157
  specificity, 319
Human,
  malarial infection and altitude, 4
  nematode, 137–8
  Trichiniasis, 217, 242
Humidity, 139–140, 143, 187
Humoral factor, 197, 236
Hyaluronidase, 88–91, 228
Hybridization among variant strains of
  Plasmodium, 14, 15

I

Immune,
  mechanisms, 96
  parents, 103
  response, 92, 94, 219
  serum, 40, 100, 101, 197
  to one species, 98
Immunity,
  active, 20, 230
  acquired, 5, 51, 195, 199, 229, 243, 246, 272, 273
  acquired by use of killed parasites, 20

capacity to acquire, 196–9
cellular factors in, 277
cortisone, effect of, 220–6, 264
development in flock, 81
development in calves, 196
duration of, 95
influence of alcohol, 261, 262
influence of age on, 24, 249
maintenance of, 234
merozoite numbers related to, 49
modifications of, 233, 278
natural, 199
of invertebrate host, 24
of rats, 229
of *Trichiniasis*, 277–81
of vertebrate host, 24
period of, 206
produced by various phases, 273
quantitative tests on, 245, 256
to coccidosis, 91–103
to *Eimeria*, 102
transfer of, 229–32
Immunization *see also* Vaccination
  by graded infections, 95
  by immune sera for husk, 197
  by irradiated larvae, 230
  by separate phases of life cycle, 256
  by stimulating infections, 240
  of calves, 196–9
  parasitic bronchitis, field experiments, 197–9
  dosage, 93, 201
  power, 93
  results of, 94
  sexual phases, 97
  vale, 203
Immunology, 46–50, 92
Infection *see also* Resistance
  concurrent, 262
  defence against, in growing mouse, 7
  dual, 235
  Eimeria, 68, 75, 81
  infective dosage, 68, 81, 95
  eyelids, 53
  graded infections of oocysts, 95
  infectivity experiments on *Plasmodium*, 20
  infective stages, 153, 164, 167, 169
  pathology, 50, 51
  precautions against, 95
  pre-natal, 181

related to age of host, 83, 181
related to antibody response, 200
related to sexual reproduction, 96
tests on infected serum, 224, 225
site of, 146
transference from pasture to pasture, 206
Trichinella, 215
via gut, 145
via skin, 135, 154
vascular tissue changes, 218
Inflammatory tissue,
  effect of cortisone, 277
  response, 276–7
Inoculation *see also* Vaccination
  of erythrocytic stages, 5
  of exo-erythrocytic stages, 16
  of merozoites of *Eimeria*, 75
  of oocysts of *Eimeria*, 75, 81, 82
  of sporozoites, 10
  of sporozoites of *Eimeria*, 75
  with Indian ink, 48
  with infected blood, 21
  with infected brain, 16
  with killed parasites, 20
Inoculum,
  results of, 82, 83
  size of, 81, 82
Intestine,
  effects of infection on mucosa, 69, 70–4
  effects of larvae in wall of, 228
  glands, 74
  inflammation of, 237
  lining, 305, 319
  of oncomiracidium, 304
  nematodes in, 131, 132
  non-cellular membrane, 304
  reserve nutrients in, 119, 120
  tissue destroyed, 219
  worms present in, 251
Ions,
  necessary for culture of *Plasmodium*, 19, 26
  permeability of capillaries to, 225
Irradiation,
  dosages, 231, 232, 267
  effects of, 11, 271
  irradiated larvae, vaccination with, 194, 200–5
  of larvae in husk disease, 194
  of larvae in *Trichiniasis*, 230, 255

of stages in life history used for infection, 255
of whole body of host, 236, 267, 268,
278
resistance to, 10
treatment, 223
vaccine, 200, 203
vaccine production, 202–7
X–irradiation on infective larvae, 200,
201, 203
γ–Irradiation, 10

K

Krebs Cycle, 128–9

L

Lactone, 115
Larvae,
ciliated, 290
climate, effect on, 138
cuticular membranes, 131
cyst wall of, 226
desiccation, 139–42
development in mice, 239
distribution by spores, 187
enzymes released by, 115
expulsion from galls, 157
heat, effect on, 134, 135
hooked, 289
hydrostatic pressure, 113
infective, 120–2
in heart, 215
in muscle, 216, 219, 281
nematode, 111
protein synthesis, 240
seasonal effects, 183, 186
size, 222
starvation, 120
substances attracting, 137
temperature, effect of, 120, 133, 134,
139, 140, 143, 182, 187
Trichinella, 215
L.D. dosage, 263, 264, 267
Lethargus of nematodes, 111
Leucocytozoon, 55
Leucovorin, 31
Leukocytes, 218, 223
Leukopenia, 268
Leukosis, 57
Life Cycle,
adaptive features in, 310

Coccidia, 69
Eimeria, 70–9
modifications for dispersal, 118–20
nematode, 110–21
self-limiting, 95
stages concerned with immunity, 255
Trichinella, 215, 221, 237, 241, 274
Light
effect on mobility of larvae, 187
effect on nematodes, 133–5, 141
heat from source of, 134, 135
Ligation of caeca, 96, 104
Lipids, 85, 88, 217, 111–3, 125, 126
Liver, *Eimeria* infection of, 76
use in culture, 35
virus effect on, 26, 27, 29
Lucite Rings, 9
Lungworm disease, 181, 188, 193
Lymphatic vessels,
carval routes in, 180, 188
Lymph nodes, mesenteric, 180, 181, 206,
208
Lymphocytes, 103–4
and infection of mice, 240, 267
changes during infection, 46, 47, 55
infected, 36
involved in inflammation, 226
neutrophil ratio, 264
Lymphoid,
nodules in husk disease, 193
reserves, 267
tissue, 103, 270, 271
Lyophilization, 142

M

Macrogametes,
DNA deficiency, 83
mucopolysaccharides in, 90
protein in, 85
Macrophages, 75, 189
Malaria,
altitude on vertebrate host, effect of,
3, 4
avian, 23, 46
bacteria, effect of, 27
biochemistry of, 32–5
chemotherapy of avian malaria, 23
coccidia, effects of, 27
cytology, 4, 12, 37, 38, 42–5
drugs, 8, 11, 13–15, 18, 20, 24, 31

electron microscope, 40–42
pathology, 46, 50
transmission of, 54
virus, effect of, 26, 27
yeast, effect of, 27
Mast Cells, 52, 231, 243, 275, 278
Megaloschizont, 55, 56, 57
Meiosis,
in *Plasmodium*, 12, 13
post zygotic, 17
Membranes,
asexual stage, 42
cuticular of larvae, 131
egg of nematode, 111, 113, 115
gametocytic, 42
nuclear, 12, 13
penetration of, 8, 9
Metabolism,
end products of, 129
host and parasite, 281
infective stages of nematodes, 128
oxidative, 128
Metamorphosis,
of parasite, 164, 165
physiological, 165, 166
Microgametocytes, content of muccoid
sulphate, 90
Microorganisms affecting infection, 27,
161, 234, 235
Migration,
of parasite larva, 132, 133
route of Dictyocaulus, 180
Mitosis in *Plasmodium*, 12
Moisture
hatching of nematode eggs, 113
survival of *Heterodera*, 143
Mortality
due to *Eimeria* infection, 76, 78
rate affected by splenectomy, 47, 48
Moulting, physiology of, 117, 118, 123,
153, 157, 165–7
Moults,
nematode, 110–111
Trichinella in mice, 237
Trichinella in rats, 221
Mucosa,
inflammatory, 252, 264, 276
in irradiated mice, 270
penetration of, 227, 229, 243
sub-mucosa, 103
villi, 221

Muscle,
bries, 242
degeneration, 234
destruction, 219
hamuli, 317
infected, 215, 219, 226, 241
movements in oncomiracidia, 289
proteins, 242
skeletal, 235
striated fibres, 218
Mutants, 11, 14

N

Nematodes
bacteria, effect of, 161
eggs, 113, 123, 139
electric currents, effect of, 136, 137
effect of light, 133–5, 141
environmental changes, 164
glycogen, 124–6
hormones in, 165, 166
in humans, 137, 138
in intestine, 131, 132
larvae, 111
lethargus, 111
life cycle, 110–21
moisture and egg hatching, 113
moults, 110, 111
nematode "wool", 142
physiology, 149
taxis, 132
transportation of, 118
migration, 132–4
plant bulbs, 142
plant secretions, 156
roots, 113–18, 136, 141, 156–62
vectors, 137
wounds, attraction of, 136
Newcastle Disease, 102
Nitrogen Metabolism, 126, 129
5–Nucleolidase, 91
Nucleus,
division in *Plasmodium*, 37, 61
structure in *Plasmodium*, 41, 42

O

Oncomiracidium, 289–91, 293, 299, 300
Ontogenetic,
development of haptor, 320
loss of hooks, 300

Oocyst,
   biometric study of, 69
   capsule, 44
   coccidial, 69
   encystment of, 75
   fine structure of *Plasmodial*, 44
   inoculation of, 75
   migration in blood stream, 75, 76
   morphology of, 77, 78
   potential production of, 81–3
   production of, in coccidia, 81–3
   cytochemistry, 5
   rate of production of, 70
   sporulated in *Eimeria*, 68–73, 76
   wall of, 86–8
Ookinetes, 12
   entry into gut wall, 43
   fine structure of, 42
Oncomiracidia, 303, 307, 308
Organic acids in culture experiments, 146
Osmo-regulation,
   canal, 304
   larval, 130
   systems, 305, 306
   use in identification, 307
Oxygen,
   increased intake of, 193
   requirements for parasites, 126–9
   tension, 4, 222
Oxytetracycline, 26

P

Palaeontological evidence, 321, 322
Parabiotic rats, 229
Parthenogenetic forms of nematode, 112, 142
Pasture,
   husk affected by, 181, 188
   infection transfer on, 206
   larval survival on, 138, 141
   migration of nematodes, 132
Pathology,
   Eimeria, 68–69, 76
   Leucocytozoon, 56
   Parasitic Bronchitis, 187
   malarian, 50
Penetration,
   capillary wall, 225
   enzyme, 227
   larval of skin, 139

   lymphatic vessel, 180
   mucosal, 229
   muscle fibre, 227
Permeability,
   capillary, 225, 276
   egg shell, 130
   larval sheath, 139
   membrane, 225
pH,
   of culture media, 17–19, 146–50, 222, 226
   of infected calf blood, 193
Phosphorylation, 91
Phosphatase, 91, 226, 227, 234
Phylogenetic,
   descent, 307
   development, 293, 300, 316
   difference, 305
   groupings, 322
   relationships, 319
Physiology,
   changes in host, 23, 276
   host and parasite, 281
   obligate malarial parasitic, 29–35
   of stimulus on nematode larvae, 149
Pilobus,
   associated with distribution of *Dictyocaulus*, 187
   occurrence in Britain, 187
Plant,
   bulb nematodes, 142
   root nematodes, 113–18, 136, 141, 156–62
   secretions affecting parasite, 169
   survival of, 140–2
Plasma, contents in infected calves, 193
   factor in development of parasite, 18
Plasmodium,
   asexual periodicity, 22
   benign strain, 13, 14
   cell division, 41, 42
   culture of, 19, 26
   culture of exo-erythrocytic stages, 36, 37, 43
   cytochemistry, 17, 41, 42
   gametogenesis, 17, 33
   genetic studies, 13
   hybridization, 14, 15
   infectivity experiments, 20
   meiosis, 12, 13
   mitosis, 12

nucleus, division of, 37, 61
nucleus, structure of, 41, 42
Plastic granules, 85, 90
  and protein-carbohydrate complex, 88
Polymorphonuclear cells, 103
Polyphenol, 90
Polysaccharide, 88–90
  globulin polysaccharide, 224, 233
  protein-containing, 228, 275
Polystomatid, 290, 292, 295
Pore size for penetration of parasite, 9
Post-larval development, 309
Precipitins, 246, 251, 255, 273
Proteins,
  in blood, 52, 233
  C¹⁴ content in, 240
  carbohydrate-containing, 227, 229
  and chitin, 112
  Eimeria, 85
  glyco-protein, 227
  immunity and, 274–5
  lipo-protein, 88
  muco-protein, 88
  membrane in lung, 190–2
  ribo-nucleo, 42
  serum, 100, 224, 235
  synthesis by encysted larvae, 240
Psychodid flies, 119

R

Refractive globule, 80, 85
Resistance,
  capacity to acquire, 195–6
  DDT, 13
  degree of, 92
  drug, 14, 15, 31
  due to protective substances, 94
  environment, 123
  fowl, 104
  importance of acquired, 187
  irradiation, 10
  of infection, 11, 76
  production of , 17
  time factor and, 5
  transference of, 95
Respiration,
  acidosis, 193
  carbon dioxide, 129
  coefficient in Parasitic Bronchitis, 193
  drug effect on, 31

energy source in sporulation, 86
enzymes detected, 91
extra-cellular parasitic, 31
Krebs Cycle, 129
quotient, 128
rate of in lungworm disease, 188, 193
rate of in vaccination tests, 203
RNA, 35, 84, 85, 224, 226, 239

S

Saline solution, *see also* Culture,
  concentrations for larvae, 131
  extract, 235
  in cultures, 18, 19, 147
  isotonic, 198
Salts (*see also* Culture), 19, 26, 131, 139
  importance of in hatching, 148
Schizonts,
  generations of, 73, 76
  in villi, 70
  merozoite numbers in, 49
  sizes of, 79
Sclerites, 290, 294, 311, 317, 321
Seasonal effects on larvae on herbage,
  183, 186
Secretions,
  aiding penetration of host, 163
  controlling stages in life cycle, 167
  host, 168–70
  plant in nematode infection, 156
Sense organs in monogeneans, 308, 309
Sensory,
  development in monogeneans, 308, 309
  reception, 136, 137
Serum, 51, 98
  antigen mixtures, 100
  antibodies, 235
  changes in, 234
  hamster, 221
  heated, 100
  immune, 100, 102
  infected rat, 224, 225
Sex ratio, 215, 222, 238
Sexual reproduction,
  Eimeria, 80, 92
  related to infection, 96
  Trichinella, 221, 222, 237
Simian Strain, 137
Size, of larvae, 222
  of male and female worms, 222

Skeletal,
  bars, 317
  muscle, 235
  structure of haptor, 294
Soil,
  factors affecting eggs, 141, 142, 143, 157–9
Specificity, 7
Spleen, 4, 5, 27, 45, 46, 47, 48, 104, 217
Splenectomy, 4, 47, 48
Spores of *Pilobus* and distribution of larvae, 187
Sporocysts, use of bile duct, 76
Sporozoites,
  cytology of, 45
  Eimeria, 74
  engulfed by macrophages, 75
  use of bile duct, 76
Sporulation,
  of stored oocysts, 70
  time of, 74
Staining,
  Baker's acid Laematin, 88
  Eimeria, 84, 85
  Fuelgen, 84
  glycogen, 86
  lipids, 85, 88
  PAS, 86–8
  techniques, 12
Starvation,
  of host, 34
  of larvae, 120
Sterility in worms, 231, 232
Steroid, 236
Stieda body of Sporocyst, 85
Stimulus,
  for hatching, 123
  for larval development, 119–20
  from host, 113, 117, 120, 167
  from root of host, 120
  mechanical from carrier host, 119
Stomata, 136, 161
Stress,
  effects on host, 34
  factors, 57, 216, 260, 261
  socio-psychologic, 280
Sucker, 321
Susceptibility,
  affected by acids, bases and salts, 26
  hypothesis as to, 20
  of mosquito host, 24

of mosquito to DDT, 13
of red cells, 8, 11
of wall of alimentary canal, 15, 16
to coccidial infection, 81, 98, 100, 101
to irradiation, 10
Susceptible stage in calves, 206

T

Taxis,
  of nematode larva, 132
  thermotaxis, 155
Taxonomy,
  importance, 300
  taxonomic range, 287
Temperature,
  body of host, 22
  culture medium, 17, 37
  differences in irradiated rats, 236
  effects of, 23, 24, 145, 149
  for culture medium, 17, 37
  for development of larvae, 120, 182, 187
  for hatching nematode eggs, 113, 139
  for movement of larvae, 133, 134
  for survival of larvae, 139, 140, 143
  reduced during host hibernation, 216
  skin, 155
  soil, 157
Thermotactic, 155
Time, effect on loss of worms, 276
Tissue,
  changes in *Eimeria* cycle, 78
  epithelial affected by infection, 81
  enzymes affected by infection, 91
  lymphoid, 103
  metabolism in infected, 217
Transmission,
  by blood inoculation, 20
  by transplanting tissue, 53
  of Dauer larvae by dung beetle, 119
  of *Haemoproteus*, 53
  of *Leucocytozoon*, 58
  of malaria, 54
  of resistance, 96
Transportation,
  of nematodes, 118
  by carrier host, 119
Trehalose, 126
Trichinella, 215, 221, 237, 274
Tropisms,
  chemo-, 136
  geotropic, 136, 137

U

Urine, 230
  of infected hamsters, 216
Ultra-violet radiation, 141

V

Vaccination, 197–200
  field tests, 201–6
  safe and effective, 205
  variations in, 206
  with irradiated larvae, 194, 200–5
Variability, 25
Vascular tissue changes due to infection, 218
Vectors,
  of *Leucocytozoon*, 54
  of *Haemoproteus*, 54
  of nematodes, 137
Villi,
  infected epithelium of, 70–2, 76
  mucosa of, 221
Virus,
  effect on Malarial parasites, 26, 27
  encephalomyocarditis virus, 235
Vitamins, 29, 32–4, 223, 262
Viviparous, 290

W

Water,
  effect on nematode migration, 132–4
  film for skin penetration, 155
  for spreading larvae of husk, 185
  inhibition of for larval expulsion, 157
  necessary for infection, 139
Weight,
  changes in infected rats, 226
  gains in vaccinates, 203, 204
  loss of, 228, 235, 243, 246, 252, 271, 276
Worms, effect of age, 238, 251
Worms, female, 249, 255
Worms, sterility in, 231, 232
Wounds, attraction for nematode, 136

X

X-Irradiation, 10

Y

Yolk stalk, site of infection, 78
Yeasts,
  effect on malarial parasites, 27
  protein, preparation of, 30